2.00
9983

FIVE HUNDRED

over

SIXTY

A COMMUNITY SURVEY ON AGING

BERNARD KUTNER

Albert Einstein College of Medicine
Yeshiva University

and

DAVID FANSHEL

Family and Children's Service, Pittsburgh

ALICE M. TOGO

Cornell University Medical College

THOMAS S. LANGNER

Cornell University Medical College

NEW YORK · 1956   RUSSELL SAGE
FOUNDATION

© 1956
RUSSELL SAGE FOUNDATION
Printed in the United States
of America

*Library of Congress
Catalog Card Number: 56-11557*

WM. F. FELL CO., PRINTERS
PHILADELPHIA, PA.

Foreword

THIS BOOK IS A COMPREHENSIVE REPORT of a study that was made of the needs of old people. At the Kips Bay-Yorkville Health Center in New York City, the health needs of the 250,000 people in the area had been met reasonably well. Maternal health, infant hygiene, school health, all were well developed. There was an excellent nursing service, also a children's dental clinic. Tuberculosis was well under control. Communicable disease was on the wane. A great deal had been done for children and young adults, but almost nothing for the old people of the district. There were a great many elderly people and the number was growing. Almost daily some problem was presented to the Health Center which involved the health or welfare of an old person in the area. However, we did nothing. Our reason was quite a simple one; we did not know what to do. We did not know what the fundamental needs of elderly people were, nor how they should be met. We were a Health Center, but it was obvious that the direct medical needs were only a part of the problem of the elderly. Social and economic factors loomed large in the foreground.

As one so often does when in a dilemma, we formed a "committee." But this group really functioned as a committee, in that it gave us sound advice and continuous guidance. It consisted of representatives from each of the following organizations: the Department of Sociology and Anthropology at Cornell University, Ithaca; Department of Health of the City of New York; Department of Welfare of the City of New York; Department of Public Health and Preventive Medicine, Cornell University Medical College, New York City; Welfare and Health Council of New York City; and Russell Sage Foundation.

3

The first decision that the Committee made was a very simple truism, namely, that the best way to learn just what the needs of old people are . . . *is to ask them*, personally and individually. Russell Sage Foundation agreed to give Cornell University the necessary funds to make the inquiry, and this book is a report of our study.

The broad vision that inspired the field research came from Professor Edward A. Suchman of the Department of Sociology and Anthropology at Cornell. His guidance was invaluable because of his rich experience in previous community studies. Dr. Leonard S. Cottrell, Jr., of Russell Sage Foundation, gave freely of his wise counsel and was a great inspiration throughout the study. We were very fortunate in securing the services of an experienced and enthusiastic social psychologist, Dr. Bernard Kutner, to direct the inquiry. He selected a capable and loyal staff to aid him and together they carried through the various stages of: (a) formulating the questionnaire, (b) directing the field work, and (c) analyzing the data. Dr. Kutner then did the hardest part of all. He wrote the report. At the time of writing Dr. Kutner was associated with Cornell University. He is now a member of the staff of the Albert Einstein College of Medicine of Yeshiva University.

It became apparent relatively early in the study that the essential need of old people in our district was an advisory and consulting service, and that this type of activity should be an integral part of the official community health and welfare structure. As a direct result of this study, therefore, and long before the work was complete, an official "Adult Counseling Center" was installed in the Kips Bay-Yorkville Health Center. This was a joint enterprise of the Departments of Health, Hospitals, and Welfare of New York City. It has received its initial support from the New York Foundation, but should soon become an effective, official, and integrated community service. For the first time we are in a position to understand, to some degree, the basic needs of old people and, thus, we know what may be done to meet these needs.

Our special thanks are due to all members of the Committee who guided us through the study and to the hard-working staff that carried the work to its completion.

Wilson G. Smillie, M.D.
Chairman of the Committee

Preface

THROUGHOUT THE NATION the steady growth of the aged population has been noted, and in many communities the importance of understanding the implications of the population trend has been recognized. This awareness has led to such efforts as the convening of state, regional, and national conferences and the formation of governors' commissions, mayors' committees, and other semiofficial organizations to study the problem and to make recommendations for appropriate governmental as well as private community action. The study upon which this report is based was initiated as a result of such recognition and is an attempt to locate certain problems and needs of the aged population of part of a major urban center. It has the specific aim of recommending the types of community service or services that would seem to be most appropriate to deal with these problems and needs. It is an effort undertaken as a cooperative venture by the Department of Health of the City of New York, Cornell University Medical College, Cornell University Social Science Research Center, and Russell Sage Foundation.

As set forth in its original prospectus, the study sought to answer three questions: (1) What social and cultural factors facilitate adjustment to aging? (2) What kinds of people successfully adjust themselves to aging? (3) What forms should be taken by programs designed to serve the needs of the aged? To find answers to these questions, three methods were undertaken: (1) a cross-sectional study of the experiences, behaviors, needs, attitudes, and values of the aged residing in the Kips Bay-Yorkville Health District of New York; (2) an inventory and evaluation of the facilities utilized by the aged persons in this area

5

as well as those in other parts of the city; and (3) application of the findings of both researches in establishing a test pilot service to deal with the needs of the aged in the Kips Bay-Yorkville area and in encouraging the extension of this test service to other neighborhoods of New York City and in other urban centers as workable plans and procedures are developed.

What we have learned in the pursuit of answers to the research questions forms the basis of this report. In the first section, we describe the objectives and problem areas dealt with by the research, the community setting in which it was carried out, and the nature of the population studied.

In the second and third sections, the research findings are spelled out in detail. Five chapters deal with the problems of adjustment among various subgroups of older persons. Three chapters examine the problems of health of the aged and their amenability, as well as actual use of various community resources.

In the final section, one chapter assesses the problems of serving the older person through community-sponsored facilities in the City of New York. In the concluding chapter, an attempt is made to draw out the implications of the research findings and the survey of resources aimed at expanding perspectives regarding community planning for the aged.

It should be remembered that the study is not intended to serve as a model or demonstration for areas less complex than Kips Bay-Yorkville or even for other sections of New York City. Rather, it aims to suggest ways of approaching the problems of aging in other social and cultural contexts. Problems of aging among recent emigrés, rural, or small town or small city dwellers are likely to be, indeed are known to be, somewhat different from those that will be shown for the area under study. Similarly, the pattern of this community's services aiding the aged is at once unique in some respects, common in others. Insofar as there are common features among the Kips Bay-Yorkville populace and the agencies and institutions serving them, this report may claim some degree of generalizability in other settings. However, its major intent is to serve as a prototype rather than as an exact model. The reader must seek to generalize from this study by selecting such aspects of it as would validly apply to other special cases.

This report is the product of many hands. Its interdisciplinary origins are testimony of the merged thinking of the medical and social domains. The study received its early impetus from the Social Science Research Center of Cornell University and Dr. Robin M. Williams, Jr., its director. For continuous consultation on various phases of the project, the authors are indebted to members of the faculty and research staff of the Department of Sociology and Anthropology of Cornell University: Dr. John P. Dean, Dr. Rose K. Goldsen, Dr. Milton L. Barron (now of the City College of New York), Dr. Gordon Streib, Miss Jessie Cohen, and Dr. Zena Blau. We are especially indebted to Dr. Edward A. Suchman, professor of sociology, who gave close guidance to the project in orienting it toward basic research as well as practical application.

Grateful acknowledgment is given to the project's Coordinating Committee for providing the organization and policy framework, as well as astute and constructive criticism of the project from its inception: Dr. Emerson Day, director of the Kate Depew Strang Cancer Prevention Clinic, Memorial Hospital, and professor of preventive medicine, Sloan-Kettering Division of Cornell University Medical College; Mr. Raymond Hilliard, director of Cook County Department of Welfare, Chicago, who served on the Committee during the project's first year, while director of the Welfare and Health Council of New York City; Commissioner of Welfare Henry L. McCarthy, New York City; Dr. Theodore Rosenthal, assistant commissioner of health; and Dr. Edward A. Suchman. Special acknowledgment is made to the Committee's chairman, Dr. Wilson G. Smillie, professor and head of public health and preventive medicine of Cornell University Medical College, now executive director of State Charities Aid Association, who inspired the project and steadfastly maintained its action-oriented direction.

The presence of the Commissioner of Health of the City of New York, Dr. Leona Baumgartner, and Dr. Leonard S. Cottrell, Jr., of Russell Sage Foundation, added greatly to the project's central focus: relating research to service across many disciplines. Special thanks are due to Dr. Irwin D. J. Bross, assistant professor of public health and preventive medicine, Cornell University Medical College, for valuable consultation during the development of the study design and sample selection procedure; to Dr. Ann P. Kent, district health officer of Kips Bay-Yorkville and member of the Coordinating Committee, for assistance in the preparation of Chapter 2 of this report; to Miss Judith Coste, Miss Francine Lang, Miss Faith Wallstrom, students at Sarah Lawrence College, for their assistance during the data analysis process and in preparing the bibliography; and to the many professional workers for their help during our survey of community services for the aged. A debt of gratitude is also due to Dr. Carol F. Creedon and Dr. Wayne E. Thompson for reading and incisively criticizing the entire manuscript, and to Dr. Edgar F. Borgatta for a careful professional review of it in the final stages.

B.K.
D.F.
A.M.T.
T.S.L.

Contents

9

PART I

A SURVEY OF AGING

Part I:

A Survey of Aging

THROUGHOUT THE CENTURIES man has striven for a full life. While for some persons life has been gratifyingly complete, until recent times only few have been able to live out the proverbial three score and ten years. And yet, from ancient times to the present, old age has brought with it mixed blessings—historical circumstance, the social conditions of the times, and unique personal experiences, all being partly responsible.

For some persons the period of agedness has brought with it unparalleled prestige, fame, and even fortune. The elder statesman, the distinguished professor emeritus, the elderly tycoon are examples. For others, age has meant unprecedented hardship, chronic degenerative illness, mental disintegration, indigency, and institutionalization. In modern times, age-determined exclusion from employment, subsistence on public financial support, and residence in custodial institutions have been some of the concomitants of aging. For the majority, however, who have neither fame nor wealth, on the one hand, nor "second childhood" or protracted terminal illness, on the other, old age ushers in a period of unique problems. Among these problems are counted the termination of gainful employment; reduced income; the onset or exacerbation of degenerative illness; isolation through death or removal of family, friends, and peers; increased periods of indolence; loss of physical and mental abilities; widowhood; a decreasing standard of living; and those feelings, emotions, thoughts, and attitudes that attend the foregoing evidences of the decline of life in our society.

While all of these problems have been with us for some time, it is only in recent years that public attention has been focused on the rapid growth of the elderly segment of the population and on recurrent problems attendant upon this growth. The comparatively rapid increase in the population surviving to or outliving the formerly expected "norm" of life expectancy has called into sharp notice certain of the repercussions of this "geriatric revolution." We not only have more of the same old problems such as indigency and widowhood, but such new problems as the care of the chronically ill and the effective utilization of years of unoccupied time as well. A series of ingenious innovations have emerged to help meet them. The last decade has produced such novel conceptions as the "golden age" club, the geriatric clinic, partial and gradual retirement, specialized housing for the aged, the sheltered workshop, foster homes, medical home care, and a science of gerontology.

Professional activities in behalf of the aged group have developed correspondingly to a point where training in social work, nursing, medicine, recreational work, and allied fields has begun to incorporate specific content and techniques for dealing with the older adult. Moreover, professional organizations are beginning to devote more journal space and conference time to geriatric and gerontological discussions. With both private and governmental support, a variety of researches have been conducted centering on problems of aging. In the past five years a proliferation of studies ranging from basic studies of the aging processes of specific organs to nationwide sociological investigations have been undertaken. The present study concerns itself with the problems of an aging population in a single segment of a major metropolis. It is to be hoped that the sociomedical data and the interpretations that follow will help strengthen the empirical and theoretical base upon which existing services can be evaluated and new ones planned.

Chapter 1

Purposes and Problems

THE RESEARCH REPORTED UPON IN THIS BOOK was conceived to meet the concerns and interests of a variety of professional and administrative agencies and individuals. It is a form of "action research," that is, an attempt through systematic scientific means to obtain clues and directions aimed at planning and developing an action program, in this instance, a service program for older people. Numbers of agencies and organizations operate in the City of New York, much as in other metropolitan centers throughout the country. Many of these organizations serve some important function centering about a particular area of immediate concern to the elderly. These facilities include: hospitals and clinics, family agencies, welfare services, employment centers, psychiatric agencies, nursing services, homes for the aged, nursing homes, domiciliaries or custodial institutions, and many others. There is no proliferation of such facilities, simply a growing list of necessary ones, each in its own way serving the older New Yorker.

Yet, despite the widely recognized and indispensable services being rendered by any community, it is proper occasionally to step back and view the existing pattern of forces mobilized in behalf of its citizens and to inquire into three problem areas:

First, are the already operating services, both public and private, meeting all the needs for which they were intended? Are there some areas that have escaped notice? Can they now be isolated and identified so that future planning can take them into account?

Second, are there new problems developing in the community that have not been sufficiently brought into fine focus and against which, consequently, no concerted attack has as yet been mounted? If such new problems do exist, what may their determinants be? Can these determinants be so conceived as to indicate the necessary steps to action?

Third, can sufficiently convincing evidence be mustered to help assess the decision, whether to attempt to cope with unmet or emergent problems and needs through existing efforts or whether new resources must be developed?

In effect, the aforementioned three areas of concern were the major foci of our attention in this study. Fundamentally, our approach was twofold. It was our belief that the best approximation of answers to the questions posed would be found first in a cross-sectional study of older people living in New York and, second, in an experience survey of officials and professionals in agencies serving them. Before turning to an examination of the study itself, let us first consider some of the theoretical and factual questions upon which this research was founded.

This is a study of five hundred noninstitutionalized persons over the age of sixty. In approaching the general areas of concern noted above, four specific problems are dealt with: (1) problems of personal adjustment, (2) factors affecting or affected by health, (3) the use of community health services, and (4) attitudes toward health and social centers. Let us consider each of these problems in turn.

PROBLEMS OF PERSONAL ADJUSTMENT

If in the later years, the person is beset with personal difficulties that multiply and are generally irreversible, those who manage to make a satisfactory adjustment to life should be found to possess one or more sustaining characteristics. We may speak of external or situational forces, though they may be fortuitous in many instances, that give the individual strength to carry on with minimal stress. Among these may be a pleasant home and surroundings, an emotionally compatible and mutually reinforcing relationship to a life partner, a respected position in the community, a variety of useful activities, companionship of family and friends, an adequate and reliable financial reserve, a sound constitution. These are factors that lend to the patterning and stability of life at any age. They help to inhibit the corrosive and demoralizing influences of retrenchment among any one or more of these forces. At the same time, there are inner or more personal forces that can make for either good or poor social adjustment. The individual's personality strengths and weaknesses, his emotional needs, the level of his demands for recognition, companionship, comfort, permissiveness are as significant to his ability to bear the brunt of the "insults" of life as are the strength of the insults themselves. Inner resources that are sufficient to offset external stresses may reduce the potency of maladjustive influences.

Sustaining or destroying forces, be they external or internal, operate simultaneously and are reciprocal in their action on the individual. Consider, for example, a man of seventy with a strong need for social acceptance who loses his job because of his advanced age. The job gave him status and, in his eyes, others respected him for his ability to carry on his work. The need remains in him but is insatiable because he can find no other work. He becomes withdrawn because he feels his associates do not have the high regard for him held previously. Any potentiality for gainful employment soon is dissipated in loneliness, frustration, and self-hatred.

One might cite, on the other hand, a widower who displays better adaptation after an initial period of maladjustment. Since the death of his wife, he has begun to drink heavily, to keep irregular hours, to be unkempt, and to be unreliable at his job. The symptoms indicate his inability to readjust to a new life pattern in the face of an environmental upset. He meets a woman who takes an interest in him. They marry and in a brief time the widower's behavioral disorders disappear. The restored pattern of his previous life gives him a sense of security and stability.

The interlocking effects of internal and external factors influencing adjustment in old age is the central theme of the analysis of our data reported in Chapters 3 to 7. More formally stated, the purpose of our research in these chapters is to provide greater clarity about the relationship between certain social forces influencing and operating in an urban area as they apply to a sample of older people within the community. Also, it is to determine the manner in which factors in the makeup of older people interact with the community and influence their personal adjustment.

Marriage and the Family

In the later period of life, family relationships take on a significance somewhat different from life in the earlier years. The altered general status of the older person has consequences for the marital relationship. The relative tranquillity of the home may be upset during this period by a variety of factors. The husband may lose his job or retire and find that neither he nor his wife is emotionally ready to accept his being at home on a twenty-four-hour-a-day basis. Tales of the husband's ineptitude in a functionless household role are legion. Difficulties may also enter the wife's situation as well, since the routines of maintaining a household are almost never the same when both marital partners are at home.

The older couple often faces the need to make adaptations in their relationship to each other. Does the man become a more docile, submissive individual after retirement and the woman more assertive than in the traditional marriage? What happens to the emotional basis of a marriage after it has lasted for forty or fifty years? In the "ideal" marriage, one might hazard the guess that there has been a gradual transformation from a marriage based upon romantic love including physical attraction and affectional interaction to one in which security and ease with each other becomes the main motif. Conversely, there may be marriages which, in the absence of complementary functional roles and the presence of children as intermediary forces, would tend to disintegrate rapidly. Just as love can be stored up over the years, it is conceivable that bitter antagonisms and frictions from basic value differences can accumulate with the passage of time and leave the marriage vulnerable in the face of strain brought on by illness or some other catastrophe. Do older couples require help in scrutinizing and rebuilding their marriages to take into account the changes mentioned above?

Relationships with children and grandchildren may also present complications. As the aging process continues, changes occur in the parent-child relationship, resulting sometimes in complete reversal of the dependency relation. Tales of intergeneration conflict, often involving grandchildren, are common. At the same time, the sentiment is often expressed that grandchildren are a great source of comfort. Little is known as to whether population shifts have created urban conditions which make contact between aged parents and their offspring more difficult. What is the effect upon family ties of the movement of adult children from the community of their aging parents, sometimes thousands of miles away? Do visits once a year or every two years help to retain any semblance of family? How does visiting with or by children affect the general adjustment of the parents?

The effects and sequelae of widowhood have received little attention in empirical research. Widows are coming to represent a sizable group in American life and there is a growing need for information regarding their patterns of adjustment. Is it a major problem for the well-to-do person who has many friends and has carried on an extensive social life? What of the widow of little means who loses the main source of her support? How does she manage her life alone after many years of close association with an economic and emotional provider? Does maladjustment increase with years of widowhood or do widows tend to work out a new life pattern? What of the widower, how does he manage his life as an enforced "bachelor"? What social and external forces play a role in the adjustment of the widowed?

If little consideration has been given to the problem of widowhood, still less treatment has been accorded the single older person. What of his or her life in retirement? How does the single person manage the relatively greater degree of social isolation in the later years? How does he fare in the face of declining health? There is considerable evidence to show that single people tend to exercise less interest in their own behalf than do married people. Are lifelong habits of personal neglect intensified in the older unmarried person and with what consequences? Considering the fact that the older person is subject to episodes of great personal stress, the nature of which tends to be generally demoralizing, the single older person should be made the subject of greater study since, potentially, the degree of stress he may experience in retirement or in poor health may more easily lead to serious emotional consequences.

Gainful Employment

At the present time it is a fact of economic life that even in a period of full employment and an easy labor market the unemployed older worker in America is in a vulnerable economic position. Economic necessity, or at least what many employers believe to be their best interests, often is given as the reason for not hiring an older person. Too frequently, it is misbelief concerning the capabilities of potential older employees or even sheer prejudice that shuts the door to economic opportunity.

We can well picture the plight of the older person making daily trips to business firms and employment agencies only to find rebuff and frustration at every turn. The sociopsychological consequences of rejection at the hiring desk so common during the depression are as devastating today to thousands of older persons, eager to work, capable of work, but for whom age is the great barrier.

Reasons for the powerful negative effects of enforced unemployment stem from a variety of factors. A person's identity is often linked to his employment. Being unemployed threatens the foundations upon which his social image is based. Then, too, we tend to identify employment with success and achievement. Those who are employed are recognized as worthy of respect, social rank, and other rewards. The unemployed are suspect as ne'er-do-wells or worse. The individual reasons for unemployment are overlooked and the fact of unemployment itself is overemphasized. In the older person a period of unemployment may lead potential employers to the feeling that he is unreliable, unfit, or unemployable. There is also a circular effect in unemployment. Coupled with it may be ill health, even if temporary. The strain of seeking work in a skeptical market may further damage the individual's less robust condition at advanced age, rendering him less fit for his normal occupation. If his morale is not over-whelmed by repeated rejections, his health may be impaired to the point where, in fact, he can no longer work. These and other factors combine to operate against the older person in his search for employment. The havoc wrought by the unemployed status in later life cannot be underestimated. The effects tend to cumu-late and probably have some role to play in enhancing degenera-tive physical and psychological processes.

Retirement is another life condition almost unique to older people. It would be of great advantage to gain insight into the older person's view of his own retirement. Here a less threatening situation presents itself. In our society, to assume the role of a retired person bears with it a certain aura of distinction. To *afford* to retire, implies that the person has achieved a station in life in which working for a living is no longer necessary. Few, indeed, attain such a position but it seems to be an idealized goal, at least of many younger people. It would appear from the present study and from others as well that, as the "retirement years" become imminent, increasingly fewer people view retirement with pleasant expectations. We would like to shed light on the question of whether expectations are met by later events in retire-ment, the extent to which retirement is viewed in retrospect as a desirable state, and some of the factors associated with satisfaction or dissatisfaction with retirement. If we find that gross discrep-ancies exist between expectations and experiences, this would suggest that considerable work is in order to attempt to correct the perception of retirement in the preretirement period. If no such discrepancies occur, it would be of value to know the degree to which both positive and negative anticipations are confirmed by actual experience.

The position of the housewife in our society has not had the attention it rightfully deserves. The situation of the older house-wife presents some interesting aspects. Her life adjustment would seem to be dictated by the nature of the changes that occur in her environment. The role of homemaker and child-rearer that occupies her middle years alters considerably as the children reach maturity, marry, leave home, and begin to rear families of their own. Moreover, this role is further modified if her husband retires or if she is left a widow. The question becomes one of whether or not the routine of life established over decades is sufficiently meaningful and satisfying after the changes take place. Does she attempt to recapitulate her child-rearing experiences through contact with grandchildren, grandnephews, and other children within the family group? Or are these efforts generally blocked by the adult children? Is the housewife better able to adjust to later life than women who are retired? Does her homemaker role retain its stabilizing character even after she is left alone by widowhood? Certainly a growing population of older women, the vast majority of whom are housewives, would call for more systematic study of their lives and problems.

The Social Self in Old Age

As indicated earlier, feelings of self-regard play as important a part in the life of the older person as in that of younger people. These self-feelings are usually determined by both the life history of the individual's personality and by his relationships to others. Hence, the self-image concept may be viewed as having a social aspect that can be investigated as readily by attitude research as by investigations of personality structure. In this study we approach the problem of self-image by making a comparison between the perception of the individual's life circumstances in juxtaposition to those of his contemporaries. To what extent does the older person feel that his life and condition compare favorably or unfavorably with that of others? What factors influence such comparisons? Are factors of self-image related to the basic adjustment of the older person? Do older people regard themselves as "old" or "middle-aged" and what factors contribute to this self-judgment? We should be especially interested in determining the relationship between the person's own age and his view of his agedness. At the same time, it would be advantageous to learn whether older people of differing stations in life regard themselves differently at various given age levels.

Much has been made of the growth of conservatism in the later years. Little is known of the degree to which conservative attitudes and behavior are related to one's image of the self and to overall adjustment. Is conservatism the hallmark of aging or is it found only in certain groups among the older population? Are people who are relatively old but who conceive themselves to be middle-aged less conservative than those of the same age group whose self-percept is one of agedness? A further intriguing problem is the relationship between conservative attitudes concerning aging and social adjustment. Are those who are least conservative or more youthful in orientation also better adjusted than those more conservative? In effect, is maintaining a youthful "outlook" a factor in withstanding the "insults" of aging?

The Problems of Isolation and Activity

It is now widely recognized that isolation consequent upon the death or moving away of family and friends is a major problem for many old people. Not yet understood, however, is the extent to which isolation is a factor in the individual's general adjustment. One immediate problem that presents itself is whether residential isolation and social isolation produce the same effects. Is the person who has lived alone during most of his life, or who lives alone though he has many contacts with friends and relations, in the same relative psychological situation as the person who is socially isolated? Further, what of the isolated widow or retired person? Are there compensations for being alone in later life? Does isolation lead to a retreat from interest in other people and in activities outside the immediate home situation? We shall also want to inquire into the degree to which the health of the older person influences or is affected by his social relationships.

Both the literature and programs of service for older people are placing greater emphasis upon activity in later life. It is contended that activities tend to reduce morbid speculation about oneself and the future, that they have therapeutic effects upon the emotional life of the individual. At the same time, there is a widespread public belief that activities in old age act as "preservatives"; they put off physical deterioration and even death. It would be good now to subject some of these assumptions and beliefs to empirical test. Is being active aside from gainful employment associated with better adjustment in old age? What of the employed person having no outside interests and engaged in few or no activities? Are active people in better health than inactive people and is there some reason to believe that activity enhances health? Are those who are retired or unemployed, yet active in outside affairs, better adjusted than those in the same groups who are inactive?

Activity programs and centers are growing in importance throughout the country. Some light shed on this problem may aid in pointing out those groups for whom these programs may prove most beneficial.

FACTORS AFFECTING OR AFFECTED BY HEALTH

Nearly everyone concerned with the problems of aging is also concerned with health in old age: its significance in respect to other aspects of being, its maintenance, its deterioration, its restoration, and so forth. Health studies of older people have in the past been interested in the ailments found among various groups of the aged. Very little work has been done in testing random samples of older people in the population to determine their health status. Yet it is of prime importance to know the extent of illness among older people, the types of illnesses, whether they are acute or chronic, the length of time they have been manifest, what type, if any, of medical care was sought and with what effects. Perhaps even more significant are the long-term consequences of illness. To what degree are older people able to carry on their usual activities despite the presence of medical complaints? Are there differences between different subgroupings of older people in their "stoicism" regarding medical complaints? Do cultural factors play some role in determining the severity of the consequences of illness?

Since older people tend to be less able to afford medical care, are there economic group differences in the state of health between those of high and low socioeconomic status and do such differences also hold for various income groups? It would be interesting to know just how older people handle their medical problems. Are their physicians consulted only for serious illnesses, or does the increased hazard of serious complaints in old age create a greater desire for regular medical checkups? Beyond this, it would be of relevance to know whether regular preventive examinations are, in fact, related to one's health status. Are those who are more "health conscious" and care routinely for their medical needs less vulnerable to the ills of aging than those who cannot or will not seek adequate medical care? In this connection, it will be of interest also to inquire into the relationship between possession of prepaid health insurance and the state of health.

A question that arises frequently in connection with health is the extent to which one's perception of his own health coincides with his actual health status. It has been contended that old people tend to extremes: either they ignore even dangerous medical conditions and gloss over their discomforts or they are hypochondriacal, spending much time ruminating over symptoms and attending clinics. An empirical demonstration of this dichotomy would be fruitful, inasmuch as it could point out the extent to which some groups are receiving unnecessary attention and others are receiving too little. Since more than 90 per cent of old people do not reside in institutions, assessment of their actual health needs in the community would be of first importance.

If a tendency to hypochondriasis is present in some older people, it would be of significance to learn to what extent health is viewed as a major life problem for older people in general. One means of determining the value position of health, aside from inquiring directly into the matter, would be to assess the degree of expressed anxiety over health. To what extent does his health worry the aging person? Is worry a general characteristic or is it clearly related to circumstances; that is, those who are ill worry and those who are well do not? Is anxiety about health a cultural phenomenon—more acute in some groups and less so in others? Who are the people who never worry about health?

Health is but one facet of life, yet it may loom large in the minds of many, perhaps as the core problem. Does the state of his health markedly affect the older person's outlook on life or are there equally potent factors that contribute to morale and feelings of well-being? These are certainly important questions to answer if an attack on the major problems that beset the older population is to prove successful.

THE USE OF COMMUNITY HEALTH SERVICES

To those charged with planning community services for the aged, the actual as well as the potential use of such services is of great importance. Therefore, in regard to health we should be in a better position to know who are the current users of community health services and who the nonusers. Are those in greatest need of services the persons who are receiving them? Is there an army of potential users who are for various reasons not now being cared for? How much truth is there in the assumption that the person who is generally busy will also be more inclined to use community health facilities than is the person who is less active in social or community life? Are those who are socially isolated not influenced by or drawn to community services in his behalf?

The use of community health services may be greatly influenced by the older person's attitudes toward health-connected institutions, the health professions, and by health personnel. Does a positive attitude toward health facilities increase the likelihood of their being used or does attitude make no difference?

An intriguing question is whether or not cultural factors play a role in the use of community facilities. Are there some groups who feel that going to a health clinic is a repugnant act or that visiting a hospital is a sign of weakness? Are there others who feel that the community should provide health facilities for them to use, or that it is in their best interests to have regular examinations regardless of their health? Among older people how prevalent is the belief that one does not call on the services of a physician unless he is seriously ill?

We shall also wish to inquire into the question of the relation of self-attitudes to the use of health services. Are those who regard themselves as older and more conservative among the greater users or are those who claim youth in age and outlook the greater users? Is age itself a factor in the pattern of use?

Specialized Services

A final issue regarding health is the question of specialized services for the aged. Although resisted by many professionals in the health field, geriatric clinics and hospitals are developing sporadically. Of serious concern, aside from the desirability of special medical facilities for the older person, is whether or not older people would utilize such services. Are there definable sub-groups among the aged who would prefer such a facility to one established for all age groups? Are there status, age, or sex differences in acceptance or rejection of the geriatric concept of health services? Planning for health services depends to a considerable extent upon a first-hand knowledge of potential users. If resistance to geriatric services is found in certain sectors of the older group, plans would have to be modified accordingly.

A similar consideration is involved in the establishment of social or recreational facilities for the aged. For whom shall these facilities be organized? Will they be for the more active residents of the community primarily, or for the very old or senile? Are feelings about old age clubs or golden age centers universal or are there divided feelings and differences in the disposition to use them? In both the fields of health and recreation, identification of a program with a particular age group may preclude from service those who do not identify or who do not care to identify with the age group concerned. On the other hand, there may be some who would not be attracted except for the fact that a special group is to be served.

PLANNING THE RESEARCH

The issues, problems, and questions raised in the foregoing sections are those dealt with in our study. Combined in it are the programmatic concerns of public health officials, social welfare planners, and the more theoretical concerns of the social scientist.

Conducting a survey as a precursor of an action program is a time-honored method of social science. Indeed, even if there were no programmatic implication, a survey of problems among a particular segment of the population can serve a number of useful functions: (1) It can point out the extent to which certain problems are felt by the sheer weight of numbers among whom they are found; (2) it can locate differences in response between various elements within the populations studied; and (3) it can put to the test certain assumptions or popularly held beliefs and, by concentrating on some special group, can draw out relatively finer points of significance concerning their attitudes and behavior. The Kips Bay-Yorkville study exemplifies each of these approaches to social planning. Its overall aim was to serve as a guide in determining the nature and extent of the problems and felt needs of the aged population of the area. Specifically, it sought to compare the responses of various groups, such as economic, age, ethnic groups, in order to bring into sharp relief those social and cultural factors facilitating adjustment to old age. It also sought to verify the validity of such oft-heard contentions as: the aged are relatively an ill part of the population; the aged are apathetic about their health; they are compulsively rigid in their habits and modes of thought, hence unable to use new services in their behalf; they do not participate in community affairs; they are miserable and unhappy as a group. Finally, the survey has focused on certain special subgroups among the aged and tried to spell out some of their problems in greater detail.

Constantly, throughout the survey, the primary consideration was: Will this question or these findings provide us with clues concerning the type or types of services elderly people feel they need most keenly but lack at present? Also, what guides to community programs will be accepted by the aged person?

The merging of interests of practitioner and social research has both positive and negative aspects when applied to a contemporary problem. The salutary contribution lies in the fact that social scientific techniques are applied to an immediate societal concern and projected upon a "living" community. Also to be listed on the credit side, is the attempt to base social planning upon more than local pressures and subjective impressions. The fact that health and social agencies have "grown like Topsy" with duplication of service and misplacement of community resources has long been deplored by social work and public health leaders. On the debit side may be the fact that the pursuit of immediate action goals has required the abandonment of some significant basic social scientific data about the general position of the aged in our culture.

The themes that run throughout this report attempt to trace the impact of urban social forces upon older persons and to show how these are internalized in the individual to create a sense of security or, conversely, elements of distress. What supports can the older person find in his urban social milieu to help meet the threats of illness, social isolation, and confusion regarding an adequate functional role? Are there contradictions in society between the standards of conduct set for all citizens and the means which would enable older citizens to meet these goals? Is it possible for the aged person to meet without demoralization the "insults" that a youth-oriented society heaps upon him? What can be added to the older person's armor by forces in the community to make him better able to withstand the stresses and strains that operate upon him? How can we prevent the dysfunctions of society from adversely affecting the individual?

In attempting to discern cultural elements that tend to have disruptive effects on the individual, the social scientist can help to provide a description of such forces. In studying the problems of the aged, this responsibility becomes most urgent. The well-being of 13 million individuals is a matter of major importance to our society. In this study of a cross-sectional group of aged persons, an attempt was made to make some sense of the aged person's relationship to his environment. It is hoped that by this means insight will be gained into a complex of problems coming daily to be among the foremost of our time.

Chapter 2

The Study Community

AT THE OUTSET, we would do well to provide two types of background for the chapters that follow. First, we shall look at the community that came under study and from which our subjects were drawn. From this brief observation, we can place the older population in the context of their homes and neighborhoods to understand better what they have to say and how they behave. Second, we shall take an overview of the group we have selected to study. Knowing who and what they are and where they came from will provide the necessary information to proceed to the central problems of the investigation.

THE COMMUNITY SETTING: KIPS BAY-YORKVILLE[1]

The survey upon which this report is based was conducted in the Kips Bay-Yorkville Health District of New York City, an area of about two-and-one-half square miles on the East Side of Manhattan Island, lying between Central Park and the East River and bounded roughly by 89th Street to the north and 34th Street to the south. It is one of New York's 30 health districts and houses about 252,000 persons according to the 1950 Census.

The health district is an administrative unit created in order to facilitate the decentralization of much of the work of the New York City Department of Health, particularly of those services dealing directly with individuals. The size and complexity of the city and the resulting variations in health problems from place to place and group to group clearly require such units which allow for corresponding local variations in health services. New

[1] This section was prepared with the collaboration of Dr. Ann P. Kent, district health officer of Kips Bay-Yorkville Health District, City of New York.

York, particularly Manhattan Island, has had many demonstrations of the effectiveness of the "district" or "neighborhood" approach to health and welfare problems in the accomplishments of settlement houses and other voluntary groups interested in various specific problems. Leaders of these voluntary agencies have been active in initiating and furthering the movement toward decentralizing of official agency services.

The present boundaries of the districts were established after taking into consideration pertinent data from the 1920 and 1930 federal censuses, local vital statistics, current and past elementary school registration figures, transportation lines, monthly rentals as an index of economic levels, hospitals and other health services and, finally, the existence of any fairly well-defined religious, ethnic, or population groupings which could be said to constitute a "community" or "neighborhood." Local vital statistics were made available by the Health Department on the basis of health areas. The boundaries of these health areas were coterminous with federal census tracts, and each area contained approximately 25,000 persons. Each health district consists of approximately a quarter-million population, or about ten health areas. In 1924 a redistricting of an area on the East Side of Manhattan took place in line with the recommendations of a study committee. As a result, the area south of 34th Street became part of the newly created Lower East Side Health District and the territory north of 34th Street became part of the present Kips Bay-Yorkville Health District.

The Kips Bay-Yorkville District consists of three essentially different areas: Yorkville East and Yorkville West, with Third Avenue as the boundary line between them; and Kips Bay, the area lying south of 59th Street.

The Kips Bay section, extending from 34th Street to 59th Street, takes its name from a prominent citizen of New York's early days, Jacob Kip, who in the latter half of the seventeenth century owned a farm of approximately 150 acres fronting on the East River in this area. The home which he built became a local landmark, and a community bearing his name grew up around his property. The northward push of the city overtook this semirural settlement in the early 1800's. The famous old Kips Mansion was demolished to make way for the eastern extension of 35th Street and hundreds of brownstone homes soon replaced the surrounding small farms. In the early part of this century, another trend became apparent—a change from a predominantly residential area into one that is primarily a business district. A few apartment houses and many hotels now constitute most of what is left of residential property in this area. The latter change became especially noticeable after World War I and has resulted in a steady decrease in the population of this area.

The Yorkville area, extending from 59th Street to the boundaries of East Harlem, has had a somewhat different history. A hamlet of this name was in existence in the late 1700's. It centered around the old Boston Post Road (Third Avenue) between what is now 83rd and 89th Streets. Nearby, along the East River, were estates of several of Manhattan's early settlers—the Rhinelanders, Astors, and Primes. In 1834 the New York and Harlem Railroad was extended to the village, and a year later a stagecoach line was established. By the end of 1880 the country mansions had disappeared and block after block of brownstone houses, the homes of prosperous citizens, covered most of the area. These homes, in turn, gave way to population pressures generated by the flood-tide of immigration at the turn of the century. Individual homes were replaced by multiple dwellings. Many of these buildings, especially east of Third Avenue, were constructed before the passage of the Tenement House Act in 1901 and consequently have furnished unsatisfactory living quarters for thousands of families from the day they were opened. They have not improved with the passage of time. The area west of Third Avenue did not experience this blight. Quite a few individual homes remain there and the apartment houses which have replaced most of them are generally of the luxury type.

In the 1920's a fringe of large luxurious apartment houses and a few small, expensive, private homes began to appear along the edge of the East River. This trend was temporarily halted by World War II, but since then other high-rent multiple dwellings have been built throughout Yorkville. Many old, substandard tenement houses east of Third Avenue have been extensively renovated and remodeled and are currently occupied by an entirely new set of tenants, since the rents are now far beyond the means of families who formerly lived there. This gradual redevelopment of the East Yorkville section into a comparatively high rental residential area is expected to continue and will undoubtedly be accelerated by the demolition of the Third Avenue Elevated structure. In contrast to Kips Bay, there is very little big business in Yorkville; commercial activity is almost entirely limited to a multitude of service trade establishments.

Yorkville, like Kips Bay to the south, has experienced a drop in population in the past thirty years. The change in both instances appears to be part of a general exodus from Manhattan which has taken place as the metropolitan area has developed and is also the result of local changes in the character of the neighborhood.

The economic contrasts in the District can be illustrated by the range of housing to be found within its boundaries. The average rental in about one-fourth of the 359 residential blocks in the area is under $40 a month, while at the other extreme average monthly rentals are $170 or more in nearly one-fifth of the blocks.[1] The District is also characterized by a large proportion of one-dwelling unit structures, which are rare on Manhattan Island. Of the 1,158 such units to be found in Manhattan, 520 (over two-fifths) are located within the Kips Bay-Yorkville Health District. Moreover, the average value of these structures in the District is considerably higher than the comparable figure for Manhattan as a whole. It seems safe to assume that in Kips Bay-Yorkville, these single-dwellings are homes of the well-to-do. These variations in rentals are accompanied by all the other conditions differentiating substandard tenements and luxury housing with all their ramifications for the individual and his family.

Of the total District population, about one-third are foreign born (a somewhat higher proportion than in New York City as a whole) and less than one-half of 1 per cent are nonwhite. The

---

[1] A breakdown of average rentals for the 359 residential blocks in Kips Bay-Yorkville is given in Table A, Appendix 1. The figures cited are from the 1950 Census of Housing.

concentration of foreign-born persons is to be found mainly in the Yorkville East area. The original village of Yorkville had a good many German settlers and many Germans moved up from the Tompkins Square section of lower Manhattan in the 1800's. In the early years of this century, other ethnic groups also made their homes here, notably Czechs, Hungarians, Irish, and Italians. There was an influx of Austro-Germans after World War I. For many years they remained in the original Yorkville settlement around Third Avenue in the eighties. However, a gradual process of dispersion is now taking place and the neighborhood no longer has the strong Germanic flavor it once had. Altogether, some 20 nationalities are represented in Yorkville.

A combination of factors have contributed to a new phenomenon that is becoming increasingly apparent in the Yorkville East area from which the bulk of our survey respondents is drawn. This phenomenon is the growing vestigial character of the older population. Young people have tended not to move into the area. Those already in it have tended to move elsewhere. Except for some mass shifts out of the area of Czechoslovakian-born residents, the old immigrants are being left behind. The situation faced by them is not entirely a happy one, since redevelopment of the area has been growing in momentum. The drab multiple-dwelling buildings so characteristic of the area are giving way to mammoth luxury apartment dwellings. If it has not yet struck him, the older person sees on all sides the gradual dissolution and replacement of old neighborhoods he has known since he migrated. Residual pockets of elderly, mainly foreign-born persons have come into being. Although the complete redevelopment of the area will take many years to accomplish, the transition is taking place. Many of our survey respondents spoke ruefully of the changes that are coming and seemed anxious about the prospects of being relocated. The City of New York plans no municipal low-rent housing developments in the area; hence, displacement and relocation seem in the offing for many.

The birth rate in all three sections of the Kips Bay-Yorkville Health District is lower than that of the city as a whole; the crude death rate is somewhat higher. Death rates from degenerative diseases are higher than are corresponding city rates, as is the neonatal death rate. Traffic is very heavy throughout the District and because of this and the existence of many dilapidated tenements the accident rate, vehicular and other, is higher here than in the city as a whole.

The economically underprivileged area, Yorkville East, has the higher birth and crude death rates, but not the higher neonatal rate. The population is comparatively younger here than in the rest of the District, but the rates for deaths from degenerative diseases are higher than for its other sections. This area has another health hazard not present in Kips Bay and Yorkville West, namely, tuberculosis. The death rate here from this disease is three times what it is in the more prosperous sections and higher than that of the city as a whole.

The health picture presented by these figures is not an entirely satisfactory one, especially in the Yorkville East area where a relatively old population containing a high proportion of foreign-born persons are living under generally substandard conditions.

Within Kips Bay-Yorkville there are some 50 nonresidential city blocks. Occupying them and some of the blocks adjacent are a variety of public, private, and commercial structures that are part of the renowned character of the city. The United Nations buildings and associated structures, the Chrysler Building, the Empire State Building, the famous Fifth Avenue shops, St. Patrick's Cathedral, and Rockefeller Center are located in Kips Bay and on its fringes. In this area are to be found also the Metropolitan Museum of Art, the Museum of Modern Art, the Frick Art Collection; many of the world's embassies have New York legations here. Also there are the Rockefeller Institute and the Sloan-Kettering Institute, both for medical research; the Cornell Medical College-New York Hospital Medical Center, the Hospital for Special Surgery, Lenox Hill Hospital, and other smaller medical facilities. The eastern portion of the Island is developing into a grand concentration of hospitals, medical research centers, clinics, and medical schools both within and south of the District. There are only a few organized social service agencies in the area. Aside from the usual municipal Welfare Center, the District

Health Center, the Visiting Nurse Service of New York, a branch of a family agency, and a local settlement house, organized social welfare services are carried on by a proliferation of ethnic and religious organizations. Social clubs, nationality societies, and local church groups are to be found on all sides. These groups tend, to a limited extent, to make some services available on a neighborhood basis.

As might be expected, the political character of the District is rather sharply divided between Republicans and Democrats. Part of Yorkville is split between rival factions of the Democratic Party and there is the lingering influence of the late Congressman Vito Marcantonio. The bulk of Kips Bay-Yorkville, at the time of writing (1955), is represented in Congress by a Republican incumbent whose major strength is drawn from the Yorkville West area, famous as New York's "Silk Stocking" district.

The history of the Kips Bay-Yorkville Health District resembles in many ways the story of the development of New York as a whole, and, as it exists now, this comparatively small area presents examples of almost all of the socioeconomic and health features to be found anywhere in the city. It is undoubtedly the least homogeneous of all the city's health districts. Kips Bay-Yorkville has aptly been described as follows by one sociologist:

> Kips Bay-Yorkville is a congeries of urban contrasts. The world's most luxurious apartments—sub-standard tenement housing; expensive hotels—mean boarding houses; exclusive private schools—outdated, crowded public schools; cathedrals—humble chapels; ranking income tax payers—families on relief for years; "the world's finest stores"—push carts; old American families—newly arrived refugees; all these and others go to make up an urban area with a thousand problems generated by too many people trying to live in too little space.[1]

Since we are most concerned with the age group past sixty, an analysis was made of the 1950 Census data and of New York City Health Department statistics regarding this group. In 1950 there were about 44,500 persons over sixty living in the District, com-

[1] Koos, Earl L., editor, *Kips Bay-Yorkville: 1940.* Department of Public Health and Preventive Medicine, Cornell University Medical College, New York, 1942, Introduction.

prising 17.7 per cent of the population of the area. This proportion is well above the general relation of those over sixty to the total population of the city. On the average city block in the area there are about 138 people over the age of sixty.

THE SURVEY SAMPLE[1]

A total of 500 residents of Kips Bay-Yorkville participated in the survey. This represents a little more than 1 per cent of the population of the area over the age of sixty,[2] the age selected as the baseline of eligibility in the survey. The sample may be described as a stratified sample and is not "representative" of the area in the literal sense of the word. It was felt early in the study that because of the economic distribution of the District, with its great proportion of well-to-do elderly residents, it would be best to weight the relative proportions of each economic group to be included in the survey, in order to lay our greatest stress upon the lower economic and social strata of the area. The decision to assign these weights was dictated by the knowledge that decisions concerning a service-oriented program for the aged should be based upon data provided by those most likely to utilize such a service: the group having less means and at a lower level of the social ladder. Hence, although a much larger proportion of well-to-do persons reside in Kips Bay-Yorkville, only 11 per cent of the sample are drawn from among them. A little less than 30 per cent come from the middle class, and the bulk, just under 60 per cent, is selected from the lower socioeconomic group. With this limitation incorporated within the sample, our findings tend to overrepresent the lower economic group and to underrepresent the upper economic group in this District. It will be noted, however, that the proportions employed for the study are not too far removed from what one would expect to find in almost any large urban complex.

With one or two exceptions, all the respondents in the survey were interviewed in their homes by a corps of 30 trained interviewers. The interviews followed a prescribed sequence of ques-

[1] A detailed account of the sample selection procedure is given in Appendix 1.

[2] As determined by the 1950 Census.

tions and each required from one to one-and-a-half hours to complete.[1] Areas covered by the questionnaire, in addition to basic personal data, were: the individual's health status with a rather detailed survey of major health problem areas,[2] their knowledge of, attitudes toward, and use of various medical and health services, social activities, extent of contact with peers and relatives, attitudes toward old age, feelings concerning their own aging, areas of satisfaction or dissatisfaction with employment or retirement, specific complaints and problems concerning their style of life, standard of living, housing, leisure time, community participation, and their attitudes toward the use of specialized services for the aged.

TABLE 1. SEX ACCORDING TO MARITAL STATUS

Marital status	Male	Female	Total	Number of cases
		(Percentages)		
Single	11	19	16	80
Married	63	18	35	174
Widowed	20	59	44	220
Divorced	2	4	3	16
Separated	4		2	10
Total	100	100	100	
Number of cases	188	312		500

The people studied range in age from sixty to ninety, with the average a little under seventy years. Following the 1950 Census proportions, slightly more than 60 per cent of the group are women. With increasing age, the number of women to men in the sample becomes greater until the oldest group (47 persons over eighty) contains nearly four women for every man interviewed.

Marital status plays an important role in the adjustment of the older person. It is of interest to note, therefore, that of each 100

[1] The interview schedule is to be found in Appendix 2.

[2] Grateful acknowledgment is made of the consultation and suggestions generously given during the preparation of this section of the questionnaire by: Beatrice Berle, M.D., Ann P. Kent, M.D., Homer C. Wick, Jr., M.D.—all members of the faculty of Cornell University Medical College, Department of Public Health and Preventive Medicine, and by John M. Weir, M.D., assistant director of the Division of Medicine and Public Health, Rockefeller Foundation.

respondents, 16 had never married (there being somewhat more men than women in this grouping), 35 were married, 44 were widowed, and 5 were either divorced or separated. As summarized in Table 1, the proportion of men who are married is three and one-half times that of the women. Correspondingly, the proportion of widows is nearly three times that of widowers. These facts reflect the tendency to greater longevity in women, partly accounting for the great numbers of widows. It is estimated that at present there are 7.5 million widows in the United States.

TABLE 2. AGE ACCORDING TO SOCIOECONOMIC STATUS

| Socioeconomic status | Age (in years) | | | | | Number of cases |
	60 to 64	65 to 69	70 to 74	75 to 79	80 and over	
	(Percentages)					
High	15	8	10	13	8	55
Middle	41	30	25	17	32	148
Low	44	62	65	70	60	297
Total	100	100	100	100	100	
Number of cases	117	139	115	82	47	500

By religious preference, 49 per cent of the sample are Catholic, 37 per cent are Protestant, and 9 per cent are Jewish. Other religions and "no preference" make up the remainder. These proportions again reflect the special population of aged with whom we are here dealing, since they vary considerably even from those of New York City as a whole.[1]

A unique attribute of the aged population is indicated in Table 2. With increasing age, there is a tendency for the proportion in the middle class to shrink,[2] swelling the proportion in the

[1] The proportions of the three religious groups in the population of New York City as a whole are estimated to be: Catholic, 48 per cent; Protestant, 23 per cent; Jewish, 26 per cent. (Deardorff, Neva R., "The Religio-cultural Background of New York City's Population," 1955). The Kips Bay-Yorkville area is further characterized by an extremely low nonwhite population (fewer than 1 per cent falling in this category), which is predominantly Protestant in New York City. Moreover, despite the great influx of Puerto Ricans in New York (many of whom are Catholic), almost no settlement of them has occurred in Kips Bay-Yorkville.

[2] While this reduction in numbers may be a function of our socioeconomic stratification, it is a fact that with increasing age it became more difficult to find respondents fitting our middle economic category. See Appendix 1.

lower economic group.[1] This downward trend is most visible during the "retirement years" (sixty-five to sixty-nine years of age).

Income-wise, of the 462 people who answered the question, 45 per cent are receiving *less* than $25 per week from all sources. An additional 25 per cent of the group receives less than $50 per week. Seven per cent are receiving more than $100 per week. If it is true that "two can live as cheaply as one," those who are still married are far better off economically than either the group that have never married or the widowed. The proportion of married men who have incomes of more than $25 per week is three times that of single and widowed men, and the similar ratio for women is five to one.

The family life patterns of our respondents reflect the situations produced by widowhood and sex differences in survival. While only one-half of the women have some kind of companionship in their households, fully three-quarters of the men live with either their spouse or some relative or friend.

Employment, or the lack of it, constitutes a serious social and economic problem among the aged. In our sample, 32 per cent of the group were gainfully employed either on a full- or part-time basis, 8 per cent considered themselves "unemployed," 33 per cent of the sample were "retired," and 27 per cent were housewives who had never worked.

Forty-six per cent of the men but only 22 per cent of the women were still working. The expected rise with increasing age in the numbers of retired individuals occurs in the sample. There are some especially interesting subgroups: 96 widowed housewives who have never worked; 42 employed widows, of whom 12 own their own businesses; and 28 unemployed women seeking to break into the labor market.

Regarding their education, the median educational attainment is grade school graduation. Thirty-four per cent did not complete grade school, but 19 per cent had some high school and 9 per cent went to college. This relative lack of formal education is understandable when one considers the fact that 70 per cent of

[1] The index of socioeconomic status used in this study is described in Appendix 3.

the group are foreign-born and 60 per cent are in the lower economic group. Further, there were not the educational opportunities fifty to seventy years ago in Europe or in the United States that there are now.

The foreign-born group is primarily European, with most of that continent well represented (Table 3). From a socioeconomic

TABLE 3. SOCIOECONOMIC STATUS ACCORDING TO ETHNIC ORIGIN

		Per cent			
Ethnic origin	High status[a]	Low status	Total	Number of cases	Per cent of sample
Germany, Austria	39	61	100	116	23
Ireland	30	70	100	66	13
United States	56	44	100	63[b]	13[b]
Hungary	33	67	100	55	11
Czechoslovakia	29	71	100	42	9
England, Wales, Scotland	52	48	100	39	8
Italy	48	52	100	27	5
Russia, Poland	51	49	100	27	5
Other	30	70	100	65	13
Total				500	100

[a] In tables where only "high" and "low" status are reported, "middle" status is included in the "high" status group.

[b] These are U. S.-born respondents whose fathers were also born in the U. S. There were 87 other U. S.-born respondents whose fathers were foreign-born; they were distributed among the various ethnic groups according to father's country of birth.

point of view, there are wide differences among the various ethnic groups that may play a significant part in understanding their respective forms of adjustment. Those of American and British birth have the greatest proportion in the high status group, while those of Czech and Irish origin have their greatest numbers in the low status group. Although our sample was deliberately drawn to form numerically fixed socioeconomic status groups, it is interesting that so few immigrants of high status are to be found in it.

These are the people in the survey—1 per cent of the aged population of Kips Bay-Yorkville. Not included among our respondents were those institutionalized in hospitals, mental institutions, homes for the aged, and nursing homes. Hence, 6 per cent (approximately) of the potential numbers eligible for the study were thereby unavailable. Moreover, those interviewed in the study who were in serious ill health, senile, or mentally disturbed are probably underrepresented in our sample; some potential respondents could not be interviewed because of their condition. Hence, the sample group probably is slightly healthier, less senile, and less emotionally disturbed than is generally the case in the aged population of this area.

PART II
PATTERNS OF ADJUSTMENT IN OLD AGE

Part II:

Patterns of Adjustment in Old Age

EXTENSIVE AND COGENT THINKING on old age as a period of personal and social adjustment has occupied numerous social scientists, psychiatrists, social workers, community welfare service planners, and gerontologists.[1] Havighurst has noted that needs that are common to all younger age groups are also common to the older person.[2] He lists these needs as: emotional security, social recognition, a sense of worth or self-respect and adequate food, clothing, shelter, and health. He asserts that satisfaction of these needs is denied to older people because of their loss of peers, status, health, attractiveness, and social roles. He goes on to define the adjustments required of older people: adjustment to death of spouse, loss of employment and reduced income, affiliation with others of the same age, decrease of physical vigor, and working out satisfactory living arrangements. According to Havighurst, adjustment to the social and psychological traumata common in old age consists of changes in behavior and attitude that permit continuation of a balanced life.

Greenleigh regards aging as a "continuum of adaptation." He defines adaptation as the mobilization of the individual's "personality strengths to meet the demands made upon him by

[1] Barron, Milton L., Gordon Streib, and Edward A. Suchman, "Research on the Social Disorganization of Retirement," 1952; Cavan, Ruth S., and others, *Personal Adjustment in Old Age*, 1949; Donahue, Wilma T., "Psychological Aspects of Aging," 1951; Donahue, Wilma T., and Clark Tibbitts, editors, *Planning the Older Years*, 1950; Idem, *Growing in the Older Years*, 1951; Havighurst, Robert J., and Ruth Albrecht, *Older People*, 1953; Nuffield Foundation, *Old People*, 1947; Pollak, Otto, *Social Adjustment in Old Age*, 1948; Schmidt, John Frank, "Patterns of Poor Adjustment in Old Age," 1951; Tibbitts, Clark, editor, *Living Through the Older Years*, 1949; Welfare Council of Metropolitan Chicago, *Community Services for Older People:* The Chicago Plan, 1952.

[2] Havighurst, Robert J., "Social and Psychological Needs of the Aging," 1952.

45

stresses in his daily living."[1] Successful or unsuccessful aging ("dissolution") depends on the older person's adaptability to stress. Greenleigh's position is that ability to adapt in old age is strongly dependent upon successful adaptation throughout the life span. Hence, constitutional, developmental, and situational factors that influence adjustment at earlier age levels are also at work during the later years. Nevertheless, the basic point made is that adaptation requires some form of "action" to meet the stresses of life in old age.

A commonly accepted point of view and one confirmed in part by research findings[2] is that activities (social participation, community work, hobbies, and other forms of expression) help to reduce the stresses created by aging by substituting one meaningful role for another or by diverting energy away from the morbid aspects of the growing-old process. Havighurst and Albrecht found, for example, happiness and good social adjustment to be functions of a large number of social roles and a high degree of activity within these roles. Burgess, however, writes: "The crucial question remains for further research: Does participation in group activities . . . increase . . . personal adjustment as measured by happiness scores? Or do those who are well-adjusted tend to engage in social activities?"[3] In other words, is social adjustment the condition making for heightened activity (and, if so, how can this adjustment be accounted for), or do activities tend to increase social adjustment?

Maladjustment is frequently associated with a lack of congruence between motivational needs on the one hand and their satisfaction on the other. Hence, maladjustment may occur when the individual makes reasonable demands upon the environment to satisfy his basic needs but his life circumstances prevent their satisfaction (for example, a man with strong dependency needs

[1] Greenleigh, Lawrence F., *Psychological Problems of Our Aging Population*, 1952, p. 6.

[2] See: Cavan, Ruth, and others, *Op. cit.;* Havighurst, Robert J., and Ruth Albrecht, *Op. cit.;* Burgess, Ernest W., "Social Relations, Activities, and Personal Adjustment," 1954; Havighurst, Robert J., "Flexibility and the Social Roles of the Retired," 1954.

[3] Burgess, Ernest W., "Social Relations, Activities, and Personal Adjustment," 1954, pp. 359–360.

whose wife dies). Maladjustment may also occur when the individual's demands are unreasonable, in that the reality situation precludes their satisfaction and substitute satisfactions are not acceptable (for example, a woman whose husband can no longer work berates him because their standard of living is declining and refuses to make appropriate adjustments).

The foregoing discussion seems to lead to the following conceptualization: Adjustment requires on the part of the individual flexibility and the capacity to change his activities, roles, motives, and social perceptions. Our concept of adjustment is not designed to cover all possible meanings ascribed to this term but is to be regarded as a concept limited to the context of this report. In this section, we shall examine this area of content and, at the same time, attempt to locate the determinants of adjustment and maladjustment in our sample population.

Chapter 3

Measuring Adjustment:
The Criterion of Morale

THE TERM "ADJUSTMENT" used in reference to personality, social relationships, or to success in dealing with life problems has proved to be a thorny problem. Although we may agree as to its components, it is often more difficult to find operational (attitudinal or behavioral) criteria by which adjustment can be systematically evaluated. Although almost any criteria can be criticized for failing to account for one or another factor, we chose as our criterion a measure of "morale."[1]

In this study we shall mean by morale a continuum of responses to life and living problems that reflect the presence or absence of satisfaction, optimism, and expanding life perspectives. It should be clear from this definition that morale and adjustment are part of the same phenomenon. Morale refers to a mental state or a set of dispositions, while adjustment refers to behaviors that stem from these dispositions. Hence, we may assume that an attitude or evaluation scale of morale measures life adjustment.

The morale scale employed is based upon responses to the following items:

1. How often do you feel there's just no point in living?
2. Things just keep getting worse and worse for me as I get older.
3. How much do you regret the chances you missed during your life to do a better job of living?

[1] A summary term adopted from the Elmira Study of Aging. The scale is derived from the same source. The Elmira Study is part of a general community study of Elmira, New York, conducted by the Department of Anthropology and Sociology of Cornell University.

4. All in all, how much unhappiness would you say you find in life today?

5. On the whole, how satisfied would you say you are with your way of life today?

6. How much do you plan ahead the things you will be doing next week or the week after—would you say you make many plans, a few plans, or almost none?

7. As you get older, would you say things seem to be better or worse than you thought they would be?

Scores of one point each were given for the following response categories. They are presented below with their distribution.[1]

Item	Scored response	Number of cases	Per cent
1. No point in living	Hardly ever	389	78
2. Things get worse and worse	Disagree	325	65
3. Regret chances missed	Not at all	252	50
4. How much unhappiness	Almost none	216	43
5. How satisfied with life today	Very satisfied	192	38
6. Planning ahead	Many or a few plans	176	35
7. Things seem better or worse	Better	117	23

For purposes of analysis, the respondents were divided into three groups of approximately equal size. The groups represent high, medium, and low morale scores.

Morale	Scores	Number of cases	Per cent
High	0 to 2	185	37
Medium	3 to 4	150	30
Low	5 to 6	165	33
Total		500	100

We can now proceed to our analysis of adjustment. To begin with, it would be valuable to assess the morale of our sample according to some of the major "conditioning" factors such as age, economic status, sex, income, and health.

[1] Scalability of these items is discussed in Appendix 4.

It might be assumed that the frustrations and disjunctive factors that afflict older people would result, to an increasing degree, in a reduction in morale in each older age group. As more trying life problems cumulate over the years, the person's efforts to face and overcome them yield diminishing returns. We see in Table 4 that a gradual systematic decrease in morale occurs over the years. The largest decline in morale or adjustment among those over sixty appears to occur in the sixty-five to sixty-nine-year-old age group.[1]

TABLE 4. MORALE ACCORDING TO AGE

Morale	Age (in years)				Number of cases
	60 to 64	65 to 69	70 to 74	75 and over	
	(Percentages)				
High	47	39	36	27	185
Medium	28	24	28	36	150
Low	25	37	36	37	165
Total	100	100	100	100	
Number of cases	117	139	115	129	500

If life entailed the same problems, conflicts, and frustrations for all older people, there would be no need to discuss the effects of role changes with aging. However, such role differences do occur, although their sharpness becomes attenuated with advancing years.[2] The male and female roles and their changes are particularly significant in later life. With this in mind, let us carefully scrutinize the sex differences in adjustment at the different age levels (Table 5).

With respect to the women first, it should be noted that morale declines *gradually* with increasing age. The proportion of those having low morale is about the same through the years, and the

[1] While the decrease in morale is significant at the .05 level between those sixty to sixty-four and those sixty-five to sixty-nine, the difference between the latter group and those over seventy-five is not significant. Statistical significance is cited throughout the text as a guide to stability of a relationship between variables being studied. Our practice will be to use the 5 per cent level of confidence as the criterion of statistical significance.

[2] This position is developed more fully in Chapter 5.

loss of numbers in the high morale group is absorbed by an increase in the medium morale group. Statistical significance of the differences occurs only between the under sixty-five and the over seventy-five group. We see here that the maladjustments and dislocations of aging include a greater proportion of women in each more advanced age category, but the group shifts slowly. For some women the matter of life adjustment may be affected by the cumulation of the problems of widowhood, declining

TABLE 5. MORALE ACCORDING TO AGE FOR MEN AND WOMEN

Morale	Age (in years)				Number of cases
	60 to 64	65 to 69	70 to 74	75 and over	
	MEN				
	(Percentages)				
High	54	40	48	30	
Medium	29	25	26	27	
Low	17	35	26	43	
Total	100	100	100	100	
Number of cases	48	57	43	40	188
	WOMEN				
	(Percentages)				
High	42	38	32	22	
Medium	26	26	33	42	
Low	32	36	35	36	
Total	100	100	100	100	
Number of cases	69	82	72	89	312
Total number of cases	117	139	115	129	500

living standards and health, loss of peers, and the loss of an important life function. Though spread over the years for some, the trend of morale for the group is gradually but continuously downward. Homemaking, housekeeping, a part-time job, involvement in the rearing of grandchildren may make their situation tolerable, and their role in life may continue to be meaningful into the seventh and eighth decades. The loss of meaningful "life roles" is obscured by the summary age figures in Table 5. For example, although the subgroupings are too small in magnitude to present, there is a tendency for the employed and/or married women to have higher morale than those who are retired and/or widowed. Compensating factors of health, friendships, and maintenance of a household tend to make the decline of morale less sharp than might otherwise be expected.

Among the men, a somewhat different picture appears. Low morale is felt by twice the proportion of the sixty-five to sixty-nine group as in the immediately preceding age group. A mild upturn in morale occurs within the seventy to seventy-four group. It may be anticipated that this increase reflects the balance between those who, having successfully navigated the passage into retirement, are now readjusting adequately to new life conditions and

TABLE 6. MORALE ACCORDING TO SOCIOECO-
NOMIC STATUS

Morale	Socioeconomic status		Number of cases
	High	Low	
	(Percentages)		
High	49	29	185
Medium	29	31	150
Low	22	40	165
Total	100	100	
Number of cases	203	297	500

those whose health status and economic position are moving downward and who are suffering some of the other disadvantages of aging. In the group over seventy-five, morale continues downgrade and begins to spread. Unlike the women, morale in the seventh and eighth decades among men is inclined to be good or bad, with a comparatively smaller intermediate group. This undoubtedly reflects the difference in adjustment between the married, employed, or successfully retired men and the widowers, single, or poorly retired men. A retired widower or retired single man, as indicated later, seems to make the poorest adjustment of the group as a whole.

Turning now to the question of social and economic position, Table 6 indicates that the relationship between morale and socioeconomic status, namely, that low status is associated with low morale and vice versa, is significant.[1] Since income maintenance, respected social position, and freedom from drudgery are associated with high status, this result is readily understood. At the same time, certain factors, such as poor health or reduced income, may be predicted to have a depressing effect on morale despite one's status position. Table 7 presents two remarkable phenom-

TABLE 7. MORALE ACCORDING TO HEALTH FOR HIGH AND LOW SOCIOECONOMIC STATUS[a]

Morale	High status Good health	High status Poor health	Low status Good health	Low status Poor health	Number of cases
	(Percentages)				
High	50	44	39	20	185
Medium	28	30	31	30	150
Low	22	26	30	50	165
Total	100	100	100	100	
Number of cases	137	66	147	150	500

[a] Health is measured by the Physical Health Index, which is described fully in Chapter 8.

ena in this respect: *the apparent failure of poor health to substantially affect morale among those of high status and the profound negative effect of poor health among those of low status.* To detail the significance of Table 7, we find:

1. There is no significant difference in morale between those in good or poor health among the high status group.

2. There is no significant difference in morale between those in poor health of high status and those in good health of low status.

3. Among those in good health there is a tendency for those in the low status group to have lower morale than those in the high

[1] This finding confirms a similar one obtained in the Elmira Community Study but contradicts the finding of the Havighurst and Albrecht (Prairie City) study. In the latter study, no significant relationship appeared. Two possible explanations could account for this difference. One is that the Kips Bay-Yorkville sample and the Prairie City sample are drawn from very different universes: a predominantly foreign-born group in the former study and a predominantly native-born group in the latter. However, it would then be difficult to reconcile the divergent findings of the Prairie City and the Elmira sample which is also drawn from a mainly native-born population. A second explanation might be that the small sample size (100 cases in a town of 7,000 population) of the Prairie City study may have obscured a socioeconomic difference that might have obtained if a larger sample were involved. At this point, the evidence leans in the direction of a socioeconomic differential in adjustment but it is left to further research to confirm or deny.

status group. The difference does not satisfy statistical significance, however.

4. Among those of low status, morale is significantly lower for those in poor health compared to those in good health.

The importance of these findings cannot be underestimated for a deeper understanding of the relation of adjustment to health in old age. The prevailing optimism and sense of well-being of those holding high social and economic status suggests that possession of the cultural marks of attainment, position in life, and other material evidences of success may serve to overcome some of the effects of handicapping conditions of the later years. Note that high status usually is associated with a longer history of personal influence, higher educational attainment, and broader cultural background. It is possible that these develop a greater degree of inner strength or personal resourcefulness to deal with the problems of aging. We can examine this possibility in greater detail now. First, however, with regard to those of low status: not only are their social and economic circumstances related to lower morale but, when ill health intervenes, morale is further depressed. At least insofar as this group is concerned, it is clear that a happier old age might be attained if adequate measures were taken to assure the maintenance of their health.[1] Low status alone acts as a depressant but when coupled with poor health the outlook becomes still more grim.

Status considerations, as we have indicated before, do not yield uniform findings with each of the status groups. With the knowledge that his social and economic position are in themselves important factors, we should want to know more about what types of experiences, conditions of life, and perceptions influence the individual's adjustment. This we shall do in the remaining chapters of this section.

[1] It might be argued that low morale among the low status group is a function of cultural factors. Since members of that group more readily admit to aging, poor health, and conservative views (see Chapters 6 and 8), they would be more ready to tell an interviewer how unhappy they are and to seek sympathy. At the same time, those of high status may be attempting to convince both the interviewer and themselves that things are far better than they actually are. The evidence seems to indicate that while the latter process of self-deception may operate for some, the material position and greater resourcefulness of the group warrants their brighter outlook.

Chapter 4

Marriage and Adjustment

CASE HISTORIES[1]

Mrs. P. is a sixty-year-old Hungarian-born widow, the mother of two daughters. Another child, a son, died in his early teens. Since her husband's death ten years ago, she has been working as a domestic, living in the home of her employer. Even with a small income, she is satisfied with her current standard of living. She has always been of very modest means.

Mrs. P. regards her health as "excellent," although she has had four minor chronic illnesses and would be rated as "fair." None of the illnesses apparently interferes with her work or other activities. Despite the ailments, she has no regular physician but attends a clinic, "though it takes you longer to find out what's wrong." She receives some medicines from her employer and usually lets her relatives worry about her health.

Although she is always eager to visit her family and friends during leisure time, Mrs. P. is very self-reliant. Poorly educated, she is, nevertheless, quite articulate: "If she's in good health a widow should work, same as I am. If you can't do anything, maybe the City will help you. I like to be independent about the dollar. The security is a wonderful thing."

She regards herself as better off than her friends but regrets not having had a better marriage from the economic standpoint. She goes out with friends regularly and invests her small earnings. Although she belongs to no clubs, she likes people. She prefers to be with the younger folk but does not want to be the only older person in the group. She would not want to go alone "and be a stranger," but enjoys attending activities with a friend.

[1] The case histories cited throughout the book are designed to illustrate in graphic fashion some of the points covered by the report. They are fictionalized composites, not representing any particular person, and are drawn in about equal numbers from two sources: the protocols of survey respondents and the case files of the Adult Counseling Services of New York. The latter organization is a sociomedical agency that developed from the results of the survey and deals with the problems of persons past sixty.

Mrs. P. is a Catholic. She goes to church only on holidays and is somewhat apologetic about this: "I figure I don't do anything wrong—no sins. I'm not against the churches. Sometimes a friend takes me. But I don't believe in heaven or hell. You're dead—you're dead."

She regards the later years of life as best and regrets her youth somewhat. She would live "like now" if she could do it over again. Her aim in life now is: "Work long, be well, not be dependent and bother nobody. No sickness—who is going to take care of you?"

*　*　*　*

The following respondent was fairly representative of the married men who seemed to have satisfying relationships with their wives. While Mr. M. has problems, these appear to be circumstantial rather than stemming from any element of personal disorganization.

Mr. M. impressed the interviewer as being a relatively happy man despite his straitened economic circumstances. He was a pleasant looking, white-haired man attired in a very neat business suit of a dark gray tweed and a colorful bow tie. When asked his age, he smilingly asked whether he should give his right age or the one he tells prospective employers. When assured that the information was confidential, he said he was seventy-five years old. He explained that he had been working since he was fourteen—some sixty years—and, as he said, "I'm ready to continue working until the end."

Mr. M. had evidently held many important positions in the business world in his time. He had once earned 30 thousand dollars a year in an export firm. Now he was forced to live on his social security benefits and whatever he could earn in the bookkeeping jobs he picked up frequently. While it was hard for him and his wife to lower their standard of living, he felt they had adjusted to their circumstances quite nicely. He had not been faced with a sudden loss of income—but a gradual decline of income as his business associates and friends died. He felt that this enabled him gradually to learn to accept the fact that he was no longer "a big shot" rather than have to experience one big jolt. Also, he felt that he was blessed in having a wife who put no pressure upon him to do more than he could. She always tells him not to mind their not having "steaks and fancy clothes" any more. They have each other and that is more important.

In exploring the manner in which Mr. M. used his leisure time, the interviewer learned that Mr. M. has always been interested in sports. For many years he had engaged in fencing to keep in trim. Even now, he goes every Saturday afternoon to the Y.M.C.A. and plays checkers. He enjoys this and likes meeting his old friends. He has belonged to this particular Y.M.C.A. since he was a young man and has a special feeling for it. He also has his family and friends to visit with, so that he does not feel completely useless. Nevertheless, when he is not working, he still finds time hanging heavy on his hands.

*   *   *   *

Mrs. Y., aged sixty-four, was a rather attractive, well-groomed woman whose looks belied her years. She seemed conscious of this fact as she laughingly remarked that she used to look like a "wreck." She had gradually reached a point where she had not cared much about her appearance and had failed to have her missing teeth replaced. She did not know why Mr. Y. took an interest in her, since she had neglected herself quite badly. There was a twinkle in her eyes when she said that she guessed her husband just had a need to rehabilitate people. Now, she has upper and lower dentures and also has been undergoing treatment by a dermatologist for "old age itch."

Mrs. Y. spoke with a good deal of warmth about the fact that she had never dreamed that she could respond to marriage as she had. She felt like a youngster again and now was convinced that love was not something restricted to those in their twenties and thirties. When her first husband had died twenty years ago, she guessed she had given up being a female. Out of a mistaken sense of loyalty to him, she did not even consider remarrying. That was wrong, she now realized. "People need to have something to live for, otherwise life is just a bore."

WHEN THE PROBLEMS OF AGING are fully considered, stress is usually laid upon those factors making for poor adjustment with advancing age. Old people are pictured as confronted with one or more major life crises that may lead to the breakdown of the organism unless suitable adaptive mechanisms are called into play. In this chapter and the one that follows, we shall examine our data with respect to levels of adjustment of subgroups in our sample population that have experienced crises in two major life areas—marriage and employment.

First, we turn to the married person, the widow and widower, and the single older person. It will be recalled from our earlier description of the sample in Chapter 2 that 16 per cent are single, 35 per cent are married, and 44 per cent are widowed. A trifling number, 5 per cent, are divorced or separated. We may now examine our sample in more detail. There are more single women than men. The proportion of married men is three and one-half times the proportion of married women, but the proportions reverse for widowers and widows.

Applying our morale scale to those of different marital status, we find in Table 8 the following items of interest:

1. Those who are *single* have a somewhat lower morale than the married men and women as well as the widowers. Within the unmarried group, men seem to be more disadvantaged. In general, people in this group who are employed make up the main part of those with higher morale.

2. Among those who are *married*, morale is approximately the same. Each of the marriage partners, in fulfilling his or her role as breadwinner or housekeeper, maintains a high average morale score.

3. In the *widowed* group, it is the employed widowers who contribute most heavily to the high morale group. Widows divide almost evenly among the three gradations in morale.

4. A relatively high morale group is made up of widowed men.

TABLE 8. MORALE ACCORDING TO SEX FOR SINGLE, MARRIED, AND WIDOWED PERSONS[a]

| | Single | | Married | | Widowed | |
Morale	*Men*	*Women*	*Men*	*Women*	*Men*	*Women*
			(*Percentages*)			
High	10	30	48	45	43	30
Medium	28	36	25	23	35	34
Low	62	34	27	32	22	36
Total	100	100	100	100	100	100
Number of cases	*21*	*59*	*118*	*56*	*37*	*183*

[a] The total number of cases used here is 474. The divorced and separated group number only 26 in all and because of this small number do not warrant reporting.

The paucity of single men in our sample is probably not an accident of our sampling method but may point up the fact that older men are usually married. Whether this means that married men tend to live longer or that elderly bachelorhood is more difficult to manage is left to future researchers to discover. We have too few cases to render any judgment.

Certainly, even a casual examination of Table 8 suggests that sex role differences have a considerable determinative part in adjustment in later life. We shall explore this and other determinants through this chapter.

A small but significant difference exists between the married and the widowed group, with the married group having the higher morale.[1] We shall consider the special problems of widows later in this chapter. As we have noted, about a third of the widows are in each of the three morale categories. While it might be assumed that widowhood might have a generally devastating effect upon morale, the length of one's widowhood does make some difference, as we shall see. This suggests that the marital state, *per se*, is not necessarily the key factor in morale. A suggestive possibility is that changes in one's marital status (in this case the onset of widowhood), or in one's role within a given status, require adjustments that some older people cannot manage successfully.

Further examination of Table 8 reveals that single and widowed women have nearly identical positions in the morale ratings. Both have higher morale than single men but lower than that of widowers. The problems of the single woman and the widow are similar, though not identical. Examination of further breakdowns of the data reveals that single women in the older group are either employed or are retired and living on a pension, government insurance, or other form of assistance. Their adjustment seems affected more by health than by problems of social role. They usually are their own housekeepers and upon retirement continue a long-established life pattern. Some single older persons continue living with one or more members of the primary family group. Serious problems of maladjustment arise if the other member or members of such "family" constellation die or

[1] Havighurst and Albrecht found marital status and "personal adjustment" related as follows: (1) Married people have better adjustment scores over single or widowed people significant at the 1 per cent level. Our comparable findings are significant and in the same direction. (2) No significant difference is found in adjustment ratings of widowed and single women. Our data confirm this finding. (3) Single men have higher "attitude" [a measure of adjustment] scores than do widowers. Our data, though our single men are few in number, indicate the reverse finding. While the measures of adjustment differ in the two studies future research should resolve this point. See Havighurst, Robert J., and Ruth Albrecht, *Op. cit.*

are seriously incapacitated. The significant fact is that an adjusted or maladjusted single person is likely to continue his usual life pattern until some event, such as illness, death in the household, retirement, or like factor, brings about changes.

Relatively high morale is seen among both married men and women. Stability of the marital relationship throughout the later years contributes greatly to good adjustment but, as seen in Table 9, this is more true among those of higher position and greater means than among those of low social status and economic hardship. In the former group, their greater resources and, in general, greater attainments may provide a firm base for dealing with changing life conditions. In the latter group, both material as well as personal resources are likely to be wanting and, when coupled with ill health, wreak havoc. In general, however, the married older couple have each other, if not their families, to enjoy. Here, there is social stimulation and the mutual need to provide for the other and for both. These stimuli and needs are the whetting stones of purposefulness, planning, and useful activity. There is no doubt that there are unhappy marital relations in the later as in the younger years that make for personal maladjustment. On the whole, however, married persons show a better adjustment, in our sample, than do either single or widowed persons.

Our next approach is to examine more closely the relationship between one's marital status and his level of morale in each of the two status groups.

There is evidence, in Table 9, of the paramount importance of the person's social position among his own friends and in the community at large. Persons of higher social and economic position seem to be especially affected. Sixty per cent of the married group in high status are classed as high in morale, while an average of only 37 per cent of those single or widowed are so classified. A married person in the upper status group possesses a marked degree of prestige within his own group. The wife, who derives status from her husband's accomplishments, continues to enjoy the prestige of his position. The social importance of the loss of one's husband among higher status women may be gleaned from

TABLE 9. MORALE ACCORDING TO MARITAL STATUS FOR HIGH
AND LOW SOCIOECONOMIC STATUS[a]

| | High status | | | Low status | | |
Morale	Single	Married	Widowed	Single	Married	Widowed
			(Percentages)			
High	39	60	36	21	32	30
Medium	33	26	33	34	23	36
Low	28	14	31	45	45	34
Total	100	100	100	100	100	100
Number of cases	18	92	81	62	82	139

[a] The total number of cases used here is 474. The divorced and separated group number only 26 and because of this small number do not warrant reporting.

the additional fact that while 52 per cent of the married group have high morale, only 25 per cent of the widowed wives of high status husbands have high morale. The husband can attend the social functions his wife arranges, meet her friends, and engage in those social and cultural activities appropriate to their social standing. Furthermore, high status married men retire from gainful employment at a comparatively late age; hence, the income of high status couples is likely to continue undiminished for a longer period than is the case among their status counterparts who are unmarried. All these factors combine to increase morale among the high status married group. Maintaining social prestige, receiving social recognition within one's own circle, and continuing to carry on the type of social life that is expected of a person are factors that lend themselves to good adjustment in the later years.

The comparatively lower morale among married people of low socioeconomic position may be accounted for by a number of interrelated factors. Many in this group are retired and, of these, the majority retired for reasons of health. Both factors tend to lead to maladjusted life circumstances. In addition, as will be shown in Chapter 5, morale tends to be low among working married women (with menial jobs for the most part), the bulk of whom are in our low status group. Hence, the factors that may act favorably upon an older couple are balanced, among people of lower social position and economic want, by ill health, unde-

sired retirement, reduced income, and unsatisfying employment.
All have a depressing effect upon morale scores.

THE PROBLEM OF WIDOWHOOD

Widowhood is fast becoming a major phenomenon of our
society. It is estimated that about 30 per cent of all people over
sixty in the United States are widowed.[1] Nationally, past the age
of sixty-five, about one of every five men and one of every two
women are widowed. A combination of factors, including the comparatively greater longevity of married women as against married
men, the tendency of widowers to remarry and of widows not to
remarry, as well as the generally younger age of the women at the
time of marriage, has made the phenomenon widespread, cutting
across all social and economic lines. The special problems that
confront the widowed both at the time of bereavement as well as
beyond have not undergone exhaustive study. Yet, both the
extent of the situation and the problems created by it call for
greater understanding. In our sample, of the 220 widowed persons, comprising more than two-fifths of the sample, only one
person in six is a man.[2] However, although the problem is primarily one concerning women, the widower presents certain
unique questions as well.

Although widowhood may occur early in marriage and in the
younger years, the vast majority of the widowed are older people.
The acute shock of losing one's spouse has far-reaching repercussions in the emotional life of the individual but its ramifications
extend into all phases of his or her life. It often means the
severance of a fundamental relationship that has given stability
and meaning to life. Since the two personalities are frequently
very closely intertwined, the separation by death may leave an
enormous emptiness in the life of the survivor that requires a long
period of readjustment. Frequently, the individual is not quite
the same person: the spouse is so much a part of the social self
that the widowed person, lacking the stimulus that was so much

---

[1] Estimated from 1950 Census data.
[2] In the Prairie City study, about one in every four widowed persons is a man.
See Havighurst, Robert J., and Ruth Albrecht, *Older People*, 1953.

a part of personality, is changed, perhaps permanently. The mutual fulfillment of emotional, sexual, and social needs is suddenly terminated. If the person is emotionally dependent upon the departed spouse, the affective impact of the loss may be irreparable. In the case of the dominant individual new expressive outlets are now required. The widow or widower occupies a special place in our society; a new role must be assumed. Grief and bereavement must be contained and an attempt made to integrate this role with the ongoing social world. Economic hardship, isolation, cessation of social participation, closer ties with other family members or friends, changed housing needs, and altered domestic activities may be consequences.

The elderly widower is less numerous in the population than is the widow. He may be as acutely stricken by his wife's death as the widow by that of her husband. A lifetime of close association with a woman whose complementary activities form the basis of a home now requires the most basic revision for which the widower may be wholly unprepared. If the wife was the homemaker-housekeeper, all those things upon which he depended and could anticipate in the management and upkeep of their mutual affairs devolve wholly upon him. The economy of convergent interests, the mutual resolution of each other's basic needs, the reciprocity of activities establishing well-ordered roles which is a bulwark of marriage are supplanted by a solitary and often disjointed independence. The vinculum that is marriage is disengaged by death and the widower may find himself incapable of remaking his life into an integrated whole. What is the nature of the widower's adjustment? How does he meet the problems of bereavement and readjustment to singleness? Does a lengthy widowhood restore organic unity to the widower's life? Is remarriage a basic solution?

Widows form the bulk of the widowed population. Since in our society only a small portion are breadwinners, the widow usually faces the problem of economic dislocations that may require her to seek employment or assistance from charity, relatives, and friends. Most widows are not economically independent, but even among those who are, status in the social milieu is derived from that of the husband's position in life. How does the widow meet the problems of social isolation and aloneness? How does she adjust to her new role without the social and emotional support of a husband and with the drastic curtailment of mobility that widowhood entails? Are there significant consequences for those who continue to live alone compared to those who move in with relatives or friends?

Among the widowed group in the present study, we find that with increasing age there are larger proportions of widowed people. Many have not remarried despite the comparatively young age at which they were widowed. For instance, among the 183 widows, 68, or 37 per cent, have been widowed for more than twenty years. The full range of the length of widowhood according to age is presented in Table 10. For some women, widowhood may stretch over half a lifetime and well into the later years.

TABLE 10. AGE ACCORDING TO LENGTH OF WIDOWHOOD AMONG WIDOWS[a]

| | Length of widowhood (in years) | | | |
Age (in years)	Less than 5	5 to 9	10 to 19	20 and over
	(Percentages)			
60 to 64	29	11	32	12
65 to 69	32	41	20	19
70 to 74	21	17	15	31
75 and over	18	31	33	38
Total	100	100	100	100
Number of cases	28	29	57	68

[a] The total number of cases used here is 182. One respondent did not answer the question.

How do these widows fare as older women? How is their adjustment compared to women who are still married? It is apparent from Table 11 that a moderate *increase* in morale occurs with greater length of widowhood. Those who have been widowed less than ten years have a greater incidence of low morale than do those widowed longer than ten years. Married women tend to have higher morale than do those widowed ten years or less. However, no significant differences in morale appear between women widowed ten years or more and those who are

TABLE 11. MORALE ACCORDING TO WIDOWHOOD STATUS[a]

| Morale | Still married | Length of widowhood (in years) | | |
		Less than 10	10 to 19	20 and over
		(Percentages)		
High	45	23	36	31
Medium	23	34	33	36
Low	32	43	31	33
Total	100	100	100	100
Number of cases	56	57	57	68

[a] The total number of cases used here is 238. One widow did not answer the question.

married. It would appear, therefore, that after a preliminary period of readjustment during the years immediately following the death of her spouse, the widow tends to find a new level of adjustment approaching that achieved during marriage. Two crucial factors, as we shall see, influence the level of this adjustment: health and employment. In both socioeconomic groups and regardless of age, where health is poor the widow's morale suffers; and if she retires or does not work during her widowhood, morale declines. It should be noted that the extent of the decline is not great, and the establishment of a pattern of life in the later years stabilizes morale considerably.

Within the higher status group, social relationships with friends and family continue through the years at a level only slightly below that found among the married group. Social isolation among upper status widows tends to become more noticeable with increasing age. In the low status group, social relations are at a low ebb in the years immediately following the death of the spouse, then increase. As age and length of widowhood increase, the difference in the relative degree of social isolation between the high and the low status widows tends to decrease. It will remain for further investigation to determine, but from our data it would appear that the life circumstances of persons of higher social position are not so drastically affected by widowhood as are the circumstances of people of lower social position. In time, however, these differences tend to decrease.

In both status groups, outside social activities increase importantly with the length of widowhood. Church functions, organizational activities, and other more passive activities occupy the elderly widow. Finally, it is of great interest to note that feelings of deprivation[1] remain about the same with lengthening years of widowhood. This is shown in Table 12. Feelings of deprivation are greatest among low status widows, as noted above, who have been widowed for less than ten years. This is a reflection, perhaps, of a sharply felt loss of husband and breadwinner. Over the years, however, in each status group there are, apparently, sufficiently compensating factors to offset feelings of comparative depriva-

TABLE 12. PERCENTAGE OF WIDOWS HAVING POSITIVE SELF-IMAGE ACCORDING TO DURATION OF WIDOWHOOD FOR HIGH AND LOW SOCIOECONOMIC STATUS[a]

Duration of widowhood	Number of high status cases	Per cent having positive self-image	Number of low status cases	Per cent having positive self-image
(in years)				
Less than 10	22	59	35	29
10 to 19	27	52	30	37
20 and over	28	57	40	38
Number of cases	77		105	

[a] The total number of widows used here is 182.

tion. The differences between the two status groups reflect the more positive self-image held by the upper status individuals in our sample generally.

A final word of comparison of widows and widowers. Although there are only 37 widowers in our sample, we may note one or two rather arresting points about them. In general, their morale remains fairly high but it is apparently severely affected by loss of employment and poor health. Of the two factors, employment appears to play the more dominant role. While only a moderate decline in morale occurs where health is poor, a severe decline in morale is noted if the person is retired or unemployed. In effect,

[1] As measured by a self-image index; it is described in detail in Chapter 6.

the two significant ties that bind an individual's life together if he is married are his family and his job. If one or the other or both of these ties are broken, the person's relative adjustment is likely to undergo a drastic impairment. It is noteworthy that there is no difference in morale between married and widowed men if their health is good and they are employed. One may surmise that with only himself to care for he would be less depressed by poor health than a married man with an older wife dependent upon him. The widower's adjustment deteriorates most if he loses his job and his health is poor—crucial factors in the adjustment of most groups.

If we were to generalize from the findings reported thus far, we would say:

1. Married older people tend to be better adjusted than single people, and the widowed occupy an intermediate position.

2. Although the level of adjustment is about the same among men and women, single men are more poorly adjusted than single women; widowers are somewhat better adjusted than widows; and married people and widowers are about equal as the groups with highest morale.

3. Older persons of high social and economic position are better adjusted than their counterparts of low position. High status married people have the best level of adjustment. High status single people are better adjusted than low status single people. The latter group make the poorest adjustment. Widows of both status groups are at equal levels on the adjustment scale.

4. Low status single men make the worst adjustment, while high status married men make the best.

5. Among widows, low morale is most pronounced among those who have been widowed less than ten years. As the length of widowhood increases, there is a rise in morale until it reaches a level approximating that of the married women.

6. Although the level of adjustment is high among the small group of widowers in our sample, it declines with the occurrence of ill health or of retirement or unemployment. Particularly crucial among widowed men is the loss of the wage-earning role. To a lesser extent, loss of health and employment has a similar effect among widows.

Chapter 5

Employment
and Adjustment

CASE HISTORY

Mr. F. is seventy and seemed to derive a good deal of satisfaction out of the small business that he was still able to conduct. He explained that he was operating a small candy and cigar stand near his place of residence. Aside from small flurries of customers in the morning and at noon, he found that he had considerable time to rest on the job. He compared his situation with some of his friends who had been forced to retire and thought that he was much better off. Aside from the fact that he was able to maintain a decent income, he liked being "out of the way" of his wife. He did not know what he would do if he had to stay at home since he had no hobbies that might absorb his interest. Although he had a heart condition, his physician thought that he was well able to continue with his employment inasmuch as he did not have to exert himself too much. Mr. F. smiled broadly as he remarked that he had never thought that some of his "successful" friends would one day really envy him.

Mr. F. spoke rather ruefully of the fact that many of his friends were "dying off." It seemed to him that he was always going to funerals. His associates had now shrunk to a very few friends and it was hard to make new ones. Laughingly, he said that he guessed that nobody wanted to go out with old fogeys. Mr. F. and his wife never went out much together because she did not like people "prying into her business."

It was the interviewer's impression that Mr. F.'s business provided him with a wonderful escape from what appeared to be a rather repressive home situation.

IT WOULD BE REASONABLE TO ASSUME that the employment, as well as the employability of the older person, is intimately related to his adjustment. Current practices setting arbitrary age criteria

68

for retirement and age restrictions on hiring, as well as the variety of stereotypes and prejudices against employment of older workers, underscore the fact that to be employed in the later years is something of an achievement. If employment gives status to the individual, permits him to maintain his standard of living, and makes it possible for him to manipulate his environment (entertain friends, buy books, go to shows, travel, attend adult classes, and so forth), then we should expect high morale to be linked to employment. To have a job when one is advanced in years implies more, however, than providing merely for social flexibility. It implies that society, or at the very least, one's employer, gives tacit recognition to the ability of the person to carry his share of the load. Such recognition requires little reinforcement. The acts of preparing for work, carrying out one's functions, and returning home are intimately tied to feelings of personal worth, self-esteem, significance in life. In fact, the individual's perception of himself is partially determined by the activities he carries on for a livelihood. The older worker, perhaps more so than his younger counterpart, becomes self-conscious of this significant status since questions of his working ability or the desirability of his continuation at a job come into focus. One has only to conjure up the pitiful image of Willie Loman in Arthur Miller's play, *Death of a Salesman*, to bring out the despair that accompanies threatened or actual loss of employment.

We should also expect to find certain differences between men and women in respect to their employment status, the reason being that for most men gainful employment and fulfilling the accepted role of provider may be so closely linked to feelings of self-esteem that a change in status during the later years may be as traumatic as the death of a spouse.

UNEMPLOYMENT

Crises of unemployment and retirement are not clear-cut entities for all persons. The point at which unemployment ends and retirement begins is often undistinguishable. Withdrawal of the older worker from the labor market by illness, accident, economic conditions, mandatory retirement age, desire to change jobs, firing, or through any one of a host of circumstances may effectively force the individual into an unwilling limbo between unemployment and retirement. This status may best be described as *disemployment*. Let us consider some of the ramifications of each of these two economic positions.

Unemployment

The aging unemployed person seeks work in a labor market that traditionally has shunned older workers. The chances of a man over sixty finding a job are slim, those of a woman over sixty almost nil. Age discrimination in industry is widely practiced and is regarded as economically sound, since, it is alleged, older workers are less productive, lose more time through lateness and absenteeism, have more accidents, and, if members of unions, command higher wages.[1] While weakness of body and symptoms of senility do exist in some older workers and reinforce an employer's trepidations, it is widely recognized that age-determined retirement and age barriers to reemployment are products of deliberate economic practice, misbelief, or sheer prejudice.[2]

The hazard of unemployment in old age is compounded by the individual's failure to acknowledge: (1) the widely prevalent managerial views regarding the employment of older persons,[3] (2) his own age and appearance together with the meanings they convey to potential employers, and (3) his own limitations, both physical and intellectual, that may in fact contraindicate employment. To what extent do older people consider themselves "unemployed"? Does unemployment signify poor health, inadequate skills, decline in physical ability to carry on active work? What is the unemployed person's outlook, his adjustment to his economic plight?

[1] Moreover, it is held that older workers are a source of economic drain upon welfare and pension funds; the "new" older worker cannot be expected to contribute greatly to the fund, yet may participate in it heavily upon retirement.

[2] For a thought-provoking discussion of this viewpoint, see Barron, Milton L., "Minority Group Characteristics of the Aged in American Society," 1953.

[3] That the picture is beginning to change a bit may be seen from a recent article by a director of a large industrial firm: Cochrane, Craig P., "Should There Be a Fixed Retirement Age? Some Managements Prefer Flexibility," 1952. For a broad survey of the problems, see Abrams, Albert J., "Discrimination in Employment of Older Workers in Various Countries of the World," 1951.

Disemployment

CASE HISTORY

Mr. L. was a short, wiry sixty-six-year-old man with snow-white hair. He appeared to be a rather nervous person, given to irritable gestures, restlessness, and a good deal of impatience in discussing his situation. The interviewer learned that the respondent had been unemployed for eight months and this was "killing" him inasmuch as he had always been a successful salesman. He now found that potential employers looked at his white hair and assumed that he could not do a good day's work. He had been going out every morning looking for work. His relationship with many of his old friends was becoming strained because they were tired of having him come around to ask for jobs. There was a desperate quality in the way he spoke and an air of defeat.

It was interesting to note that this respondent had considered the possibility of doing other work, such as serving as a watchman or messenger, but found the idea of such work "repulsive." He felt that being a salesman was in his blood. The fact that a salesman has to be aggressive and sell himself as well as his product appealed to him. He thrived upon the competitiveness that he found in his work. Besides, he was not ready to take a job as a watchman because it was for "doddering old men."

The most painful part of the situation confronting Mr. L. was that he had to depend upon his children to help him out financially during this period. The interviewer gathered that Mr. L. had always been a rather strict parent, who had trained his children to be strong and independent. He had never shown any weakness to them before.

In the past few months this respondent had been suffering from dizzy spells, insomnia, and a gastric upset. He admitted having been in a panic a number of times as a result. He had gone to his family physician, who had cautioned him to try to relax more. Mr. L. was very vituperative in deriding this counsel.

Among those who utilize the appellations "unemployed" or "retired" are the "disemployed." They are persons who are not employable because of age but not for reasons of poor health, loss of vigor or stamina, or lack of special skills. They have lost their "right" to work because they have passed the mandatory retirement age and are pensioners or, having been forced through circumstances to leave the labor market, they are denied reentry because of age. Some continue to regard themselves as potentially employable, others have resigned themselves to the "retired" status, albeit unwillingly. They do not fully regard themselves as "not available" for work, nor do they fully accept the role of retiree. This group are potentially among the more maladjusted inasmuch as they do not accept the position into which they have been unilaterally placed by society. In resisting the weight of economic realities, reduced income, and changed living standards, as well as changed life habits brought about by loss of employment, frustrations are inevitable. The greater the struggle, the more pain they suffer in their futility.[1]

Turning now to Table 13 we note that in our sample the persons who are working are by far those with higher morale. Al-

TABLE 13. MORALE ACCORDING TO EMPLOYMENT STATUS[a]

Morale	Employed	Unemployed	Retired	Housewives
	(Percentages)			
High	56	29	27	29
Medium	26	16	32	34
Low	18	55	41	37
Total	100	100	100	100
Number of cases	161	38	164	133

[a] The total number of cases used here is 496. Data were not available for four persons in the sample.

though there are only 38 who regard themselves as "unemployed" we might, on the basis of the data they provide, speculate a bit about them. If the same proportion in each morale group were to be found in a larger population, we could conclude that compared to all other conditions of employment, the unemployed are the worst off. Undoubtedly many, perhaps all of them, represent examples of what we have termed "the disemployed." For whatever reason, they have been shut out of the labor market with little likelihood of being able to reenter. Their psychological position appears extremely weak. Not only are they losing the advantages that employment brings and suffering the ignominy of

[1] In the analysis that follows we have not been able to separate the unemployed from the "disemployed." It is to be hoped that future research will make this distinction and account for its consequences.

having no fixed status, but since they consider themselves to be "unemployed" rather than "retired" they also suffer the frustrations of attempting to rejoin the labor force in an essentially closed market. They are out with little chance of getting in; however, they cannot or at least do not acknowledge this fact. Their state of suspension understandably leads to a deterioration of outlook and to dismal perspectives. When this is coupled with the fact that unemployment was often caused by ill health or accident, the negative influences are compounded.[1]

If we now examine our findings within each socioeconomic group, interesting results emerge. As shown by Table 14, within

TABLE 14. PERCENTAGE HAVING HIGH MORALE ACCORDING TO EMPLOYMENT STATUS GROUP FOR HIGH AND LOW SOCIOECONOMIC STATUS[a]

Employment status	Number of high status cases	Per cent having high morale	Number of low status cases	Per cent having high morale
Employed	82	66	79	46
Unemployed	11	55	27	18
Retired	24	37	140	26
Housewife	84	34	49	20
Number of cases	201		295	

[a] The total number of cases used here is 496. Data were not available for four persons in the sample.

each status group the employed have the highest morale rating. The size of the decline in morale within the low status group is noteworthy. Factors other than not being in the labor market are clearly evident. The 20 per cent difference in high morale between the two employed social status groups is statistically significant, as is the difference between the housewives. The retired samples are too small to yield significant differences but the direction is the same. The small number of unemployed do not lend themselves to statistical comparison, although the curiously high morale in the high status group of 11 unemployed would bear careful scrutiny in a larger population. In all, status wields

[1] The percentages of those in poor health in each employment status group are: employed, 29 per cent; unemployed, 71 per cent; retired, 51 per cent; housewives, 44 per cent.

a potent force in determining morale. We shall point out other determinants but status considerations must be recognized as particularly important.

Since we shall examine the situation of the retired group later in this chapter, it would be appropriate here to look at the housewives. There are 133 housewives or 27 per cent of the total sample. These are women who have never worked outside the home for any substantial portion of their lives but who were or are dependent upon the earnings of their husbands for support. A little more than one-fourth of this group are still married and the remainder are widows.

TABLE 15. MORALE OF MARRIED AND WIDOWED HOUSEWIVES[a]

Morale	Married	Widowed
	(Percentages)	
High	50	22
Medium	22	39
Low	28	39
Total	100	100
Number of cases	36	92

[a] The total number of cases used here is 128.

A striking difference in morale is found among the widowed and married housewives, as shown in Table 15. This substantial difference is clearly determined by a multiplicity of factors operating simultaneously. Not only are married housewives continuing their normal activities associated with maintaining a home but in our particular sample all but six have husbands who are still employed. The lower morale of the widowed housewives is virtually the same in each economic status group. In effect, in both groups the loss of their husbands (accompanied by the departure of children) is not only a financial blow but their ensuing life leaves them without a significant role to perform. They are neither rearing a family nor caring for a home, roles that have sustained them over a major portion of their lives. Most of them are therefore unsuited or maladjusted to the role of an isolated self-sustaining person. The emotional and material deprivations of widowhood after the family has "left the nest" are matched by the lack of a focal "purpose" in life. Hence, lower morale and poorer adjustment follow. It may be presumed that where a new purpose exists or is found, morale will rise. While the numbers are too small to be anything but suggestive, the data indicate that a widow having a job in later life tends to be better adjusted than a housewife who has never worked. This information is given in Table 16. It will also be noted that widows who have never worked and retired widows appear to be similar in adjustment. It would seem, therefore, that employment may lift

TABLE 16. MORALE OF WIDOWS ACCORDING TO EMPLOYMENT STATUS[a]

Morale	Employed widows	Retired widows	Widowed housewives
	(Percentages)		
High	46	30	22
Medium	28	34	39
Low	26	36	39
Total	100	100	100
Number of cases	39	44	92

[a] The total number of cases used here is 175. Eight "unemployed" widows are not included.

the spirit, mobilize energy, and brighten the individual's perspectives. *To play a role in the productive economy, when coupled with good health, is predictive of a favorable adjustment.*

The widows among the aged are the fastest growing group since female survivorship in the later years is far outstripping that of males. Considering the lowered adjustment of this group, future planning should aim toward helping them in special ways. Perhaps planning for widowhood would be indicated, but this may be too unpalatable a suggestion. This kind of stark facing-of-reality is pleasantly avoided by the protection of life or retirement insurance. If the problem could be headed off by programs appealing to the older married woman, many of the tragic consequences of widowhood might be avoided.

Another comparable group[1] are those who have never been married. In our sample, this group is largely made up of women.[2] Of the 24 single persons who are employed 19 are women, about half of whom are rated as having high morale. Of the 12 retired single men not one has a high morale rating, while nine are rated as having low morale. Women in the same category appear to have a slightly better adjustment. Of the 40 retired single people in our sample, only six achieve a high morale rating. *Being single in old age does not seem conducive to good adjustment except for those who are still employed.* Major life satisfactions undoubtedly become as closely bound to gainful employment in this as in other segments of the population.

An illuminating example of role differences and comparative adjustment may be found in the married group. Nearly two-thirds of the employed married men are in the high morale group. These men are fulfilling the traditional and accustomed roles of breadwinner and husband. At the same time, although we have but 12 cases, the married working women are about evenly divided within our three morale levels. This is suggestive of the possibility that working in the later years is far less meaningful for a woman than for a man, particularly if she is married. By comparison, only two working widows in ten and only one working single woman in ten are rated as "low" in morale. Undoubtedly, working past sixty in the case of a woman is often motivated by the need to provide the means for caring for a sick husband or to supplement his small earnings. As indicated above, those women who do fill the traditional homemaker role in the later years tend to be better adjusted. Five of every ten in this group are high in morale and fewer than three in ten are low.

While homemaking is the accustomed function of the married older woman, gainful employment is the most acceptable activity for the older man. Less than a third of the retired married men have high morale. Apparently, employment lightens the burden of the years. It should be borne in mind that poor health often

[1] Data not presented here.
[2] In general, older men tend to be married while older women tend to be either single or widowed.

accompanies retirement. Hence, the generally lower morale among the retired may be a function of health rather than the loss of a meaningful role in life. While to some extent one's health does play a part in reducing morale, role-filling would seem to account better for the following facts:

1. *The lower morale among widowed working women when compared to working men.* Here, although leading a fairly active life, the woman may have been forced to go to work to support herself at a time in life when she may expect or wish to retire.

2. *The apparently low morale of married working women.* The employed status seems to be objectionable to this group, possibly because inadequate income or illness made finding a job imperative.

3. *The low morale of widowed women when compared to married housewives.* Death of the spouse undermines the social ties to the community, reduces living standards, and removes the family role. The woman is often left alone in the world, a position causing great difficulties in adjustment in the later years.

4. *The very low morale of the retired single person.* Not only living alone but withdrawn also from activities and people associated with work, this group may experience extreme isolation. Only an individual of considerable personal resources can readily adapt to the relative vacuum of retirement.

All these factors would point to sheer loss or withdrawal from occupation as less significant to morale than change to a less desirable or less familiar social role.

Perhaps the most convincing evidence of the potency of meaningful roles in later life is provided by a comparison of the levels of morale of those employed and retired whose incomes are identical. It might be assumed that morale would increase with a rising level of income and this would hold regardless of the sources of the person's income. A substantial income may permit the person the freedom and leisure that his available free time provides. He may also maintain a relatively high living standard generally if income is substantial. Our findings, however, are not conducive to so simple a relationship. *How* one derives his income seems to be more importantly related to one's level of morale than *what* the income is itself.

TABLE 17. MORALE ACCORDING TO INCOME FOR EMPLOYED AND
RETIRED PERSONS[a]

	Employed			Retired		
Morale	Less than $25 per week	$25 to $49 per week	$50 and over per week	Less than $25 per week	$25 to $49 per week	$50 and over per week
	(Percentages)					
High	31	49	65	23	37	35
Medium	31	30	25	33	29	35
Low	38	21	10	44	34	30
Total	100	100	100	100	100	100
Number of cases	29	44	80	100	35	17

[a] The total number of cases used here is 305. Twenty cases in which the respondent
did not answer the income question are not included.

As seen in Table 17 a person who is working but receiving less
than $25 per week has a morale rating similar to that of a person
who is retired but receiving a higher income. It is also quite
clear that as earnings or income increase, morale rises. However,
note that while the extent of this rise is great among the employed
group (probably reflecting differences in style of living, type of
occupation, and satisfaction derived), it is only moderate among
the retired group.[1] The social role that provides the greatest
degree of gratification for most persons is the employed role, particularly for men. The less desirable role is that of the retiree.
Morale responds accordingly.

Statistical analysis does not reveal significant differences between the employed and retired groups at each income level.
However, note that the direction of the finding is the same in each
instance: whatever the level of income in each income group, the
morale rating tends to be higher among those who are employed
than among those who are retired.

There is no doubt that our data reflect what is apparent to
workers in the field generally and to many who observe the
problems of older people. Changes in role and function brought
about either directly or indirectly by aging upset the balance of
deep-seated personality needs that have been satisfied by certain
environmental conditions to which the individual has grown ac-

[1] The differences within the retired group are not significant.

customed and upon which he has become highly dependent. Unless the reorganization of the individual's life pattern brings about those changes that will serve as functional substitutes for previous sources of satisfaction, maladjustment follows. The termination of working life, the death of a spouse, disabling illness, or a decline in one's normal style of living requires fundamental modifications in the individual's life plan if he is to readjust with a minimum of stress. As we shall see, for some people even the fact of having grown old is difficult to acknowledge. Aging itself is a changing status that demands certain behavioral and attitudinal adjustments.

Readjustive or adaptive tools or techniques can come from two directions: from the individual himself or from the environment. Inner direction—the setting of goals, new aspirations, new activities, and the like—usually is found in an individual who is less dependent, more capable of flexibility and possessing a history of varied, self-sustaining interests to occupy and absorb him. A person who possesses these qualities may be capable of mobilizing his personal resources to offset the reverses that accompany aging. He can manipulate his environment and achieve a new balance in his life with a minimum of help from the outside.

Far from possessing such internal strengths, the majority of people are considerably disturbed by the crises of later life and experience much stress. Although their maladjustments may take forms that are socially acceptable (developing "senility" without evident organic reasons, passive crankiness, reminiscence and boastfulness about the past, faddism, ultraconservatism, and allegiance to bizarre "causes"), these patterns tend to prevent the individual from achieving lasting personal and social gratifications. In general, although societal measures to help the individual through his more trying experiences are increasing, many of the "solutions" thus far propounded and put into practice tend as often to increase as to decrease the individual's maladjustments. Since frequently he cannot himself reverse or halt the dislocations brought about by job disfranchisement, widowhood, enforced retirement, reorganized family life arrangements, loss of prestige and influence, two courses remain open to him. He attempts to "adjust" to the world by becoming demanding, abusive, interfering, withdrawn, hostile, hallucinatory, or rigid; these are neurotic or psychotic solutions. Or he turns to the community for aid. Here he may, if he is fortunate, receive the help and understanding he needs; or he may, instead, encounter callous rejection. In Chapter 11, we shall indicate the need for additional services for the aged in New York City. These "environment influencing" services should be the mechanisms to diagnose, evaluate, and recommend courses of action that will remove or alleviate some of the unhappiness and maladjustment found in older people. As we have indicated, role changes tend to affect morale or adjustment adversely. The challenge to the community is to help smooth over these transformations by preventive programs undertaken before their onset and by diagnostic and therapeutic programs when disruption occurs. It is in the area of preparation and prevention that the least work has been done. More specifically, it is in the areas of employment and planning for retirement that the least effective effort has been made in behalf of those over sixty.

THE QUESTION OF RETIREMENT

CASE HISTORIES

Mr. Y. is a sixty-eight-year-old pleasant, mild-mannered man who seemed pleased to speak about himself. He had been a plant engineer and had done very well financially. He had managed to provide an attractive home for his family in the suburbs, send his children to expensive eastern colleges, and have household help for his wife. About fifteen years ago, he suffered a "nervous breakdown" as a result of tension experienced on his job. He had been given a very responsible position as the head of a division in the company and had had to do the work of several men. At the time his physician advised him to retire completely since the work posed a hazard to his health.

Mr. Y. now regrets his decision to retire. He had then thought he had sufficient funds to care for himself and his wife in a comfortable manner. He had had many interests, such as the church, gardening at home, and reading foreign languages, which were enough to keep him busy. However, he did not anticipate that his funds would become depleted in time. Unfortunately, he and his wife had required several serious operations during the past few years and he had had to spend large sums of money. If he had remained at work, he would not be crimped for funds. He now thought it was a mistake for physicians to advise their patients to retire without taking into account factors in the situation, other than health.

* * * *

Mr. P., aged sixty-five, seemed to have realized all of the goals that he had set for himself. He appeared to be quite well adjusted, despite the very limited income on which he and his wife lived.

Mr. P. was dressed in overalls which he wore over a wool undershirt. Although he spoke in faltering, broken English, there was a sense of quiet dignity and self-respect that characterized the interview with him. He explained that he had worked hard all his life as an electrician and was proud of the fact that from the day he "got off the boat" he had never had to accept charity. He had brought up five children and they had all turned out fine—he had done his job well. His "kids" came to see him and the "Missus" often and he enjoyed his grandchildren very much.

There was little trace of bitterness as Mr. P. described how he missed his old line of work. He guessed he had been happiest when he had tools in his hands. He had only to listen to an auto engine to know what was wrong—a carburetor needing adjustment, spark plugs needing replacement, electrical system showing a short. He gave up his work only because his arthritis became so severe that he could not splice wires or handle his tools firmly enough. Perhaps it was just as well that he quit when he did, "what with these new things like electronics and automation."

At best, retirement seems to be a mixed blessing. Even for those who are economically prepared for retirement, the sudden acquisition of time—"unoccupied," "leisure," "unfilled," "available" time—creates problems. How to avoid a sense of uselessness, boredom, monotony? How to compensate for the loss of responsibility in one's life endeavors, to retain the prestige and status often tendered the older worker or executive, to find or acquire functional and satisfying substitutes for gainful employment to fill the vacuum created by retirement? How successful are retirees in crossing this gap? How difficult are the adjustments? How satisfying? Does retirement meet expectations? What are some of the social and psychological concomitants?

For those ill-prepared to meet the economic dislocations engendered by retirement, there are the added burdens and hardships of removal to smaller, often inadequate living quarters, "doubling up" with family members who may not too eagerly extend the helping hand, reduced or inadequate diets, and all the manifest and subtle deprivations attendant upon a reduced standard of living. Are those older persons whose style of life becomes cramped by the evaporation of the means of support more subject to maladjustment than those who have experienced privation all their lives? Is income the crucial element in satisfaction with retirement or are there other important factors? Does retirement mean loss of health and mental decline? What of the retiree's social perspectives? Does he lose friends, reduce his participation in the affairs of the community; or does the unprecedented existence of "free" time facilitate his involvement in outside activities? Since a rapidly growing group of Americans are facing or are about to face retirement, it becomes vitally important to study and understand the problems of a growing retired population.

Although we often tend to think of retirement as beginning at a definite point in time (that is, at some specific age), frequently this is not the case. If a person is self-employed, he may gradually turn over the control of his interests to other members of his family or firm. Some find themselves inadvertently retired. A sudden illness, accident, or disability precludes return to their usual jobs and without preparation they find themselves "retired." At a sudden shift in the economic structure, they may become "temporarily" unemployed and only gradually come to realize that they are, in fact, retired. There are those who "retire" more than once. Either they cannot adjust to being retired or they are induced to return to the labor force when their special skills may be needed. During World War II innumerable older people came out of retirement for the war effort. No doubt many an older worker who was "retired" by the Great Depression of the 1930's came back to work as much because of the desire to restore his former income, living standard, and sense of worth as to contribute to the war effort.

In a national survey of Old-Age and Survivors Insurance beneficiaries, fewer than 4 per cent of the more than 15,000 persons studied stated that they had retired for a life of leisure. Four out of each ten said they retired because they could not work (for health reasons); more than one in ten were out of work because of action by the employer; and nearly four others of each ten had left to find other work, were forced out by a reduction in personnel, had their jobs discontinued, or their employer left his business.[1] Thus, for many people retirement seems to be an accident of health or employment circumstances rather than an anticipated event. Recently, in a study of 3,515 employees drawn from a wide variety of industrial and governmental sources, it was found that compulsory retirement at fixed ages was considered undesirable by about two-thirds of those surveyed.[2]

TABLE 18. AGE AT RETIREMENT[a]

Age (in years)	Number of cases	Per cent
Under 40	1	1
40 to 49	3	2
50 to 59	25	15
60 to 64	34	21
65	15	9
66 to 69	45	28
70 to 74	23	14
75 and over	16	10
Total	162	100

[a] The total number of cases used here is 162. Two persons did not answer the question on age of retirement.

Turning to those among our sample, we find 164 persons, or just under one of every three persons in the total group, who classify themselves as "retired." The average length of retirement is between two and three years. The greatest number, however, about 40 per cent, have been retired more than five years. Table 18 indicates that more than half of the group retired after sixty-five with a median retirement age of 66.1 years. The group is equally divided between men and women. For about 80 per cent, the job held at retirement was their regular life-time occupation.

[1] From a report prepared by the Interstate Clearinghouse on Mental Health, Council of State Governments, Chicago, 1955.

[2] *The Study of Occupational Retirement:* First Progress Report. Department of Sociology and Anthropology, Cornell University, Ithaca, N. Y., 1953.

Nearly three-fourths of the group retired suddenly rather than gradually. *The major cause of retirement was attributed to ill health.* This figure may be somewhat inflated, since "ill health" as a cause of retirement is more socially acceptable than is, for example, "replaced by a younger man" or "fired for inefficiency." Only one person in ten retired because of reaching a mandatory retirement age. More than 90 per cent asserted that they had enjoyed their last job before retirement, with nearly two-thirds strongly emphasizing their enjoyment. In passing, it is interesting to note the similarity when comparing the job satisfaction reported by those still working to those retired:

Like(d) job	*Still working*	*Retired*
	(*Percentages*)	
Very much	57	64
Fairly so	29	28
Not much	11	7
Not at all	3	1
Total	100	100
Number of cases	*161*	*164*

The differences between the two groups are insignificant. The generally high level of satisfaction may be influenced, in the case of the retired group, by the high value placed upon any kind of employment; and in the case of the employed group, by that same value where the job is threatened by aging and their possible imminent retirement.

Table 19 indicates the income of the retired group at the point of retirement. Of those reporting their income, the median was $37.50 per week.[1] It is interesting that when asked to state what were the most important factors to them when they were working, those given prominence were money, the work itself, and a feeling of being useful, in that order.

[1] The fact that our retired group are people of small means, whose incomes at retirement are relatively low, derives from our sample selection procedure. It will be recalled that three-fifths of the group were drawn to represent the lower economic stratum.

Each retired person was asked to rate his retirement as "better" or "worse" than expected. Responses to this question are presented in Table 20. It is abundantly clear that there is no unanimity regarding the appraisal of retirement. Approximately as many find it better as find it worse than expected. It is not

TABLE 19. INCOME AT TIME OF RETIREMENT[a]

Weekly income	Number of cases	Per cent
Less than $25	45	29
$25 to $49	62	40
$50 to $74	31	20
$75 to $124	7	5
$125 and over	9	6
Total	154	100

[a] The total number of cases used here is 154. Ten persons did not answer the question on income at time of retirement.

clear, however, what is implied by the fairly large group who find it "about as expected." What had they expected? Was their anticipation of retirement pleasant or unpleasant?

To meet this question, those interviewed were asked to state how they had felt about retirement at the time that they actually

TABLE 20. EVALUATION OF RETIREMENT BY THE RETIRED[a]

Evaluation	Number of cases	Per cent
Better than expected	45	29
Worse than expected	49	31
About as expected	63	40
Total	157	100

[a] Seven persons who are retired did not respond.

did retire. Of the 149 who responded, 34 per cent said they had looked forward to retirement. Another 53 per cent said they had disliked the idea, and 13 per cent were noncommittal or gave qualified responses.

From Table 21 we see that the group making the ambiguous assessment of retirement as being "about the same as expected" is

TABLE 21. ANTICIPATION OF RETIREMENT ACCORDING TO CUR-
RENT EVALUATION OF RETIREMENT[a]

Recalled anticipation of retirement	Current evaluation of retirement			
	Better than expected	Worse than expected	About the same as expected	Total
	(Percentages)			
Looked forward	51	19	32	34
Disliked	27	66	64	53
Noncommittal or qualified	22	15	4	13
Total	100	100	100	100
Number of cases	45	48	56	149

[a] The total number of cases used here is 149. Fifteen cases were not included
because of lack of information.

comprised largely of retirees who now felt that they had unfavorable preretirement anticipations. Favorable anticipations of retirement are frequently reported by those who assess retirement
favorably and negative anticipations are reported by those who
assess their retirement negatively.

We turn now to Table 22 to make clear the association between
anticipation of retirement *compared* to present evaluation. Did
retirement meet, exceed, or fall below the expectations of retirees?

TABLE 22. EVALUATION OF RETIREMENT ACCORDING TO RECALL
OF ANTICIPATION OF RETIREMENT[a]

Current evaluation of retirement	Recalled anticipation of retirement		
	Looked forward	Disliked	Noncommittal, qualified
	(Percentages)		
Better than expected	46	15	53
Worse than expected	18	40	37
As expected	36	45	10
Total	100	100	100
Number of cases	50	80	19

[a] The total number of cases used here is 149.

Of those who looked forward to retirement, 46 per cent found
it "better than expected" and 36 per cent found it "as expected."
Since the group who "looked forward" to it doubtless expected

pleasant things from retirement, we see that 82 per cent of the retirees who expected retirement to be satisfactory have found it so. At the same time, approximately the same proportion of those who disliked the idea may be assumed to have had their expectations confirmed.

There is a slight tendency for women who looked forward to retirement to be more satisfied. No sex difference is found in degree of satisfaction among those who took a dismal view of retirement.

When economic and social status groups are compared on the question of satisfaction with retirement,[1] we find that 59 per cent of the high status group have found retirement better than expected, but only 24 per cent of the low status group have found it so.

TABLE 23. MORALE ACCORDING TO CURRENT EVALUATION OF RETIREMENT[a]

| | Current evaluation of retirement | | |
Morale	Better than expected	Worse than expected	About the same as expected
	(Percentages)		
High	33	12	35
Medium	40	22	35
Low	27	66	30
Total	100	100	100
Number of cases	45	49	63

[a] The total number of cases used here is 157.

Earlier in this chapter, we noted the low level of adjustment of our retired sample—41 per cent of retired persons were in the low morale group and 32 per cent were in the medium morale group. Do one's satisfactions or dissatisfactions with retirement have any effect on one's level of adjustment? Does satisfaction with retirement enhance general adjustment? In Table 23 we see that those who found retirement to be disappointing contribute most heavily to the overall low morale ratings of the retired group. Note especially the levels of adjustment among retirees assessing

[1] These data are not presented here.

their retirement as "worse than expected" and those stating it is "about the same as expected." We know that both groups had approached retirement with feelings of dislike, and further, in both groups persons of low socioeconomic status predominate. But among those who found their negative expectations merely confirmed, morale is higher and, in fact, compares favorably with morale ratings of those who found satisfactions in retirement. On the other hand, when unhappy expectations are not only confirmed but exceeded, morale is sharply depressed. This occurs among both retired men and retired women.

There is no significant difference in morale between recent retirees and those who have been retired longer, nor is there any

TABLE 24. MORALE ACCORDING TO LENGTH OF RETIREMENT FOR MEN AND WOMEN RETIREES[a]

	Men		Women	
Morale	Retired less than 2 years	Retired 2 years or more	Retired less than 2 years	Retired 2 years or more
	(Percentages)			
High	19	30	42	25
Medium	48	26	16	36
Low	33	44	42	39
Total	100	100	100	100
Number of cases	*27*	*54*	*19*	*64*

[a] The total number of cases used here is 164.

significant difference in morale within sex groups at varying lengths of retirement. A significant difference in adjustment does occur, however, between recently retired men and recently retired women (Table 24). Only 19 per cent of the recently retired men achieve a high morale rating. Although our numbers are small, the data suggest that for men the years immediately following the loss of the traditional male role of breadwinner is a period of considerable stress and add support to our other findings regarding impact on adjustment of loss of a major life role.

Summarizing these and related findings, a negative evaluation of retirement is found among those: (1) whose self-image (reflecting feelings of deprivation) is also negative; (2) who are relatively isolated socially; (3) who tended to dislike the idea of retirement in the first place; and (4) who had to give up their jobs because of poor health.

Evaluations of retirement differ little between those who have been retired for less than two years and those whose retirement has been longer, suggesting that evaluations remain fairly stable regardless of the passage of time. At varying lengths of retirement, there is no change in the relatively low morale and low level of social activity and social relationships that characterize the retired group.[1]

Although it might have been predicted otherwise, it is of particular import to note that income at retirement and one's present income are *not* factors in determining the individual's attitude toward retirement. In fact, there are about equal numbers receiving Old-Age Assistance and Old-Age and Survivors Insurance, or being assisted by relatives in each of the groups evaluating their retirement as "better" or "worse" than expected. *This would indicate that of all the values involved in adjustment to retirement, the feeling of being useful and wanted is paramount.* It would seem that the maintenance of good social relationships and the discovery of self-fulfilling activities would contribute to adjustment during retirement. A great deal more research is needed, however, to determine whether a well-adjusted person who looks forward to and plans for his retirement is also the sort of person who succeeds at retiring. We should be particularly eager to learn whether those with poor earlier adjustments are also maladjusted in retirement. Our data seem to indicate that the majority approached retirement with trepidation and, for the most part, their fears were realized. Since retirement forces many persons out of a lifelong routine into unwanted leisure, it is understandable that resistance to retirement should be so great. Further, it appears that it is not lack of money but lack of a significant role that is one of the main sources of deprivation in retirement. The blow to the ego signified by retirement in our society is due to the

[1] Social isolation and nonremunerative activities as they relate to adjustment are discussed in detail in Chapter 7.

fact that retirement tends to imply uselessness, which is reinforced by the behavior of others toward the retiree.

Before concluding this section, it may be well to emphasize that
were it not for poor health, many of our older respondents could
have worked many more years. Not only does declining health
force early retirement but during retirement it serves to sharpen
the person's sense of helplessness. A clear implication is that
health maintenance or restoration could do much to alleviate
many of the social ills deriving from retirement.

Chapter 6

Morale and the Social Self

CASE HISTORIES

Miss L. is sixty-four and presents a rather dramatic appearance. She was wearing a long black coat over a velvet gown, a large fur piece, and many trinkets. She carried herself in a very dignified, haughty manner and mentioned frequently that she came of very fine background and that her life was filled with activities of all kinds: lectures, recitals, parties, and so on. In the course of the interview she said that she had been cautioned by her physician to taper off her activities because she suffered from hypertension. She laughingly scoffed at such advice, however, saying that she would rather cut her life short than diminish her activities. The interviewer gathered that she had also been cautioned to lose weight and to give up smoking but had decided not to heed that advice either.

In revealing that she had never married, Miss L. scoffingly referred to men as being like "animals" and not interested in the finer things in life. She needed to assure the interviewer that she had had many opportunities to marry but could not consider sharing her life with anyone who was intellectually her inferior. She knew many people who feared to live alone, but she was just the opposite—she loved it! The company she enjoyed most was herself. She liked to read, listen to good music over the radio, and make her own clothes. "To live alone one has to be creative."

The interviewer learned that Miss L. was unable to afford her present living accommodations but was reluctant to give them up for less fashionable arrangements. However, she gave the impression of being very resourceful about meeting critical emergencies and had evidently often been in the position in which she was about to be evicted only suddenly to find a friend who would "stake her" until she obtained some employment. She had also done editorial work, involving the preparation of manuscripts for publication. She said that she was known to be an extremely efficient secretary.

It was difficult for the interviewer to decide whether Miss L. was putting up a good front, and suppressing a good deal of tension, or whether her surface behavior could be accepted. At any rate, she carried off the appearance of the "grand lady" very well indeed.

* * * *

In the cases that follow, both women are seventy-four years of age, natives of Ireland, and in substantially good health. Miss L. is a maiden lady who is still employed, while Mrs. W. is a widow who for many years was a domestic but no longer works. Both are Catholics; both are in the lowest income group; and neither completed grammar school.

Miss L. lives in the home of her employer, an elderly, feeble lady of means; she receives room and board and "expense money" but no wages. She regards herself as a "professional companion" and says she needs little money of her own, although she has some saved from previous jobs. Describing herself as "middle aged," she said her standard of living is better now than during most of her life. Her life is circumscribed by her domestic activities, although these are not taxing. Her greatest joys derive from reading and religion. She goes to church regularly twice each day and spends her evenings immersed in books. She reads about six hours a day. Said she: "I'd rather lie in bed with my nose in a book than go out. I always read lying down in bed."

She considers herself "antisocial," preferring to have others come visit her. She would "love to live in a hotel," where she would find seclusion. Most of her friends have died but she sees a brother once a week usually.

Quite understandably, she regards religion as the most important thing in life. Her ambition is not to be in want in her later years or even to be dependent on anyone. In line with these feelings, she fears the day when she may be as feeble as her charge. She regards the age of "fifty" as the time when people begin to get old but has considered herself "middle-aged" for the past twenty years.

A widow more than thirty years, Mrs. W. lives alone in a furnished room in a blighted neighborhood. Her husband died before she migrated to the United States. She has worked at various jobs as domestic and cleaning woman, but now feels depressed because "they won't give me a job—I'm aged." A nephew who had been living with her for two years following his separation from his wife had left about a month prior to the interview and as a result Mrs. W. was somewhat distraught. But she reported herself as being both proud of and thankful for the good health she enjoys despite her years. She is afraid of doctors and avoids clinics and agencies since, as she put it, "I am a private person and don't like to tell anybody my business."

She identifies being employed with youth: "When you're working when you're young, you're happier 'cause you have money and clothes and everything—car, radio, TV, getting a kick out of the world."

Although devoutly religious, Mrs. W. does not go to church often because she is "lazy" and feels her clothes are not good enough. "I like to be like everybody," she remarked. But she ruefully added: "God knows when you don't go. He'll put a distress on you."

Her private world keeps Mrs. W. from seeking others. She would not go to any form of social or recreational club. Her relatives offer enough social life for her needs. A brother and his children are the main sources of her social experience. She remains stoic about her meager existence. She would like more money but regards money in the same vein as evil: "The good people are never rich. I'd hate to be selfish. I'd help the poor if I had it."

Her main ambition in her later years is to lead a "comfortable" way of life. She fears being buried in an unmarked grave. She looks longingly at some of the Catholic homes for the aged but asserts she would rather live with relatives if necessary. She stressed the good food she had heard was served there and by contrast said: "There are some like myself who just live on bananas." She feels her life is somewhat useless now that she has stopped working.

OFTENTIMES, ADJUSTMENT IS CONCEIVED OF as being modified by influences external to the person. Thus, a change of employment, a new residence, marriage, and so on are regarded as factors that play the primary role in the relationships between the individual and his environment. In this section, however, we turn our attention internally. We attempt here to determine the associations between the person's view of himself as compared to others and his general adjustment.

Self-perception, the social image of oneself, is of basic importance in understanding the responses of the person to other human beings, as well as to things and to situations. The older person who regards himself as relatively young may find himself embittered by the attitude of a prospective employer who regards him as old. The person who perceives himself as middle-aged and attempts to behave accordingly may find himself accepted into social groups that would not admit him if he regarded himself as old. In our society the admission of one's aging and the view of agedness are so distinctly negative that to regard oneself as "old" or "elderly" is considered an aspect of a "negative" self-image. It implies, as used in the following analysis, merely the admission of a disadvantageous or undesirable state. The person who says he is older is therefore regarded as comparatively deprived. It should be noted that this is not a unique position of the authors but is common social usage. Hence, if aging is generally regarded in a negative light, our scale must reflect this usage.

First of all, let us examine the background of the problem in terms of our data. Do older people feel deprived or disadvantaged? We have attempted to answer this question by means of a Self-Image Scale. The scale consists of three questions based upon the individual's comparisons of himself to others of his age group or his friends. His answers give us a picture of the individual as he sees himself against a social measuring rod. Not only do his responses tell us something of the person's self-estimate but they also reveal his perceptions of others.

The Self-Image Scale consists of the following questions:

1. Would you say you feel older or younger than most people your age?
2. Do you think your health is better or worse than that of people your age?
3. Would you say it [your standard of living] is better, or worse than the standard of living of most of your friends and acquaintances?

Positive self-image scores are given if the individual advantageously compares himself to others.[1] The distribution of the scored responses follows:

Response	Score	Number of cases	Per cent of total
Feel younger	1	326	65
Better health	1	252	50
Better living standard	1	70	14

[1] The use of the term "self-image" does not necessarily imply an evaluation of the self. It is used here in the sociological sense, derived from social comparisons. It does not necessarily connote self-esteem, self-rejection, or self-hatred.

Our sample was divided into two nearly equal groups. Those with low scores are called the "negative" and those with high scores the "positive" self-image group.

Does one's self-image affect adjustment? As Table 25 indicates, the effect is pronounced. While 45 per cent of the negative image group are low in morale, only 19 per cent of the positive image group are low.

TABLE 25. MORALE ACCORDING TO SELF-IMAGE

Morale	Positive self-image	Negative self-image
	(Percentages)	
High	46	29
Medium	35	26
Low	19	45
Total	100	100
Number of cases	*225*	*275*

We might be able to explain this result by pointing to the fact that the items comprising the index deal with *relative* deprivation or advantage. Since the high socioeconomic group has most of the advantages, we should expect that those in the high status group have a positive self-image and those in the low group a negative self-image. We find, in fact, that significantly more of those in the higher status group have a positive self-image than do those in the low status group (55 as compared to 38 per cent). However, the size of the difference between the two status groups amounts to no more than 17 per cent. Does this, then, mean that a negative self-image among those of high status is as great a determinant of low morale as we might predict would be the case in the low status group? We see from Table 26 that this is actually the case. Among those of low status, the difference between the positive and negative image groups is obviously large. The difference between the image groups among those of high status, while smaller, is still significant statistically.

In effect, we are saying here that while there is no doubt that high status tends to be associated with higher morale, to an im-

TABLE 26. MORALE ACCORDING TO SELF-IMAGE FOR HIGH AND LOW SOCIOECONOMIC STATUS

| | High status | | Low status | |
Morale	Positive self-image	Negative self-image	Positive self-image	Negative self-image
	(Percentages)			
High	53	43	40	23
Medium	32	25	37	27
Low	15	32	23	50
Total	100	100	100	100
Number of cases	112	91	113	184

portant extent members of both status groups are adversely affected if they believe that their peers are or have been better off than they in certain respects. That those who feel deprived as related to their peers among the low status group show so low a level of morale is dramatic testimony of the interrelationship of the self-concept and adjustment.[1] At the same time, it should be borne in mind that the relationship between self-image and morale may be mutually reinforcing. Those who do not feel deprived but regard their lot as comparatively good may be influenced by their present state of adjustment. If adjustment is good, their outlook on life may be wholesome even if their objective circumstances are not all desirable.

As would be expected, those having a negative self-image are proportionately greater among employment status groups characterized by low morale. Among the employed, the proportions having negative and positive self-image are about equal, but among the combined unemployed-retired group, only two out of five show a positive self-image. Within each employment status group, the association of low morale and adverse self-comparisons occurs, the association being particularly marked in the unemployed-retired group where adjustment is generally poor. The converse association of high morale and positive self-image does

[1] In this connection, Greenleigh has stated: "The importance of the self-concept in aging cannot be overestimated. It is more common for people to handicap themselves by their concepts regarding aging than to honestly accept their capacities and potentialities, making the most of them." Greenleigh, Lawrence F., *Psychological Problems of Our Aging Population*, 1952, p. 16.

not hold. On the other hand, where morale is relatively high—
that is, among the employed—the concurrence of low morale and
feelings of deprivation is not marked; indeed, over half of the
employed persons who compare themselves adversely with others
still achieve the high morale rating. From our data, we do not
know what is the causal relationship between morale and self-
concept; but the data suggest that there is some kind of mutually
reinforcing relationship.

In any event, to regard oneself as disadvantaged or deprived
makes for considerable unhappiness. An unfavorable comparison
of oneself to others has often been regarded as typical of a
neurotic adjustment.[1] Such comparisons dwell upon one's defects
and shortcomings to the neglect of saving features and positive
potential. No doubt, among the aged as in younger populations,
exposure to social rejection (being considered too old to work, too
old to participate in civic functions, and too old to be taken
seriously) eventually leads to the conviction that the individual *is*
too old to function meaningfully in society. He withdraws and
broods about how much better off are his friends and neighbors.
As a result of his exclusion from familial or societal roles, he may
turn to noncompetitive or noninteractive activities of his own
making, that is, a compulsive and exclusive concern with gardening, hobbies, reading. Or he may join activity programs or clubs
that permit him to exercise these functions in an organized setting. The fundamental factors associated with feelings of fulfillment and social recognition are overlooked. Activity, *per se*,
whether carried on in solitary or social surroundings, does not
necessarily provide such fulfillment. In fact, so long as the individual regards himself as repudiated by society and sees others
securing satisfaction of their "need to be needed," activity can
only serve as a palliative for his basic social needs to be loved,
understood, respected, and sought. Our findings point to the need
of older people to understand the problems they have in common
with other older persons. Group education, "group therapy," or
"counseling" may provide this type of understanding. Discover-
ing how a similar problem is experienced and coped with by

[1] Horney, Karen, *The Neurotic Personality of Our Time*, 1937.

others can reduce the individual's sense of aloneness in his later years.

THE PERCEPTION OF AGE AND MORALE

Earlier, we touched briefly on the question of adjustment and the individual's self-identification with broadly defined age groups. To obtain the individual's subjective estimate or perception of his own age, the following question was asked: "We'd like to know how you think of yourself as far as age goes—do you think of yourself as middle-aged, elderly, old, or what?" The responses to this question were distributed as follows:

Response	Number of cases	Per cent
Old or elderly	212	42
Middle-aged, young, or denies being old	244	49
Evaded direct answer	33	7
Refused to answer	11	2
Total	500	100

We can now proceed to determine the relationship of age self-perception and adjustment. We have already found that morale declines with age. As Table 27 indicates, however, those who regard themselves as younger or who deny that they are old have higher morale than those who admit to being old or elderly.

TABLE 27. PERCENTAGE HAVING HIGH MORALE ACCORDING TO OLD AND YOUNG SELF-PERCEPTION

Age (in years)	Self-perception old or elderly		Self-perception young or middle-aged	
	Per cent having high morale	Number of cases	Per cent having high morale	Number of cases
60 to 64	31	32	52	78
65 to 69	34	41	40	80
70 to 74	24	58	51	47
75 and over	16	81	41	39
Number of cases		212		244

[a] The total number of cases used here is 456. The remaining persons did not respond directly to the question of age self-perception.

Here is an instance, particularly among those who are, say, seventy or over, of seeming self-deception or delusion in an otherwise "adjusted" group. Upon closer scrutiny, however, much of the deception or delusion evaporates. Undoubtedly, at least two groups form to comprise the elderly people who regard themselves as young or middle-aged. There are those who are, in fact, deluded and whose self-percept is so distorted that they cannot conceive of themselves as being old. While we do not have the data to support this contention adequately, it is the authors' opinion that only a relatively small segment of this group are so mentally unbalanced as to produce such a distortion. Rather, it is more likely that the person who regards himself or at least reports himself as young or middle-aged does so as a matter of enlightened self-interest. The bulk of "younger" or "middle-aged" people are from the high status group. As we have noted, to lose one's youth, to admit to aging, is equivalent for many older people to "giving in" or admitting defeat. He may be subject to subtle ridicule that "Old Father Time has got the best of you" or that he has "hung up his shoes." The acceptable ethic in this group is to fight against time and aging, to purchase all those goods and services that purport to preserve youthfulness. A pattern is evident here: those who attempt consciously to remain "youthful" are also among those who take a nonconservative attitude toward aging, are optimistic about their health, and have high morale. It is to be expected, and it remains for a longitudinal study to test, that such a person comes upon his agedness suddenly and with more traumatic sequelae than do those who more readily admit to aging.

The state of one's health has a controlling influence over morale, as we have seen. Similarly, health also influences one's estimate of his aging. Of those who responded to the question of how they came to feel "old" or "elderly," more than half mentioned a specific disease, a disability, hospitalization, or the development of physical weaknesses as the determining factor. Those who claim to be younger are generally more optimistic about their health, are higher in the socioeconomic scale, and are more often employed than those who say they are old.

To summarize this chapter: We have attempted to determine the relationship between the self-concept of our older respondents and the state of their adjustment. Employing a self-image scale based upon comparisons between the person and others, we find the following:

1. Self-image and morale are fairly closely associated.

2. Persons of high socioeconomic status are generally more positive in self-concept than are people of lower status.

3. Within each socioeconomic group, those with more positive self-image are higher in morale.

4. Unemployed and retired people show both poor self-image and low morale.

5. Even among those with a negative self-concept, a substantial proportion of the employed still have high morale.

On the question of their perception of their own age status, we find that:

1. Although morale, in general, declines with increasing age, people who say they are "young" or "middle-aged" have higher morale than those who depict themselves as "old" or "elderly."

2. Those who claim to be youthful are higher in socioeconomic status, in better health, and more often employed than those who regard themselves as older.

These findings indicate the complex nature of adjustment in old age. Feeling deprived or disadvantaged is related to both the person's *view* of the world as well as his adjustment to it. Both of these factors are conditioned by life circumstances: his economic security, social position, job status, and so on. Those who accept or are resigned to being old generally are also less well adjusted. We have noted, however, that a person who says he is "middle-aged" at seventy-five may be expressing a self-view determined as much by a desire to keep in the youthful social swim as by his actual perception of himself. While the self-concept may not be a cause of adjustment in old age, it is contributory as well as part of the individual's pattern of adjustment.

Chapter 7

Activity, Isolation, and Adjustment

CASE HISTORIES

Mrs. M., aged seventy-five, lives in a rather dilapidated tenement house. It was obvious from her home furnishings that she had once been a person of means. Despite the fact that the apartment needed redecorating, it was neat and meticulously kept. Mrs. M. was fairly well dressed and seemed delighted with the interviewer's visit. She rambled a good deal and obviously was starved for social contact. She insisted upon showing photographs of herself as a young girl, as a bride, as a young mother, and on through middle age until the current time. A most attractive woman she had been, indeed, showing a very delicate and sensitive face in all her photographs. She said that she liked to look at her album and review her life. Tears came to her eyes as she said how hard it was to be wrinkled, gray, and living in such surroundings. She had always been an active, vibrant person. Now, she was reluctant to "go out and face people."

Despite her efforts to keep up old ties, Mrs. M. confessed that she often waited until her friends approached her rather than calling upon them. She admitted that she was a proud person and felt sad that she could not reciprocate by entertaining her friends as they would her.

In the course of the interview, Mrs. M. spoke rather bitterly of her sister-in-law. She accused her of being "aloof" and resentful of the fact that her brother helped her financially. Mrs. M. had not visited in her brother's home for several years because she felt that his wife had made it very clear that she was not welcome. As a result, Mrs. M.'s brother comes alone to visit her.

The interviewer was impressed with the intensity of feel that Mrs. M. showed during the interview. She revealed pent-up feelings of self-pity and resentment because of her situation. She showed derogatory feelings toward other racial and ethnic groups. The interviewer was also interested to note that Mrs. M. took pride in the fact that she was known to most of the clinics at a nearby hospital. She seemed to take satisfaction in enumerating in great detail an imposing array of physical complaints.

*   *   *   *

Mrs. S. is a sixty-nine-year-old widow, native-born, with two professional sons and a "well-married" daughter. At an early age Mrs. S. married a physician who became prominent professionally, socially influential, and well-to-do. Her husband died recently of heart disease after forty years of marriage. She now lives alone in a large, expensive apartment in a fashionable neighborhood.

Reporting herself to be in good health but in rather poor spirits, Mrs. S. said that she feels her aging acutely and more alone than ever, since her children visit her only infrequently. With time on her hands she has found a part-time temporary clerical job, although she does not seem to need the money. She spends her evenings crocheting and doing other needlework.

Mrs. S. has not yet adjusted to the death of her husband and suffers the consequent social vacuum. She describes a woman's reaction to widowhood in these words: "They start to bellyache if they don't have something to do. It's no good lounging around and staying in bed. If you have a definite thing to do, you can forget sorrow. I don't like gadding about playing cards and gossiping like other widowed women." In response to a question about her standard of living, she remarked: "I can't return their [friends] courtesies. I don't socialize with the kind of people I did before. Being a widow puts you in a different class. Half of my contemporaries are dead."

Formerly Mrs. S. attended lectures, but now assists in a charity one day a week. She sees her older friends usually only when they are ill. She prefers reading and needlework to "gadding about." She attributes her reduced activities to "cold weather," but wistfully remarked that her husband would normally take her about in a taxi when they went out but now she walks unless it is raining. She belongs to no social organizations; she considers them to be below the level she would prefer. To quote her directly: "I'd want to go higher not lower—get culture out of it."

Mrs. S.'s relative isolation is reinforced by her lack of contact with her children. She feels that companionship is the thing she now misses most. Her feeling of resentment becomes clear in answering a question about placing the blame for problems of older people: "It's what you think the other fellow will think. The older person's attitude—his anxiety about what others will think. It's not true in my case, but *the young are cruel*." (Italics ours.)

She dates her loss of status and changed life from the date of her husband's death. She feels that she suddenly felt "middle-aged" at sixty-four upon his death. Losing her husband was the hardest change to which she had to adjust and now she feels, despite her activities, somewhat useless. She has a bleak outlook on life. Her need for someone to replace her husband whom she revered is revealed in her statement: "These days a person doesn't really know whom he can count on."

ONE OF THE ALLEGED BENEFITS deriving from retirement, and of old age generally, is that it brings great freedom. For some people it is a time for doing as one pleases, with ample free and uncommitted hours, a time when one can realize the secret ambitions of travel, writing, devotion to home and family, or "jest settin' and lookin'." For others, however, free time can signify only an overabundance of void. For a man, to fill satisfactorily the usual working hours with meaningful activity may be an arduous labor indeed. For a woman, the care and maintenance of the home after children have grown and established themselves elsewhere may provide meager satisfactions. It is not merely a matter of providing recreational or leisure-time pursuits that will help avoid boredom or prevent morbid reminiscing that is required. *Many older people require activities in retirement that will be substantial functional substitutes for the responsibilities of gainful employment, family rearing, and homemaking.* For many, mere leisure-time pursuits will be felt to be the expressions of indolence and of the useless role to which society has relegated them.

Levine[1] has made the useful distinction between free time and leisure. He defines free time as time that, until retirement from gainful pursuits, had been devoted to work activities. Usually, it means the hours from nine in the morning until five in the afternoon. Leisure hours are those that had been available for nongainful activities in and about the home—the evening hours. Retirement produces a situation in which free time and leisure time are contiguous, uninterruptedly, each day. In effect, every day is "rest" day. The key problem is to fill the amount of free time available with activities that provide meaning to the person, meaning that is inherent in doing one's daily work, in caring for a home or in rearing children.

[1] Levine, Harry A., "Community Programs for the Elderly," 1952.

ACTIVITY AND ADJUSTMENT

Many who have worked with older people have noted a change in behavior and attitude among those who adopt some form of activity. They report that the association between increased activity and a more positive disposition is often quite marked. One of the more interesting hypotheses concerning aging is that the person who "keeps busy" is much happier as he grows older than the person who is indolent. Some have even adopted the position that keeping active promotes longevity.[1] The belief that activity and activity programs promote individual as well as community health has achieved rather wide acceptance in this country. In the field of aging, some have attempted to demonstrate that activity in day or recreational centers maintains the physical and/or mental health of the person.[2] This notion, although it has never been systematically studied to determine its validity, is frequently used as an argument to extend the mandatory retirement age as well as to develop activity programs for the nonworking older adult. Our contention, based upon the findings that follow, is that not *any* activity but only activities that provide status, achievement, and recognition can lift morale, and that those that are not basically satisfying needs do not contribute much to the individual's adjustment. In the analysis that follows, we concentrate upon gainful employment as contrasted with nongainful activities on the assumption that, in general, gainful activity is more meaningful than are some other forms of activity.

Not to be overlooked, however, is the possibility that through sheer activity the individual may incidentally find outlets for his feelings or find social relationships that might provide the key to satisfying some of his more fundamental needs. The probability of fortuitously uncovering hidden personal resources or of developing meaningful relationships with others is greater among persons who involve themselves or are drawn into activities than would be the case with the withdrawn or seclusive person. The great chal-

[1] University Research Corporation (Chicago), "They Live on Their Interests," *Hobbies*, vol. 4, December, 1950, p. 55.

[2] Haas, Walter A., and Joseph Bunzel, *A Study of Psychological and Social Adjustment of Aged Individuals Attending Day Centers for the Aged.* New York City Mayor's Advisory Committee for the Aged, 1953. Mimeographed.

lenge to those who would provide the means to attract the isolate from his home or off the park bench is not only to encourage activity but to learn something of the individual himself, so that "busyness" does not become the end in itself. To neglect the person and the personality in the attempt to activate him is to throw a buoy to a drowning man. It does not rescue him from his plight but it keeps his head above water.

The activity scale employed in this study is based upon the respondent's report of activities in which he engaged "fairly regularly." A score of "one" was given for a positive response to each of the following items:

	Per cent of sample
Reading and/or going to library	43.0
Work on hobbies	8.0
Write letters	24.4
Go to the park	18.4
Take rides or walks	32.6
Attend classes	2.6
Engage in religious activities (other than church attendance)	8.4
Play cards	12.0
Go shopping	42.8
Go to a bar	5.0

If the person belonged to a voluntary organization, one point was given. An additional point was added if membership occurred in more than one organization. Membership in a labor union received one point. Thirty-five per cent of the sample received scores for membership in organizations or unions.

For purposes of analysis, scores of "0" through "2" were combined into a "low activity" group and scores of "3" through "9" were combined into a "high activity" group. The groupings are as follows:

	Number of cases	Per cent
Low activity	300	60.0
High activity	200	40.0

Applying our activity scale to our measure of morale, we find in Table 28 that high activity level and high morale are significantly related.[1] At the same time, it is to be noted that nearly a third of the low activity group are rated at high morale and about one-fourth of the active group are rated at low morale.

We have already seen that if an older person has a significant role to play in life (particularly if he is employed), morale is high. With this in mind, let us compare the relative morale ratings of those who are employed, unemployed, or retired, and those who are housewives. If our position is correct, those who have the meaningful and ego-satisfying activities (that is, the employed

TABLE 28. MORALE ACCORDING TO ACTIVITY LEVEL

Morale	Activity level	
	High	*Low*
	(*Percentages*)	
High	46	31
Medium	28	31
Low	26	38
Total	100	100
Number of cases	*200*	*300*

group) but who are otherwise inactive will have higher morale than will the unemployed and retired *though active* group. Table 29 presents the results of this comparison.

First, we see that among the otherwise active group, those who are working have considerably higher morale than those who are not employed. The equivalent morale levels of the unemployed-retired and the housewives, all of whom are active, are functions of the common existence of opposing factors in each group.[2]

---

[1] This finding confirms the results obtained by Havighurst and Albrecht in their Prairie City study (Havighurst, Robert J., and Ruth Albrecht, *Older People*, 1953, p. 287). As we shall show, however, when the population is subdivided into employment categories, the greatest contribution to better adjustment among the more active group comes from those who are employed. Employment and good health are far more important as determinants of adjustment than activity level.

[2] The unemployed group and the widowed housewives bring the two sets of figures down to a common level.

Second, within the inactive group those who are employed have a higher percentage of people with high morale than do those who are not working.

Third, there is a 16 per cent difference in the high morale group between the employed active and employed inactive categories. This, however, is not statistically significant.

TABLE 29. MORALE ACCORDING TO EMPLOYMENT STATUS FOR ACTIVE AND INACTIVE PERSONS[a]

	Active			Inactive		
Morale	Employed	Unemployed and retired[b]	Housewife	Employed	Unemployed and retired[b]	Housewife
			(Percentages)			
High	63	32	35	47	25	25
Medium	21	34	35	33	26	36
Low	16	34	30	20	49	39
Total	100	100	100	100	100	100
Number of cases	87	61	49	74	141	84

[a] The total number of cases used here is 496. Four respondents did not answer the employment question.

[b] The unemployed and retired are combined since we are interested in comparing the working and nonworking populations.

The crucial question is, therefore: Do those who are inactive but employed have higher morale than those who are active yet unemployed or retired? This should provide a test of the relative strengths of activity and employment as factors determining the level of morale. Although the difference is not statistically significant, we find that there is a greater percentage of cases of high morale as well as a smaller percentage of cases of low morale among the inactive-employed as compared to the active-unemployed or retired.

In other words, there is a tendency for employed people who are not otherwise socially active to be better adjusted than those who are active but without gainful employment. We have not here inquired into the nature of the work done or the status it gives the person among his colleagues, despite the obvious range of occupations involved.[1] Also, we have not inquired here into the nature of the activities performed, other than to distinguish gainful employment from all other forms of activity. Overall, however, morale is higher when the individual is employed even if he is not otherwise active. There is no question that activity level does play a role in morale or general adjustment in old age. Table 28 seems to confirm this. We see in Table 29 that even among those who are retired or unemployed (the group that would be most available for outside activities) there is a suggestion that lower morale is found more often among the inactive than among the active group, but gainful employment appears to be more crucial in good adjustment.

Advocates of activity programs as the solution to problems related to aging will not be especially heartened by these findings. They may draw satisfaction, nevertheless, from the fact that at least a portion of the older group may be substantially benefited by increasing the individual's general activity. It is important to keep in mind that it may not be the level of one's activity that increases morale but that people whose adjustment is good tend to be more active, and those who are not well-adjusted are less inclined to be active. More fundamental considerations than mere activity are involved in adjustment.

THE FACTOR OF SOCIAL ISOLATION

With advancing age, nearly every old person is brought to the realization that infirmity and death are claiming more and more of his peers. This attrition of one's generation also makes painfully clear to the individual the fact that he is becoming increasingly socially isolated. Close friends are not easily acquired and with the years it becomes increasingly difficult to form new friendships comparable to those enjoyed for the better part of a lifetime.

In addition, for reasons that we shall make clear shortly, many older persons change their residence and, in so doing, leave or are left by old friends. Moving away is a common cause of isolation and, together with death and the illness of one's associates, pro-

---

[1] Expected differences in morale do appear at different occupational levels; higher status positions are related to higher morale.

vides its major bases. Moreover, as others have shown, such moving is often "centripetal," that is, away from established residential neighborhoods toward the center of business areas. Life here is more anonymous and centered less around friends and relations. In terms of the needs of many older persons it appears far from satisfactory.

Widowhood tends to encourage isolation, since the survivor is usually less able to continue the acquaintanceships, attend the social functions, and do as much visiting without the spouse. Friends of one's spouse are less likely to continue to visit the widow or widower, and he or she in turn often does not continue visiting.[1]

Other factors that tend to isolate the older person are chronic illnesses, of either himself or his spouse, unemployment, and retirement. All of these create situations in which the individual is cut off from contact with work associates, friends, neighbors, and relatives. The range of potential social relationships is reduced because opportunities for developing and furthering them are minimal.

Isolation is a serious problem in old age but not much is known about its concomitants or consequences. Are maladjustments more acute when the individual's social life is curtailed? Are there substitute satisfactions that forestall bitterness, loneliness, and decrepitude? Are there health and psychological resultants stemming from isolation? To what extent can isolated older people be expected to respond to social and health advice? What steps, acceptable to older people, can be taken to reduce the sense of social isolation?

We may inquire into other ramifications of this condition of life that accompanies so many older people through their later years. First, we should take note of an important difference: that between *social* and *residential* isolation. While the two are commonly concurrent, there are many who live alone who are not

---

[1] This is not meant to imply that isolation is not in many instances a matter of personal preference. Hibbard and Lee recently asked 1,290 widows of Presbyterian ministers whether it was wise for a widow to live in the household of her married children. Fully 97 per cent replied in the negative. In addition, 43 per cent stated that they prefer to live alone. See Hibbard, Donald L., and John P. Lee, "Presbyterian Ministers and Their Widows in Retirement," 1954.

socially isolated, and there are persons who live with others who may be considered to be isolated since their social lives may be wholly restricted to a boarder-landlord relationship or some other simple symbiotic social arrangement.[1]

Social isolation was determined by the use of an index of isolation, based on items dealing with the degree of human contact with friends or relatives. The lower the index score, the higher the degree of social isolation. A score of one point each was given for the following items: (1) seeing children at least once a month, (2) seeing other relatives at least once a month, (3) having very close

TABLE 30. RANGE OF INTERPERSONAL RELATIONS (RELATIVE SOCIAL ISOLATION) ACCORDING TO RESIDENTIAL STATUS, AGE, AND SOCIOECONOMIC STATUS

	Broad range of interpersonal relations Not isolated	Limited range of interpersonal relations Isolated	Total	Number of cases
Residential status		(Percentages)		
Live alone	35	65	100	201
Live with others	50	50	100	299
Age (in years)				
60 to 64	52	48	100	117
65 to 69	47	53	100	139
70 to 74	49	51	100	115
75 and over	30	70	100	129
Socioeconomic status				
High	58	42	100	203
Low	35	65	100	297

friends living, (4) having personal friends, (5) having made new friends. For analysis purposes the score groups "1" and "2" were combined into a "limited range of interpersonal relations" (social isolation) group, and those with scores "3," "4," and "5" were combined to form a "broad range of interpersonal relations" group.

From Table 30 it is plain that residence with others is no guarantee of substantial social contact, while residential seclusion frequently accompanies social isolation.

[1] One of the commonest social complaints of older persons living in the households of children is the feeling of isolation within the family group.

In addition, we note that about 56 per cent of the sample are designated as having limited range of interpersonal relations. About 60 per cent of the men and 53 per cent of the women are in this category, a difference that, although not statistically significant, is important, since a majority of the men are married while the bulk of the women are widows, of whom a great proportion live alone. As might be expected, relative social isolation increases with advancing age, although the most marked single increase occurs past the age of seventy-five. Table 30 indicates the relation of age to relative social isolation. Although the downward trend is nearly the same for both men and women, there is an interesting sharp decline in the extent of social interaction among men between sixty-five and sixty-nine, the "retirement years."[1] We have already explored the possibility that the crisis years for men, sixty-five to sixty-nine, bring about a marked withdrawal from participation in social life. There is also a tendency at all age levels, but most marked in the group over seventy-five years of age, for those having had more education to be less isolated. Those who have had a high school or college education are, on the whole, less isolated than those who have had limited education. It is possible that the style of living, interests, and social values of those with more advanced education sustain their ability to continue to seek out others, as well as to place a higher value on social affairs. It is also possible that those with more education have led lives that afford them greater human resources to draw upon in their later years.

In line with these findings, it is not surprising to learn that social isolation is a function of socioeconomic status. Of those in the high status group, 58 per cent are not relatively socially isolated, while only 35 per cent of those in the low status group are among those with a broader range of interpersonal relations.

From Table 31 we see that the extent of relative social isolation does not affect the generally high level of morale of high status persons. Among those of low status, however, isolation has a depressing effect on morale. Ill health may be a factor making for low morale in this group, or low status with its attendant lower

[1] These trends are not shown in Table 30.

income may force unwanted restrictions on the individual's social life. Depressed morale is understandable if a person feels compelled to circumscribe his life because he considers himself unable to uphold his part of social relationships in a manner which he deems appropriate.

TABLE 31. MORALE ACCORDING TO RELATIVE SOCIAL ISOLATION FOR HIGH AND LOW SOCIOECONOMIC STATUS[a]

Morale	High status		Low status	
	Isolated	Not isolated	Isolated	Not isolated
	(Percentages)			
High	51	47	25	37
Medium	28	30	28	36
Low	21	23	47	27
Total	100	100	100	100
Number of cases	*85*	*117*	*194*	*103*

[a] The total number of cases used here is 499. One respondent could not be classified on the Isolation Index.

Except in those families where strong in-family ties are fostered to a point where the older person is drawn closer to the family of the child, the lower the socioeconomic position of the person, the more likely he is to be left more and more alone with advancing age. In Czech, Hungarian, and especially Italian families, for example, protection of the elderly father or mother by inclusion in the household of the adult child is somewhat more common than among native-born, British, German, or Irish families. Hence, there is understandably a considerable difference in degree of isolation of members of these various ethnic groups.

British writers, for example, have stressed the importance of maintaining independence in the later years:

. . . Where possible, old people should be provided with small convenient dwellings where they can live alone. The independence and the effort involved in living alone can, as an example in one housing trust has shown, help old people to remain young for their age.[1]

[1] Comments of Mrs. A. V. Hill of the Advisory Council of the National Corporation for the Care of Old People, cited in Adams, G. F. and A. T. Welford, "Some Social and Psychological Problems of Ageing," *Nature* (London, England), vol. 171, March 7, 1953, pp. 422–423.

Similarly:

> The traditional pattern in which the family, old and young, lived together under one roof has largely broken down, with the result that many old people are extremely lonely. A return to the traditional pattern is clearly impossible and, even if it were, it might involve satisfying the needs of old people at an undue cost in terms of freedom and privacy for those younger.[1]

It was pointed out that some solution such as older people living alone but near younger relatives often works well. It was stressed, however, that a large part of the responsibility for the success of such arrangements rests upon the older person. Such statements epitomize British and, to some extent, North German, Irish, and American cultural values regarding the aged. It is clear that a high premium is placed upon independence and privacy but these in turn often lead to isolation. At least among those in the lower economic group, these views seem to be shared by those of West and North European origin as well as by Americans.

It might be argued that it is religious rather than cultural dicta that affect isolation. To test this assumption it would be best to examine the isolation pattern in two ethnic groups sharing the same religious beliefs. Our Irish and Italian samples afford such a test. *While two-thirds of all Irish-born respondents are in the isolated group, only a little more than one-third of the Italian-born are in this group.* Both ethnic groups are predominantly Catholic. Thus, the Irish group in which the three-generation family ties are relatively loose, encourages greater independence among its older members. However, instead of the older person's adapting to the condition of self-reliance, the effect is to place upon him the burden of maintaining social relationships in the face of declining capacities. The individual thereby becomes less able to use his freedom to sustain adequate social contacts. Among the Italian group, on the other hand, three-generation ties are culturally sustained, and the older person tends to find himself in closer touch with younger family members, if not actually living with

---

[1] *Ibid.*, Comments of Miss S. R. Burstein of the Wellcome Historical Medical Museum.

them. Thus, values and customs regarding family life, attitude toward old age and the aged, and the place of self-reliance in each ethnic subculture play some part in determining the extent of social isolation. It should be pointed out here that the isolating tendencies are less present in the higher strata of society *among nearly all ethnic groups.*

We shall see in the next section that social isolation is associated with relatively poor health. We can first examine some of the health concerns and dispositions of older people in connection with their social relationships. It might be assumed that a person who leads a busy social life, seeing family and friends frequently, would tend to be less given to preoccupation with his health. In effect, health would be a secondary matter among those who shared a rich social experience. By contrast, we may assume that the social isolate has time to brood, to concentrate his attention upon his own problems, since he is cut off from associates who might distract him from morbid self-observation. We come, therefore, to the question: What influence does social isolation play in concern with health among those good and poor in health? We may answer with conviction that isolation has no influence in *increasing* worry about health problems in either group. In fact, among those in good health *there are significantly fewer worriers in the relatively socially isolated than in the nonisolated group!*

We can only speculate on the meaning of these findings. There is no confirmation of the assumption that among the relatively socially isolated group, lacking in the comfort of human relationships, there would tend to be an inward turning, an inordinate concern with bodily well-being, even hypochondriasis. Although this does occur in some cases in our sample, it is not widespread. It should be noted that most people, though friendless or without relatives, may have acquaintances, radio or television "friends," books, magazines, and pets that provide the degree of "contact" necessary to avoid being preoccupied with health. In this case, it might be surmised that the friends and relatives who concern themselves with our relatively healthy respondents tend to raise their health-anxiety level.

Further evidence on this point stems from health self-ratings made by our respondents.[1] The proportion of worriers about health to nonworriers is significantly greater in the nonisolated group both among those who rate themselves in good, as well as those rating themselves in poor health (Table 32). It does seem, especially among those who view themselves as ill, that having relatives and friends tends to raise considerably the level of concern about health. It is a question, however, whether this is a virtue or a vice, for, while some worry may be needlessly engendered, it might in some cases act as a spur to activity in caring for present or potential health problems.

TABLE 32. WORRY ABOUT HEALTH ACCORDING TO RELATIVE SOCIAL ISOLATION FOR GOOD AND POOR HEALTH SELF-RATINGS[a]

	Self-rating good health		Self-rating poor health	
	Isolated	Not isolated	Isolated	Not isolated
	(Percentages)			
Worry about health	18	30	56	65
Do not worry about health	82	70	44	35
Total	100	100	100	100
Number of cases	125	149	153	71

[a] The total number of cases used here is 498. One respondent could not be classified on the Isolation Index and one did not answer the question of worry.

Relative social isolation, we have found, is most common in the low socioeconomic status group. Social contact we have found to be more characteristic of the high status group. If having considerable contact with friends and relatives raises one's anxiety about health, what is its bearing on social adjustment? To test this question, we examine in Table 33 the frequency with which children visit, or are visited by, our elderly respondents and compare the relative effects upon morale in each status group.[2] It will be observed that although the differences do not reach sta-

[1] These ratings are reported upon in full in Chapter 8.

[2] A high frequency of visiting may include parents and children residing in the same household.

tistical significance, there is a tendency for morale to be higher among those who see their children less frequently than among those who see them once a week or oftener. This is more striking in the higher than in the lower status group. It is also of interest that the same level of morale is found among those having no children as among those seeing children often in each status group.

TABLE 33. MORALE ACCORDING TO VISITING FREQUENCY OF CHILDREN FOR HIGH AND LOW SOCIOECONOMIC STATUS[a]

	High status			Low status		
Morale	Visit often[b]	Visit seldom[b]	Respondents having no children	Visit often	Visit seldom	Respondents having no children
	(Percentages)					
High	47	65	43	28	36	27
Medium	29	21	35	30	28	31
Low	24	14	22	42	36	42
Total	100	100	100	100	100	100
Number of cases	101	29	72	109	45	143

[a] The total number of cases used here is 499. One respondent did not answer the question of frequency of visits.

[b] "Visit often" = at least once a week. "Visit seldom" = less than once a week.

What of relationships to relatives other than children? In Table 34 we see that in the high status group there is a 16 per cent difference with lower morale in the "frequent" as compared with the "infrequent" visiting group. This relationship is statistically significant as is also the fact that *morale is highest if one has no relatives*. The reverse trend is found in the low status group, although the difference between the groups with high and low incidence of visiting is not statistically significant. Here low morale is greatest among those who have no relatives. One further relationship completes the picture: that between morale and visiting with friends. This is presented in Table 35. No difference in morale is found among the high status group regardless of the frequency of visiting. Among those of low status, morale decreases with increasing isolation. Fifty-seven per cent of

TABLE 34. MORALE ACCORDING TO VISITING FREQUENCY OF RELATIVES OTHER THAN CHILDREN FOR HIGH AND LOW SOCIOECONOMIC STATUS[a]

Morale	High status			Low status		
	Visit often[b]	Visit seldom[b]	Respondents having no relatives	Visit often	Visit seldom	Respondents having no relatives
	(Percentages)					
High	45	43	54	36	27	27
Medium	20	38	30	36	34	28
Low	35	19	16	28	39	45
Total	100	100	100	100	100	100
Number of cases	51	58	89	65	88	140

[a] The total number of cases used here is 491. Five respondents did not answer the frequency of visits question and four others did not indicate the number of relatives in the New York area.

[b] "Visit often" = at least once a week. "Visit seldom" = less than once a week.

persons without friends in the low status group are among those at the lowest morale level.

An examination of the previous three tables seems to indicate that among high status older people social relationships with children or other relatives tend to be associated with a decrease in good adjustment. Some of the visiting is attributable to health problems, but, even among those in good health, morale declines with the increased frequency of visiting. On the other hand, no decrease in morale occurs with a decrease in visits with friends.

TABLE 35. MORALE ACCORDING TO VISITING FREQUENCY OF FRIENDS FOR HIGH AND LOW SOCIOECONOMIC STATUS[a]

Morale	High status			Low status		
	Visit often[b]	Visit seldom[b]	Respondents having no friends	Visit often	Visit seldom	Respondents having no friends
	(Percentages)					
High	49	48	47	35	29	23
Medium	29	27	33	37	33	20
Low	22	25	20	28	38	57
Total	100	100	100	100	100	100
Number of cases	88	77	36	102	100	87

[a] The total number of cases used here is 490. Ten respondents did not indicate whether or not they had friends.

[b] "Visit often" = at least once a week. "Visit seldom" = less than once a week.

It is possible that visits with one's own relations may affect morale adversely because of two factors: friction between the older person and his younger relatives over the rearing of the grand-children[1] and, touching upon the central problem among this group, recognition of the facts of aging. Perhaps the older person may be harassed by suggestions on how to keep healthy and young, or the sheer contrast in ages of the two generations reinforces the fact of his own aging process. We have seen how anxiety over health is raised among the less isolated group. It is notable also that, even if one has no children or no relatives, morale does not decline. In the latter instance morale is considerably higher than it is among those whose relatives see the respondent frequently.

In the lower status group, visiting with children has little impact upon morale. The same is true of visiting with other relatives, although a downturn in morale is noted with decreasing frequency of contact. Morale is lowest among those with no relatives.

Friendship patterns produce the widest variations in adjustment. In the high status group, morale remains relatively high regardless of the frequency of visiting and even among those who have no friends. From this result we may surmise that although visiting is quite high generally in this group, there are some persons who do not respond adversely to social isolation. In fact, they may be perfectly content to be recluses or "deviates" in their own group, placing privacy above other values more socially acceptable among their status group. For some people whose personal and inner resources are sufficiently strong, old age may provide the only period in life when they may escape "the madding crowd." Some are to be found in residential hotels, where they may lead a secluded, unperturbed life. Others closet themselves in old family homes, rooming houses, or apartments, and have their food and other needs delivered to them. It is inescapable that social animals though we are, at least some prefer nonhuman companionship or utter privacy in the later years.

[1] In a study of the families of our sample, to be reported separately, the most commonly cited disadvantages of having one's aged parents live in the same household were the "conflict of generations" and "spoiling grandchildren."

Social isolation has an important bearing on one's own view of his health status. It is clear from Table 36 that the relatively socially isolated group is primarily responding to its objective health status[1] in making its judgments on health. On the other hand, the nonisolated group, while rating themselves overwhelmingly as in good health when health is in fact good, are sharply divided in their ratings when they are in poor health. While the number of cases is small, the 41 per cent who rate themselves in good health (though they are, in fact, in poor health) suggests that a selective factor may operate for this group, which tends to exaggerate the expressed degree of health they possess. It will be recalled that a close relation exists between nonisolation and high

TABLE 36. HEALTH SELF-RATINGS ACCORDING TO HEALTH STATUS FOR THE SOCIALLY ISOLATED AND NOT ISOLATED[a]

| | Isolated | | Not isolated | |
Health self-rating	Good health	Poor health	Good health	Poor health
		(Percentages)		
Good	67	23	82	41
Poor	33	77	18	59
Total	100	100	100	100
Number of cases	139	140	144	76

[a] The total number of cases used here is 499. One respondent could not be classified on the Isolation Index.

economic status. We have here evidence that exaggeration of concern (worry) about health is, in fact, a concealed characteristic of the nonisolated high status person, inflating the good health estimates of the healthy and deflating the poor health estimates of the ill. It is conceivable that there exists among them considerably more illness and considerably greater effort to live with illness than was reported during their interviews. The evidence on self-deception or the public view of the self in the high status group is impressive. It includes denial of self as aged or old, overestimation of own health status, lower degree of expressed concern over illness, and a generally negative attitude toward aging and the aged.

[1] Health status as used here derives from an index reported upon more fully in Chapter 8.

From the evidence, it would seem that social isolation, despite the fact that it is accompanied by poor health, does not raise the degree of concern about one's health. It is related to a sense of futility, to feelings of frustration, to a negative self-image, and to relatively conservative attitudes toward aging. In line with the relatively poor morale of those in the low status group who are friendless or who have no family, we find more isolated persons who feel that the love and affection they had received when they were younger is no longer given. Table 37 indicates that isolation cuts off deep emotional gratifications and ties, and probably the latter have the reciprocal effect of reducing the individual's desire to develop further social relationships.

TABLE 37. ESTIMATE OF RECEIPT OF LOVE AND
AFFECTION ACCORDING TO SOCIAL
ISOLATION STATUS[a]

	Isolated	Not isolated
	(Percentages)	
Receive as much love and affection as formerly	58	75
Receive less love and affection now	42	25
Total	100	100
Number of cases	256	200

[a] The total number of cases used here is 456. Forty-three respondents did not answer this question and one other could not be classified on the Isolation Index.

Among low status people, where destitution, loss of social graces or of presentability may follow upon illness, social isolation brings loneliness, feelings of uselessness, and deprivation most severely. It is from this relatively isolated and friendless group that we find, although their frequency is not very great, most of the suicidal thoughts, concern with death, and feelings about the worthlessness of life. It is in this group also, comprising about one-tenth of our sample, that restorative and rehabilitative efforts are most needed.

In this chapter, we were concerned with questions of social activities and relationships as they relate to adjustment in old age.

1. We have found that activity and morale are associated, high participation being associated with good adjustment.

2. Within each activity level group, the employed have higher morale than the other employment status groups.

3. Furthermore, those who are gainfully employed but otherwise inactive have a higher level of adjustment than do the unemployed or retired who engage in nongainful activities.

It would seem from our data that sheer activity to fill increased free time is less satisfying and less conducive to good adjustment than gainful activity. At the same time, this possibility should be borne in mind: it may be that the well-adjusted person is more inclined to engage in general activities than one who is less well adjusted. In any event, our findings give only partial support to the assumption that the busy older person is the happy individual. For some, activities such as those provided by recreation and activity programs *are* satisfying and are helpful in promoting good adjustment. But for many, meaning and satisfaction are to be found in other activities.

On questions of social relationships, a social isolation index was employed. Slightly more than half of the sample group were classed as having a limited range of interpersonal relations, that is, as relative social isolates. Findings are as follows:

1. Residential isolation and social isolation are not necessarily coincident.

2. As might be expected, social isolation increases with advancing age, with a sharp decrease in social relationships occurring past the age of seventy-five.

3. Social isolation is significantly more marked among low socioeconomic status persons than among those of high status, and isolation has a depressing effect on morale among low status individuals. The relatively high level of morale among the high status group is maintained regardless of the extent of social isolation.

4. Ethnic group variations in social isolation reflect cultural differences with respect to in-family ties. Among the North and West European and American-born groups, where independence of the older person is valued and family ties are loose, social isolation tends to be more frequent than among other ethnic

groups where two- and three-generation ties are fostered. These cultural differences obtain even within the same religious affiliation; but within most of the ethnic groups in our sample the association of high status and active social life is found.

5. The supposition is not confirmed that social isolation, with its increased opportunity and time for self-observation and introspection, may result in an exaggerated concern with one's health status. In fact, when health is good, social isolates express less concern about health than do nonisolates.

6. Among nonisolates in poor health, self-estimates of health are inflated and conform least to an objective health status rating. It may be that in this group, many of whom are of high status, there is an effort being made to dissociate oneself from one of the signs of aging—that is, ill health.

7. Although it might be expected that frequent social relationships with children, relatives, and friends would be conducive to good adjustment, we did not find this generally to be the case. Among the low status group, frequency of visiting with family and associates was found to have no relationship to morale. Among those of high status, increased proportions of persons having *low* morale was found to accompany frequent visiting with children and relations. This was not true of frequent contacts with friends. We can only suggest what may enter in here. Involved, perhaps, is friction between generations or about suggestions to the older person for maintaining the youthfulness and health which are highly prized among this group. Or, perhaps, the contrast between the two generations may emphasize for the older person that which he would deny—his own aging.

One further comment should be made. Social isolation does have its negative aspects. It is often accompanied by—sometimes even the result of—failing health. The death of his peers, the circumscription of his social relationships bring home to the older person the fact of his aging. Not to be forgotten, however, is the possibility that some older individuals may prefer the state that we have here termed "isolation." Some are living out cultural traditions and values. To repeat what we have said before, the aged are not a homogeneous group.

PART III
HEALTH IN OLD AGE

Part III:

Health in Old Age

PERHAPS ONE OF THE MOST STUDIED ASPECTS of aging is disease associated with the process of growing old.[1] Old age has been characterized as a time of illness, often of a chronic nature, when the individual is more susceptible to certain diseases, when physiological failure is more common, and when homeostatic balances become upset.[2] Geriatric science has undertaken to describe and analyze the illnesses to which older people seem more susceptible, their respective prevalence, courses, prognoses, and therapies. Despite the existence of this widespread knowledge, these conditions are often not greatly responsive to medical or other corrective care. Frequently, the control or management of an ailment is considered a more realistic goal of medical attention than is complete healing or cure.

There is considerable agreement among geriatricians that ailments common to old age are no different in nature from those to be found among younger people, although certain of them have prevalence and intensity that are peculiar to the aged. Among these are the cardiovascular diseases, cancer, arthritis, rheumatism, the collagen disorders, hearing impairment, and certain mental and nervous disorders.[3] It is also more difficult to achieve

[1] Among the most recent studies in this field are the Hagerstown, Maryland, survey and the ongoing study in Hunterdon County, New Jersey. See also: Cowdry, E. V., editor, *Problems of Ageing*, 1952; Monroe, Robert T., *Diseases in Old Age*, 1951; Kaplan, Oscar J., editor, *Mental Disorders in Later Life*, 1945; Stieglitz, Edward J., editor, *Geriatric Medicine*, 1954.

[2] Carlson, Anton J., and Edward J. Stieglitz, "Physiological Changes in Aging," 1952.

[3] Monroe, Robert T., *Diseases in Old Age*, 1951.

rapid restoration to health in an afflicted older person. Lesions are more resistant to closing, bone breaks more refractory to mending, respiratory infections more unyielding to antibiotics. The period of recuperation is therefore often protracted and the process of rehabilitation often involves discouragingly slow progress.

The basic aims of medical research on the problems of aging have been to comprehend the basic degenerative processes, to combat them actively when they occur, and to institute preventive measures where possible to forestall or arrest the disorder as the case may be. Prevention or control of the major illnesses common to older people involves not only the development and application of specific medical procedures (for example, gold therapy in arthritis, insulin therapy in diabetes) but a considerable measure of dependence upon the individual's consistent application of principles of self-care. Regular preventive examinations, maintenance of prescribed diets, self-administration of prescribed drugs, utilization of auxiliary services (such as housekeeping, visiting nurse), and adherence to a style of life consistent with the limitations imposed by the particular conditions— these are aspects of health care in old age that depend for success on the older person's diligence and motivation in his own behalf.[1]

Ill health, with its attendant economic, social, and psychological consequences is therefore a major problem facing older people. What is its extent in the population, what are its manifestations and its consequences? Is the threat or existence of infirmity regarded as the "natural" or "expected" outgrowth of aging? If this is true, what effects do these attitudes have upon the older person's desire for medical care and preventive health measures? How responsive is he to health education or specialized geriatric services? How willing is he to be realistic about his health needs? Community health planning must proceed not only from a knowledge of the scope and variety of health prob-

---

[1] The notable achievements in the area of physical rehabilitation have found wide application among the aged. For an illuminating account of some of this work, see Dacso, Michael M., "Physical Restoration in the Older Person," 1951.

lems but from accurate estimates of the utilization of health resources by their consumers. How ready older people are to accept health services and what their dispositions are toward new facilities will necessarily condition the nature of health planning for the later years. In considering the health problems of 500 persons in the Kips Bay sample, therefore, we shall keep in mind their dispositions and attitudes respecting preventive health measures and self-care, since these factors have a crucial bearing on this fundamental aspect of the adjustment of the older person.

Chapter 8

Health Status and
Orientations

CASE HISTORY

The interviewer learned that Mr. C., now seventy-six years old, had stopped working ten years ago because of failing eyesight. Previously he had been employed as a laborer. His vision has been deteriorating over the years to the point where he could scarcely see. The interviewer was struck by the fact that there had been almost a total neglect of the respondent's medical condition. It was difficult to determine whether this was due to the economic impoverishment of the family or a provincial attitude toward obtaining medical care. The need for medical attention was apparent. It was learned that Mr. C. had once been told that his urine contained an abnormal amount of sugar. While he suspected that he suffered from diabetes, he has never followed through on any plan to obtain medical care. When the interviewer expressed surprise about this, he smiled wanly and just shrugged his shoulders.

Mr. C.'s wife had died about twelve years earlier. He was described by his daughter, who was present during the interview, as having been unusually dependent upon his wife for all the important decisions; she had managed the family's finances and had had the major burden in rearing the children. The children had always known the father as a quiet, withdrawn man. Yet they all loved him because he was so gentle. Whenever they would suggest that he go to the doctor, he would smile at them wistfully and say that he would, in time. They suspected that he really had little incentive for living since their mother died.

OUR FIRST MAJOR PROBLEM in this section revolves about the question: What is the extent and nature of illness in old age? Further, we are interested in knowing the extent to which illness results in incapacitation. How basic the problem of health is, may be gleaned from examining the functional consequences of illness: the extent of confinement to bed or home, of being prevented from carrying on normal activities, from engaging in usual social relationships, and from employment.

Close questioning of our aged sample revealed a sizable number free of both reported physical illness and comparatively mild consequences among those reporting current illnesses. More than 43 per cent of the group stated that they had no physical or health problem bothering them at the time of the interview. Further questioning focused on specific illnesses or physical disabilities, however, reduced this proportion to 23 per cent of the sample having no health-connected complaint.[1] Some chronic ailment was reported by over half the sample (53 per cent). More

TABLE 38. INCIDENCE OF REPORTED
COMPLAINTS

Number of illnesses (complaints) per person	Number of cases	Per cent
None	115	23
One	164	33
Two	105	21
Three	61	12
Four	32	6
Five and over	23	5
Total	500	100

than 800 specific complaints, including dental problems, were mentioned—an average of between one and two for each older person in the sample, and more than two complaints per person among those having some complaint.

While this degree of illness may seem considerable at first glance, an examination of its functional consequences presents a less serious picture. Considering the sample as a whole, fewer than one person in ten are totally homebound by ill health.[2] How-

[1] The discrepancy between reports of health problems "bothering" an individual and of actual health problems raises an interesting question concerning one's attitudes toward and feelings about one's illnesses. Reporting a health complaint to an interviewer may or may not represent the existence of an illness or disability. On the other hand, some persons having legitimate medical complaints fail to report them.

[2] It is estimated that about 6 per cent of the aged population of the country are institutionalized. Total combined bed capacities for the aged in the Kips Bay-Yorkville District indicate about the same figure, although many institutional residents are not permanent residents of the area.

ever, of those chronically ill, more than two of every three are able to carry on their usual activities. Still others are able to continue some activities. Table 39 presents the full range of consequences of the illnesses of the sample.

Only a few people find that their illnesses require their spending considerable time in bed. In the year immediately preceding their interviews, about one person in 17 was bedbound for as much as a month or longer. Nearly 70 per cent of those having had some type of illness did not require bed care. The average length of bed care for those who *were* bedbound at all was from three to four weeks. Hence, where serious illness does occur, in which bed rest is mandatory, the length of bed care is considerable.

TABLE 39. CONSEQUENCES OF ILLNESS

Consequences	Per cent of those ill[a]	Per cent of total sample
No serious consequences	–	44
Keeps person at home	24	13
Keeps person from doing things	32	18
Keeps person from seeing people	7	4
Keeps person from work	23	13
Keeps person from all the aforementioned	14	8
Total	100	100
Number of cases	*285*	*500*

[a] These are respondents reporting at least one complaint.

The types of illnesses and physical complaints reported are shown in Table 40.

It may be noted that no active cases of tuberculosis or cancer were revealed by the survey, although 14 persons reported having had cancer at some time in their lives. The absence of active tuberculosis or cancer in a survey is probably explained by the fact that persons with such serious disorders are hospitalized or were otherwise unavailable to our interviewers.[1] It is, of course, possible that some instances of cancer existed among our respondents without their knowledge. The stigmatic nature of

[1] In a number of instances, serious illness—usually heart attack or stroke—precluded an interview.

tuberculosis in our society may have obscured the presence of this disease among the sample.

There were numerous complaints registered of a neurological or psychiatric nature that are not included in the foregoing analysis. Eighty-three persons, or about one-sixth of the group, had at some period in their lives been "so worried, nervous, or emotionally upset that they could not carry on their usual activities." Half of those so afflicted had required medical care. Only

TABLE 40. INCIDENCE OF ILLNESSES OR COMPLAINTS REPORTED

Illness reported	Number of cases	Per cent of sample
Arthritis	130	26
Hard of hearing	102	20
High blood pressure	87	17
Heart disease	52	10
Visual disturbances	33	7
Cataracts	32	6
Gall bladder disease	28	6
Urinary troubles	27	5
Paralysis and muscular disability	27	5
Asthma	24	5
Kidney disease	22	4
Stomach ulcer	13	3
Prostate disease	13	3
Diabetes	13	3
Cirrhosis	5	1
Genital troubles in women	5	1
Glaucoma	3	a
Total medical illnesses	616	
Dental complaints	218	44
Total	834	

a Less than 1 per cent.

19 persons had experienced such an episode within the past four years.

Nearly one in five reported being frequently troubled by nervousness, and a like number, chronic insomnia. Nearly one-fourth of the entire group usually awake tired and exhausted. Almost one person in eight mentioned protracted depression. About one-tenth of the sample admitted to frequent preoccupation with death, while not quite 5 per cent of the total has considered committing suicide within the past ten years.

Insofar as the group as a whole is concerned, the extent of present recognizable emotional troubles is limited to from 4 to 18 per cent of the group. There is considerable overlap in reported symptomatology. Thus, about one-third reported nothing indicative of emotional distress.

Employing the Elmira study scale of senility,[1] we note that not quite 6 per cent respond positively on all three items used as indicators of senility, an additional 20 per cent having two of the three "senile signs." While the scale cannot be said to offer presumptive evidence of senility, we may say, nevertheless, that senile symptomatology is strongly present in about one person in twenty and moderately present in one of five others in the survey.

Use of the Elmira study Compulsiveness Scale[2] produced little evidence of compulsiveness in this group. No person scored positively on all three items of the scale. More than a third indicated disturbance on two of the items but nearly two-fifths of the sample show no compulsive signs on this scale.[3]

In sum, while other comparative data are lacking, it would appear that despite the mental degenerative processes of aging to which most older persons are allegedly heir, about one-third show practically none of the emotional wear and tear of life in a large city. Furthermore, only one-fourth of the sample show substantial intellectual or emotional changes indicative of senility, and these, of course, increase with advancing age (Table 41).

Thus far, we have dealt with the sample as a whole. Just who are the ill among this surveyed group? Let us now turn to an examination of sample subgroups.

As one would surmise, the older the individual, the more likely is he to be afflicted with some illness. As seen in Table 42, the general trend of illness rises with the later years. Nevertheless,

---

[1] A scale based upon items dealing with thoughts of death, daydreaming, and forgetfulness. The study was concerned with problems of the aged of Elmira, New York, and was carried out under the Department of Sociology and Anthropology of Cornell University. It has not yet been published.

[2] A scale composed of items dealing with being interrupted, having belongings disturbed, and having others rearrange the house.

[3] It is conceivable, of course, that compulsiveness for some is not a pathologic disorder but a mechanism serving a useful purpose in circumscribing the individual's life concerns.

TABLE 41. SIGNS OF SENILITY ACCORDING TO AGE

Signs of senility	Age (in years)			
	60 to 64	65 to 69	70 to 74	75 and over
	(Percentages)			
None or one	79	80	71	66
Two	15	15	23	28
Three and over	6	5	6	6
Total	100	100	100	100
Number of cases	117	139	115	129

it cannot be said that illness dominates old age. As indicated earlier, the nature of many of the listed ailments is of sufficiently minor character as not to cause the individual undue proscriptions upon his life activities. Although we shall consider the fact and its significance subsequently, it should be noted in passing that one of these proscriptions is the continuous need for medical care. Hence, clinic visiting absorbs the attention of a large part of our chronically ill sample. The greater the number of illnesses, the greater the likelihood that the person has visited or is currently a patient at a clinic. But whether attendance at clinics as a result of the health problems of aging is necessarily a constricting or limiting experience is a matter for debate, and we shall discuss it in another section.

With any degree of illness, the proportions of men and women are about equal. There is a slight tendency for never-married people to report more illnesses than either married or widowed

TABLE 42. INCIDENCE OF REPORTED ILLNESSES ACCORDING TO AGE

Number of illnesses reported	Age (in years)				
	60 to 64	65 to 69	70 to 74	75 to 79	80 and over
	(Percentages)				
None	26	29	20	18	15
One or two	57	48	58	56	49
Three and over	17	23	22	26	36
Total	100	100	100	100	100
Number of cases	117	139	115	82	47

people.[1] There is considerably more reported illness as one descends the economic ladder. About 10 per cent fewer instances of no illness occur among low as compared to high socioeconomic status persons, with those of medium status occupying a middle ground. There are about twice the proportion in the low group reporting three or more illnesses as there are in the middle or high economic group (Table 43).

TABLE 43. INCIDENCE OF REPORTED ILLNESSES ACCORDING TO SOCIOECONOMIC STATUS

| Number of illnesses reported | Socioeconomic status | | |
	High	Middle	Low
	(Percentages)		
None	31	25	21
One or two	55	58	52
Three and over	14	17	27
Total	100	100	100
Number of cases	55	148	297

This finding suggests that various other factors, components of the general variable of "socioeconomic status," are also related to the degree of reported illness. Is it possible, for instance, that membership in the upper economic and social class carries the cultural dictum that a person of high station must minimize evidences of failing health or incapacitation, must in fact stoically present an exterior of youthful vigor and "preservation"? At the same time, does low status remove barriers to admitting one's aging? In the same connection, it will be of interest to know whether chronic ill health, a commonly accepted sign of aging, is less acceptable to higher status than to lower status people.

AN INDEX OF PHYSICAL HEALTH

Before turning to these questions, it becomes necessary to refine our measure of health status, since the mere enumeration of illnesses does not provide us with a yardstick of their seriousness or

[1] It is interesting to note in this connection that the never-married group have more instances of being without the services of a regular physician who treat their illnesses than any of the other marital groups.

of their social, economic, or personal consequences. Thus, while one person may report three or four minor ailments, none of which bothers him greatly, another may suffer from a single major illness that may be partially or totally incapacitating. The presence of several minor ailments that do not confine or restrict the person's normal activities is certainly less consequential than is, say, cancer or tuberculosis or any major ailment that demands the reordering of the person's life pattern. At the same time, it should be emphasized that the degree of seriousness of an ailment as measured by medical standards may be quite different when measured by those of the sufferer. Certainly a blinding migraine attack may be subjectively as devastating to the person's ability to operate normally as the presence of a brain tumor. Moreover, minor ailments are often exaggerated beyond all reasonable objective criteria, as in hypochondria, and the individual's *felt* disability or incapacity effectively reduces his functioning.

We must therefore weigh illness simultaneously with its functional significance in the person's life. Toward this end, a Physical Health Index was constructed in which a weighted score was assigned for each of several aspects of health. These consist of: (1) amount of time confined to bed because of illness in the past year; (2) social and economic deprivations due to ill health; (3) number of illnesses; (4) certain "critical" diseases if reported, such as cirrhosis of the liver, cancer, angina pectoris. The scoring scheme follows:

Confinement to bed because of illness during past year	*Score*
Less than 1 week	1
Occasionally	1
1 to 3 weeks	2
3 weeks to 1 month	3
1 month and over	4

Deprivations due to illness	
Illness keeps individual in house	1
Illness keeps individual from doing things	1
Illness keeps individual from seeing people	1
Illness keeps individual from work	1
Illness keeps individual from all of the above-mentioned	4

Number of illnesses
One   1
Two   2
Three   3
Four and over   4

Serious diseases if reported (angina pectoris, asthma, stomach
ulcer, cirrhosis of liver, vaginal bleeding or spotting,
cancer, paralysis of part of body)
One   1
Two   2
Three   3
Four and over   4

A total weighted index score was determined for each survey
respondent. For purposes of analysis and comparison, the scores
are arbitrarily divided at certain points and an evaluative term
is used to describe the health status of those within each group
of scores. Thus, the following divisions are adhered to in this
report:

Physical Health Index score	*Health status*	*Number of cases*	*Per cent of total*
0	Excellent	*67*	13.4
1 to 2	Good	*217*	43.4
3 to 5	Fair	*131*	26.2
6 and over	Poor	*85*	17.0
Total		*500*	100.0

For analytic and comparative purposes, the first two categories
are combined to form a "good health" group, and the latter are
combined to form a "poor health" group.[1]

It is significant to note that about 56 per cent of the total can
be placed in the "good health" group. Moreover, in some instances where poor dentures, frequent common colds, or sprained
ankles may have been the turning factor, an individual may have
been placed in the "fair" rather than in the "good" category.

As in the case of sheer numbers of illnesses, men and women
are about equally distributed at each level of health. With respect

[1] Such combinations are possible since the groups that are combined show no differences between them when analyzed against other major factors being studied
such as socioeconomic position or adjustment level.

to age differences, although there is a decline with advancing age in the number of people without a major health problem, the Index indicates *relatively little difference in health status as age increases.*[1] The proportions of people at each health level were nearly the same for each age group. The significance of this fact should be stressed. It is not the factor of age alone that determines the seriousness of the social dislocations brought about by disease. A minority of each age group *is* in poor health. However, not only is there no great increase in the frequency of illness with advancing age, but increase of incapacitation or social handicap due to illness is also slight.

TABLE 44. PHYSICAL HEALTH STATUS ACCORDING TO SOCIOECONOMIC STATUS

| Health status | Socioeconomic status | | |
	High	Middle	Low
		(Percentages)	
Good health	80	64	50
Poor health	20	36	50
Total	100	100	100
Number of cases	55	148	297

On the other hand, socioeconomic position bears a positive relationship to good health. Arranging the sample into "good health" and "poor health" groups, we see in Table 44 that low socioeconomic status is associated with poorer health. Not only are there proportionately more illnesses at the lower socioeconomic levels, but also a greater proportion of instances of serious consequences. These differences, particularly those between the lower and middle and between the lower and upper socioeconomic groups, are so great that they demand careful scrutiny.[2]

[1] It will be recalled that the number of *complaints* does increase with age, but here we say that regardless of this fact the seriousness of those complaints or their social resultants as measured by the Physical Health Index are not greater as age increases.

[2] It should be pointed out that owing to a sizable sampling error, the three groups are probably somewhat selective. Relative ease of access of high economic status persons to nursing homes and the relative difficulty of interviewing ill people, especially in the high socioeconomic group, as well as the generally greater willingness of lower socioeconomic status people to be interviewed make it likely that these differences are, in fact, not so large as they appear to be.

Since there are only small and insignificant age differences on the Physical Health Index, we can predict that health status differences between each socioeconomic group will hold at each age level.

Does low status, with its attendant circumstances of slum dwelling, low income, and large families induce ill health among older people? Or do higher status people with more income, greater awareness of preventive health measures, and greater access to medical services have such superior care that they do not fall prey to illness or debility? Indeed, is it high social status and the greater need for maintaining robust health that is crucial to good health, or is it sheer income and the ability to command health resources both of a preventive and a therapeutic nature that is the more important factor?

TABLE 45. PHYSICAL HEALTH INDEX ACCORDING TO INCOME[a]

Physical Health Index	Income per week			
	Less than $25	$25 to $49	$50 to $74	$75 and over
	(Percentages)			
Excellent	11	11	11	26
Good	37	36	57	51
Fair	29	34	20	15
Poor	23	19	12	8
Total	100	100	100	100
Number of cases	207	116	74	65

[a] The total number of cases used here is 462. Thirty-eight respondents did not reply to the question on income.

The evidence on this point seems to show that both factors play a role in depressing the reported illness and its consequences in the higher economic groups. Through high income, the individual has the ability to mobilize health resources as the need may arise. One might argue, however, that a person of means is usually well educated and, hence, well informed about the need and the resources available for adequate medical care. But it is a striking fact that a person's education is not a significant factor in health status if considered by itself regardless of his economic status. Yet income does differentiate the poor in health from those who are comparatively well. Table 45 indicates the nature of the relationship. In general, as income increases the health picture brightens. The proportions reporting no illness and no effects of illness do not show a rise except in the wealthiest group. At other levels of health status, the trend is clear. Table 46 consolidates the health groups to present a vivid picture of the meaning of income to health in old age.

TABLE 46. HEALTH STATUS ACCORDING TO INCOME[a]

Health status	Income per week			
	Less than $25	$25 to $49	$50 to $74	$75 and over
	(Percentages)			
Good health	48	47	68	77
Poor health	52	53	32	23
Total	100	100	100	100
Number of cases	207	116	74	65

[a] The total number of cases used here is 462. Thirty-eight respondents did not reply to the question on income.

Thus, economic deprivation or loss of income would seem to play a major role in the health status of the aged. It suggests that those best able to muster the health resources of the community may survive in old age without undue physical hardships or their social and psychological concomitants.

HEALTH CONDITION AND HEALTH SERVICES

One may now ask just what types of medical service, if adequately utilized, have a significant effect upon the older person's health. Does health depend upon the availability of a regular physician in the event of illness? Does it depend upon preventive health examinations, health insurance programs, or other factors? An examination of the survey findings makes it clear that the availability of a *regular* physician in time of illness is *unrelated* to health status. Presumably, if the individual is sufficiently ill, in one way or another he does receive some form of medical care. On the other hand, selective factors may be at work here, since we do not know the mortality rates for those who received insufficient care as compared with those adequately cared for and per-

sons who do not have the care may have higher age-specific
death rates.

More than half the persons in each health status group have
physicians who regularly care for their illnesses. Further, we see
in Table 47 that the proportions in good and poor health are no
different within each socioeconomic group. Socioeconomic status,
on the other hand, seems to be of considerable importance as a
factor influencing health status.

TABLE 47. HEALTH STATUS ACCORDING TO SOCIOECONOMIC
STATUS OF PERSONS HAVING AND NOT HAVING A
REGULAR PHYSICIAN

	Have regular physician		Do not have regular physician	
Health status	High status	Low status	High status	Low status
	(Percentages)			
Good health	65	51	75	48
Poor health	35	49	25	52
Total	100	100	100	100
Number of cases	155	158	48	139

It is illuminating to learn the reasons offered for not having a
regular physician. While no preponderance of any one reason is
discernible in the upper or middle groups, lack of funds is the
primary reason in three out of ten cases in the lower economic
group, with an additional three in ten explaining that, not being
ill, they have no need for physicians.[1] But this does not mean that

[1] Differential treatment of patients from different social classes has been demonstrated by Myers and Schaffer. These authors conclude that "in a situation where
the economic factor was held constant . . . the higher an individual's social class
position the more likely he was to be accepted for treatment, to be treated by highly
trained personnel, and to be treated intensively over a long period." (Myers, Jerome
K., and Leslie Schaffer, "Social Stratification and Psychiatric Practice: A Study of
an Out-Patient Clinic," 1954, p. 309.) The hypothesis was offered that part of the
reason for these findings is the lack of understanding or acceptability of psychotherapy to lower class persons. In the present study, failure to acquire a physician
may reflect a similar devaluation of medical service as well as an apprehension that
these services would not be offered in an acceptable manner or setting. While the
situations are not entirely similar, since it is probably more difficult for the public to
understand the value of psychotherapy as compared with medical care, many older
people do experience frustration in seeking medical assistance for chronic illnesses
that do not readily respond to treatment. In recent years, though medical interest in
chronic illness is increasing, the perception of an indifferent attitude on the part of
physicians may still persist on the part of many patients.

medical care is not received during illness. It is possible that medical care during illness is only one factor in health maintenance and preventive measures, taken in time to ward off or contain an illness, also need to be considered.

While we shall examine the older person's utilization of other health services presently, we should note here that *having regular medical examinations bears no relation to the state of an individual's health.* Among those who have a checkup twice or more a year a greater proportion are in poor health than among those who have a yearly checkup or who seldom or never see a physician (Table 48). It is probable that those who have a checkup frequently have

TABLE 48. HEALTH STATUS ACCORDING TO REGULAR CHECKUP[a]

| Health status | Have regular physical checkup | | |
	Twice or more a year	Once a year	Seldom or never
	(Percentages)		
Good health	42	57	60
Poor health	58	43	40
Total	100	100	100
Number of cases	79	127	187

[a] The total number of cases used here is 393. This question was asked only of those who affirmed that "it's a good idea to have a regular thorough checkup by a doctor even if there's nothing wrong." Three subjects did not respond to the question.

some illness requiring continuous attention. Further refinement of these data reveals that a substantial proportion of those in the low status group and in poor health do not see a physician regularly because of inability to pay for medical services.[1]

Significantly, there are almost no differences between socio-economic groups concerning these tendencies. This suggests two possibilities: one is that not to have a preventive health examination is an American or even a universal cultural phenomenon transcending ethnic and religious differences; the other is that the accessibility of health facilities to upper and middle class people is

[1] Webber reports in a study of 734 retired persons in St. Petersburg, Florida, that 61.8 per cent had not visited a physician in the previous six months and 83 per cent had not had a physician come to their homes in the same period. See Webber, Irving L., "The Retired Population of a Florida Community," 1951.

balanced by the required character of these examinations among lower class people who generally are found to have more numerous medical complaints.

While health examinations and having the regular service of a physician seem to bear no relation to health, the possession of some form of health insurance does have some relation. Among the 75 per cent of the survey group who do not own health insurance, there are as many in one as in the other health classification.[1] But for the 25 per cent who *do* own some form of health insurance, *there are nearly twice as many in the good as in the poor health group*. Of the 176 persons who own some prepaid health insurance, two out of three belonged to a hospitalization plan, while one out of three was a member of a health insurance program.

It would be erroneous to assume that prepaid health insurance automatically reduces health hazards. It is at least equally possible that those who possess such insurance are already generally healthy or are "health conscious," or both. Therefore, they may be disposed to go out of their way to receive early medical attention. The significance of these findings may also reside in the fact that membership in a prepaid health or hospitalization program may *induce* an older person who might otherwise hesitate to undertake expensive diagnostic or therapeutic procedures to carry them to the ultimate goal of possessing better health.

We may at once question whether possession of health insurance is related to one's economic status and, if so, do not our findings mean that those who are in better economic station can afford to secure health maintenance through insurance? The answer is not clear-cut. Certainly, within the middle economic group (who proportionately own the most health insurance) there is no difference at all between the numbers having health insurance in either health group. About half of each middle class health group own health insurance. In the upper economic group, there are as many owners as nonowners of insurance among those in good health but, although the numbers are too small to gauge accurately, more people among those in poor

---

[1] Nationally, participation in health insurance plans approximates coverage of 25 per cent of the population.

health do not own health insurance. This finding can be discounted by the fact that the wealthier group is more likely to seek medical aid from their own physicians as needed rather than to purchase health insurance. In the lower group, about two-thirds of those in good health, but three-fourths of those in the poor health group, do not own health insurance.[1] These data do not represent incontrovertible evidence that health insurance in some manner induces conditions that lead to health improvement. However, their direction suggests that, at least for some, health insurance may mean better health. From the figures given there is some implication that, if more individuals had the benefits of a prepaid health service, fewer cases of poor health would ensue.

The acquisition and retention of these health insurance services implies a certain degree of concern or motivation in regard to health matters. In some cases, perhaps in most, this is true. But regardless of the reasons, be they motivational or the sheer accident of coverage by one's employer, the fact of better health with the possession of insurance is noteworthy.

One interesting sidelight to this general point is worth mentioning. Since health insurance provides a measure of protection to health, does it also provide peace of mind concerning one's health? As we shall point out, for a variety of reasons worry about health is relatively low among the sample as a whole. Indeed, only 13 per cent of the entire group say they are often worried about their health. What proportions who own health insurance worry? Likewise, what of those who do little or no worrying? Interestingly, we find a tendency for those who have insurance to be less apprehensive about their health than those who do not have insurance. For at least one portion of the aged population, ownership of prepaid health insurance is significantly associated with reduced anxiety concerning health.

HEALTH AND EMPLOYMENT

Another variable relevant to health status may be employment. It is important from a planning standpoint to determine whether health problems are a major concern of those not gainfully em-

---

[1] The difference is not statistically significant.

ployed. We should expect that those who are employed are in better health than those who are unemployed. Those who are retired and housewives should hold some intermediate position between them. The relationships should hold, since to be employed requires a certain degree of good health, while unemployment often is brought about through illness. Likewise, some retired persons may be ill—fewer than among the unemployed but more than among the employed. Table 49 presents these findings. The employed are divided into those employed by others and the self-employed. Nearly three-quarters of the employed group are in good health, there being a somewhat greater proportion of self-employed than those employed by others in the good health group.[1] About half of the housewife and retired

TABLE 49. HEALTH STATUS ACCORDING TO EMPLOYMENT STATUS[a]

Health status	Self-employed	Employed by others	Retired	Housewife	Unemployed
		(Percentages)			
Good health	78	69	49	56	29
Poor health	22	31	51	44	71
Total	100	100	100	100	100
Number of cases	41	120	164	133	38

[a] The total number of cases used here is 496.

groups are in good health, while more than 70 per cent of the unemployed are in poor health. What is crucial here is the temporal sequence. Did the unemployed group become ill before or after their unemployment? Does working keep a person in good health, or does good health extend a person's work-life?[2] While we do not have direct answers to these problems, it is interesting to note that approximately two-fifths of the retired group left their employment for health reasons. It is probable that many people continue working just as long as health or employment

[1] The difference is not statistically significant.

[2] Some have suggested that employment tends to ward off the degenerative processes by keeping the individual within certain rigidly proscribed limits of activity. See, for example, Stern, Karl, "Problems Ecountered in an Old Age Counselling Center," 1950.

practices permit. Among those who have retired, inasmuch as the period of nonemployment may last for many years, some health problem may eventually arise. In general, the employed group, being considerably younger than the retired or the housewife groups, are probably less subject to ill health. The process is selective: ill health may lead to retirement or unemployment; those who are younger have fewer ills and continue in employment; those who are older are subject to more illness regardless of their employment status but become candidates for retirement if illness becomes severe.

AWARENESS OF HEALTH STATUS

When considering the person's health status, a question arises concerning the individual's awareness of his own health condition. It is logical to assume that when an individual's health is threatened (as it may be in old age) or when illness or accident occurs, there will be a significant rise in the individual's consciousness of his general condition. It has been argued that older people tend to ignore warning signs and symptoms of illness or degeneration, since they do not expect good health in old age in any event. They postulate that older people tend to be unrealistic, to turn away from their health problems by ignoring or failing to recognize them. Upon close inspection of the survey data, however, it becomes clear that, while this seems to be the case in some instances, awareness of and concern about health are generally commensurate with the extent of the problem. If we compare their own judgments of the state of their health with evaluations based upon the Physical Health Index, we find a considerable degree of correspondence, though this is only a rough estimate at best.[1] From Table 50, we see that of those who are rated as being in excellent health by the Index, 85 per cent rate themselves as either "excellent" or "good." Nearly half of those rated "good"

[1] It is, of course, true that the two ratings are not based upon the same criteria. The Physical Health Index judgment takes into account both illnesses and consequences and is weighted to give a comparative rating. At the same time, the individual judgment is based on a continuum ranging from "excellent" to "poor." Both may be said to be roughly equivalent if it is agreed that the evaluative "excellent," "good," "fair," "poor" are commonly understood.

by the Index use the same rating for themselves. Only ten persons
rated themselves as "poor" in health who were rated "excellent"
or "good" by the Index. Only 8 per cent of those rated as "fair"
or "poor" in health rated themselves as "excellent." In general,
therefore, older people cannot be said to be ignorant of their
health condition.[1]

TABLE 50. HEALTH   SELF-RATING   ACCORDING   TO   PHYSICAL
         HEALTH INDEX

Health self-rating	Physical Health Index			
	Excellent	Good	Fair	Poor
		(Percentages)		
Excellent	48	25	10	6
Good	37	46	26	12
Fair	15	24	35	27
Poor	–	5	29	55
Total	100	100	100	100
Number of cases	67	217	131	85

Despite the generally reality-oriented judgments of the sample
regarding their health, certain class differences do appear that are
worth noting. *Those of higher socioeconomic status tend to judge themselves as being in better health than do those in the lower socioeconomic
levels whether in the good health or poor health groups.* As seen in
Table 51, it is apparent that competence to judge one's own
health status is not equally good among all subgroups. When
compared to the Physical Health Index, health self-judgments are
relatively accurate for those in the low economic group in both
health status groups. But while self-ratings among those of high
economic status and good health are very accurate, judgments of
poor health by this economic group are the most unrealistic of all.

In each status group opinion of one's own health condition is,
in general, high among those in good health; it tends, however,
to be higher among the upper socioeconomic group. Similarly,
although the number of cases is small, the persistence of this trend
in the poor health group suggests that upper status people tend to

[1] The Pearson correlation coefficient of the Physical Health Index and the Health
Self-Rating is .57.

overrate their health, while those in the lower group match more closely the objective condition, in their own judgments. When combined with a lack of overt concern about health and considerable resistance to having preventive health examinations, this "unreal" judgment of health on the part of higher status people would suggest that a sociocultural role is being played by older high status persons who feel impelled to deny their "symptoms of aging." It may be that the differences between one's self-perceived health status and the facts as determined by the Physical Health Index may stem partly from a desire (though it may be subconscious) to avoid identification with the older age group.

TABLE 51. HEALTH SELF-RATING ACCORDING TO SOCIOECONOMIC STATUS FOR GOOD AND POOR HEALTH STATUS

Health self-rating	Good health		Poor health	
	High status	Low status	High status	Low status
	(Percentages)			
Good	80	70	41	24
Poor	20	30	59	76
Total	100	100	100	100
Number of cases	137	147	66	150

Although more than 40 per cent of the sample rated themselves as being in fair or poor health and a like number are found in these same categories by the Physical Health Index, most older people in the survey in general did not feel themselves to be disadvantaged as far as health is concerned when compared to others of their age. In fact, about half the group attested to the fact that their health was better than that of their peers and an additional third of the total felt their health to be the same as others of comparable age. Only 44 persons, less than 10 per cent of the sample, felt their health was worse than that of others. This generally favorable appraisal of one's own health is best seen when contrasting the actual health assessment of the Physical Health Index with their feelings about health in respect to others. Thus, nearly two-thirds of those in the good health group feel their health is better than that of others but less than half of those in the poor health group feel this way. Only six persons in the good health group feel their health is worse than others, and but 18 per cent of those in the "poor" group believe themselves to be in worse health than their age contemporaries. This suggests that many older people regard their chronic illnesses, disabilities, and incapacities as "natural" consequences of old age. Tolerance for incapacity or disability may reflect a generally passive acceptance of life circumstances with advancing age. We may hypothesize that older people have an unusual tolerance for illness. If it is correct, one may then predict that health problems do not represent a central focus of attention of older people. Hence, their readiness to attend to minor illnesses or complaints that may lead to chronic or fatal maladies, their responsiveness to health education programs, their inclination to have regular preventive health examinations, and their interest in geriatric centers may all be affected. As will be seen in Chapters 9 and 10, motivation in utilizing services is not universally high, and in general these predicted negative dispositions are at least partially confirmed. Unless we understand the meaning of old age to older people themselves and the role that health plays in this meaning, programs to aid the aged may not be geared to meet their needs.

Two avenues of approach may be taken to the question of the prominence and significance of health matters in the adjustment of older people. The first is to determine the place health holds in the hierarchy of problems seen by older people to require special attention. The second is to determine the extent to which health anxiety exists. We shall examine each approach in turn.

HEALTH AS A CENTRAL VALUE

Each respondent in the survey was asked this question: "If there was a center which dealt only with the needs of older people, what do you think it should deal with?" It was hoped that a comparative rating could be established concerning the importance of various life problems or unmet needs among the aged. There were 851 responses to the question and, as shown in Table 52, health ranks equally with financial problems and slightly lower than employment as areas with which a center should concern itself. *Of the full sample, only 25 per cent mention health as an area to be dealt with.* It is clear that at least in this sample of aged persons, health or its decline in old age does not loom as quite the specter that it is so often assumed to be. While health does play a potent role in adjustment to aging, the fact seems to be that it is embedded within the context of other life problems of at least equal significance.

An interesting side issue that will concern us again is the difference between the economic status groups on this question. Proportionately, more older people in the upper economic group

TABLE 52. PROBLEM AREAS WITH WHICH A CENTER SHOULD DEAL

Problem areas mentioned	Number of responses[a]	Per cent of all responses	Per cent of total
Recreation	175	21	35
Employment	132	16	26
Health	127	15	25
Financial	126	15	25
Housing	71	8	14
Help meet new friends	67	8	13
Education	38	4	8
Legal	18	2	4
Family	17	2	3
Other	80	9	16
Total	851	100	

[a] More than one area could be given by a respondent.

than in the middle group and more in the latter than in the lower economic group name health as a problem. More than twice as many of those in the upper group mention health as those in the lower group. This is a curious result since, as we have seen, there is far less reported illness as well as less overt concern about health among those in the higher socioeconomic group. It would seem likely, therefore, that upper socioeconomic status persons would see a medical center for the aged as of less importance than it is accorded here. Is it possible that responses to this question are more indicative of anxiety about health that is not expressed in other ways? To project a general need such as health as a major concern for a center for the aged while denying the existence of ill health or any anxiety about it suggests that considerable unexpressed concern for health exists in people of high social and economic position.[1] Another, but less plausible, explanation is that high status persons are generally more favorable in attitude toward health facilities, although they personally may not wish to use them.

Two additional facts must be reported here. Men name health as a concern more frequently than do women, although there is no sex difference on either the Physical Health Index or the health self-rating. An age differential also appears that is even more interesting. A significant decrease in mentioning health as a concern for a center occurs among those seventy-five years of age and older, although no corresponding decrease in health problems actually occurs. Again, we shall reserve analysis of these problems for a later point.

WORRY ABOUT HEALTH

It will be recalled that more than 40 per cent of the sample were rated as poor in health and a like proportion rated themselves similarly. To what extent is health regarded as a matter of serious concern to those who have most reason to worry? The answer to this question will provide additional evidence concerning the general attitude of older people toward health maintenance. Only 30 persons (6 per cent of the group) admit to worrying "all of the time" about their health and about an equal number are worried "most" of the time. The great majority of the sample are either only "sometimes" or "never" worried. Three out of every five respondents claim never to be worried about health. We may now inquire what bearing health status has to concern about health. Table 53 provides the answer to the question. The poorer the health of the individual the greater the likelihood of concern. This seems a likely finding until one considers the fact that more than a third of those who are in the poorest health *never worry* about their health. Perhaps most

[1] As we shall see, overt anxiety is very low among higher status persons. This suggests, and we shall explicitly deal with this issue, that health is, in fact, a major area of deep concern to those of high social and economic position.

TABLE 53. WORRY ABOUT HEALTH ACCORDING TO PHYSICAL HEALTH INDEX

	Physical Health Index			
Worry about health	Excellent	Good	Fair	Poor
		(Percentages)		
All of the time	–	3	7	18
Most of the time	–	1	14	14
Sometimes	18	25	33	31
Never	82	71	46	37
Total	100	100	100	100
Number of cases	67	217	131	85

dramatic is the fact that two-thirds of those in the consolidated "poor health" group worry little about their condition. If worry about health and spontaneous recommendations on the concerns of a center for the aged are criteria of the centrality of health in the lives of older people, the judgment seems to be that it does not occupy the salient position it would deserve if illness alone were considered the significant factor. While numbers of older people are ill and the vast proportion of them have chronic ailments, undue anxiety does not seem to be aroused.

Worry about health is not uniformly low in all segments of the sample. For example, economic status seems to have a bearing on expressed health concern. Thus, there is less concern about health expressed by the upper economic group than would be expected. As seen in Table 54, very few in this group admit to worry about health all or even most of the time, while correspondingly greater numbers profess such concern in the lower group. It is interesting

TABLE 54. WORRY ABOUT HEALTH ACCORDING TO SOCIOECO-NOMIC STATUS FOR GOOD AND POOR HEALTH STATUS

	Good health		Poor health	
Worry about health	High status	Low status	High status	Low status
		(Percentages)		
All or most of the time	2	4	17	29
Sometimes, never	98	96	83	71
Total	100	100	100	100
Number of cases	137	147	66	150

to note that although worry is greatest among the lower economic group, of the 150 cases among them who are in relatively poor health, more than half *never* worry about health and an additional fourth worry only "sometimes." Clearly, the discrepancy between conditions of health (and, incidentally, acknowledgment of this condition) and expressed concern is quite large.

In attempting to explain this discrepancy—a discrepancy having wide action implications—one rather obvious hypothesis suggests itself: for the vast majority of older people[1] tolerance for illness and its consequences is part of a more general pattern of *adaptation to adversity*[2] that involves the acceptance of harsh circumstances including economic deprivation, social isolation, the recession of the abilities and capacities of youth, and the general withdrawal by society of opportunities for self-expression, creativity, and contribution. We have already seen that the major portion of the surveyed group feel themselves to be healthier than others their own age or, at least, just as healthy. Moreover, while there is overwhelming agreement that people should have health examinations regularly, only about two-fifths of those advocating examinations actually do have them, and most of these latter have serious health problems requiring extensive medical care. Adding the relatively low level of anxiety about health to be found even among those who are poorest in health (and the denial of health problems among those in the higher economic group), we gain a picture of the older group as generally stoic, realistic but resigned and, in some cases, apathetic to their condition. Whether this pattern of adaptation is a significant aspect of successful aging in populations other than our own sample is difficult to say.

Ethnic Factors in Concern About Health

While those in good and poor health according to the Physical Health Index are about equally divided among other ethnic groups, the American-born and those of British and Italian extraction seem to enjoy somewhat better health. Nevertheless,

---

[1] Based on our findings, we estimate about three-fourths of them.

[2] See Greenleigh, Lawrence F., *Psychological Problems of Our Aging Population*, 1952.

health status alone does not determine the degree of expressed anxiety over health. People born in the United States, Germany or Austria, Britain, and to some extent Ireland may be said to be "health optimists;" there are more among them who never worry about their health and fewer who rate their health as poor. On the other hand, Czechs, Hungarians, Russians and Poles, and Italians tend to be "health pessimists;" they are more concerned about their health. Table 55 shows the relationship of ethnicity to worry about health, both among those who are in good as well as among those in poor health. It would appear that fundamental

TABLE 55. WORRY ABOUT HEALTH ACCORDING TO ETHNIC ORIGIN
FOR GOOD AND POOR HEALTH STATUS

Ethnic origin	Good health			Number of cases	Poor health			Number of cases
		Do not				Do not		
	Worry	worry	Total		Worry	worry	Total	
	(Percentages)				(Percentages)			
Germany, Austria	23	77	100	62	54	46	100	54
Ireland	31	69	100	35	52	48	100	31
United States	18	82	100	44	37	63	100	19
Hungary	44	56	100	27	57	43	100	28
Czechoslovakia	52	48	100	23	74	26	100	19
England, Wales, Scotland	7	93	100	28	36	64	100	11
Italy	47	53	100	17	80	20	100	10
Russia, Poland	21	79	100	14	85	15	100	13
Other	15	85	100	34	58	42	100	31
Number of cases				284				216

cultural factors play major roles in the expression of concern with health. Certainly, if these data are substantially correct, health education programs geared to the "sensitive to health" Czechs, 52 per cent of whom worry about health even if healthy, are not likely to meet with the same response among those of British extraction, of whom 64 per cent of the poorest in health stoically maintain that they never worry.[1]

[1] Zborowski has detailed the cultural differences in response to pain among war veterans of varied background. Our findings indicate a marked similarity to his: stoicism and disdain over personal suffering among native-born Americans and Irish-born veterans but much expressed anguish and "social suffering" among Jewish and Italian veterans. See Zborowski, Mark, "Cultural Components in Responses to Pain," 1952.

Similar results emerge from an examination of the health self-rating. While not a single Britisher rates himself as "poor" in health if he is actually in good health, about three out of ten Italians, four out of ten Czechs, half of the Russians and Poles, as well as half of the Hungarians rate themselves "poor," although they are in good health. Similarly, with the possible exception of those of British origin, there are like degrees of optimism and pessimism among those in poor health. Although the numbers are too small to judge accurately, the British tend to appraise realistically such poor health as exists.

An additional cultural factor emerges in a consideration of age differences in health ratings among the various groups. With increasing age there is a sharp decline in the proportion of "good health" self-estimates among those born in the United States, Germany or Austria, Ireland, England, and Italy (the latter having a drop of 21 per cent in "good health" rating between sixty and seventy years of age) compared to those from Russia or Poland, Hungary, or Czechoslovakia. Among the latter group (the pessimists) there are similar proportions of about two-fifths of each group regarding themselves in good health. Among the "optimists" (with the Italian group puzzling in this respect) initial estimates range about two-thirds in good health before seventy years of age, with a drop to about one-half after seventy regarding themselves as in good health.

In the area of preventive health measures, cultural differences are wiped away. Thus, nearly four-fifths of all groups agree with the necessity of having regular physical checkups (although fewer Czechs than others feel this way). But only half of those in each ethnic group who feel that such examinations are important actually have them regularly. Likewise, no important differences appear concerning recommended areas for a center for the aged to deal with. Health is mentioned on the average by about 25 per cent of each group and ranks about third in frequency of mention.

HEALTH AND FUTILITY

It has long been contended that one of the most unfortunate aspects of aging in our society is the fact that the older person loses his purpose in life. Since one's lifetime occupation, one's family and circle of friends, and one's capacities all recede or disappear, the individual—so the argument runs—becomes disillusioned and bitter and his life becomes aimless or goal-less. If all that gave meaning to life in one's younger days is gone, effort becomes futile; hence, many old people present a picture of apathy and indifference to much that goes on around them.

To test these suppositions, an index of "futility" was employed as part of the questionnaire.[1] Such items as: "Nowadays a person has to live pretty much for today and let tomorrow take care of itself"; "It's hardly fair [for young folk] to bring children into the world with the way things look for the future"; and "In spite of

TABLE 56. FUTILITY FEELINGS ACCORDING TO AGE

Futility	Age (in years)					Total sample	Number of cases
	60 to 64	65 to 69	70 to 74	75 to 79	80 and over		
	(Percentages)						
Low	41	34	42	38	45	39	195
Moderate	49	55	50	46	49	50	250
High	10	11	8	16	6	11	55
Total	100	100	100	100	100	100	
Number of cases	117	139	115	82	47		500

what some people say, the life of the average man is getting worse, not better" are examples of the scale's components. In terms of the distribution of responses to the scale, Table 56 presents a summary analyzed according to age. As seen there, futility does not seem to increase with age. Widowhood, loneliness, retirement, and illness notwithstanding, attitudes toward life as depicted by responses to the scale are relatively positive. Some have argued that men are more disillusioned and disorganized by old age than are women but no sex differences occur on the futility scale. Small but insignificant differences appear among the various employment status groups with slightly less futility ex-

[1] The scale was devised by Dr. Leo Srole and is known as the "anomie scale". See Srole, Leo, "Social Dysfunction, Personality and Social Distance Attitudes," 1951.

pressed by the self-employed group and slightly more by the unemployed.[1]

Poor health and relative social isolation are the two factors most closely associated with a sense of futility in old age. While most of the survey respondents fall in the center of the futility scale, there is more expression of futility among those in poor health than among those in good health (Table 57).

TABLE 57. FUTILITY FEELINGS ACCORDING TO
GOOD AND POOR HEALTH STATUS

Futility	Good health	Poor health
	(Percentages)	
Low	47	29
Moderate	46	55
High	7	16
Total	100	100
Number of cases	284	216

Feelings of futility are strongly associated with relative social isolation (Table 58). While 41 per cent of those in the isolated group show high futility, only 27 per cent of the nonisolated

TABLE 58. FUTILITY FEELINGS ACCORDING TO
RELATIVE SOCIAL ISOLATION[a]

Futility	Isolated	Not isolated
	(Percentages)	
Low	59	73
High	41	27
Total	100	100
Number of cases	279	220

[a] The total number of cases used here is 499. One respondent could not be classified on the Isolation Index.

group show high futility. An interesting question presents itself. The development of a sense of hopelessness may emerge not from

[1] One might explain the lack of differences here by hypothesizing that attitudes toward age and self are so well fixed by the age of sixty that only minor changes occur in the later years despite the many presumably demoralizing experiences common to the aging person.

isolation alone but from isolation in the face of declining health. The question is then: Are social isolation and physical health also related to each other? An examination of Table 59 reveals they are definitely related. While about one-half of those in the non-isolated group are in poor health, nearly two-thirds of those in the isolated group are in poor health. Inasmuch as poor health is closely related to low economic status as well, a pattern emerges from the data. Among those of poorer means, though not universally, a tendency to become isolated from the social world accompanies declining physical health. More than likely, the two factors reinforce each other—ill health imposing additional social proscriptions. From illness and isolation arises a sense of

TABLE 59. HEALTH STATUS ACCORDING TO RELATIVE SOCIAL ISOLATION[a]

Health status	Isolated	Not isolated
	(Percentages)	
Good health	35	51
Poor health	65	49
Total	100	100
Number of cases	279	220

[a] The total number of cases used here is 499. One respondent could not be classified on the Isolation Index.

futility, cynicism, or resignation that expresses itself in a variety of ways. For example, attitudes toward dress and activity in old age are more conservative as well as more rejective. Those who feel more acutely the futility of life also feel in general that older people should associate with others of their own age and should dress more conservatively than do people who do not feel such frustrations.[1] Again, we are faced with the unresolvable problem of sequence. Do lifelong frustrations, or those that accompany the aging process, engender feelings of irreconcilable bitterness in some older people that eventually culminate in the contraction of

[1] It should be pointed out that futility or anomie is a relative thing and that only about 15 per cent of the total sample would seem to fit under some such category as "totally futile."

the individual to a solitary shell, cut off from friends or relatives?[1] Or do the accidents of circumstance that leave the individual alone in the world develop these feelings of futility which we find? While we cannot resolve this issue, it is probable that either course may lead to the same result. It is important in this connection to point out that those in the lower socioeconomic stratum are significantly less free of feelings of futility than those in the higher socioeconomic group. A life comparatively untroubled by financial concerns and relatively free of illness would seem to be adequate reason not to expect futility in the higher economic group. We are led to expect more frustration in the lower economic group.

In summarizing the problems of health in old age, three significant trends should be noted.

Within the limitations imposed by sampling a large population and taking into account its special character (foreign-born predominance, noninstitutional, high Catholic proportion, and low socioeconomic status), the health of the aged seems sound though marked by numerous minor as well as major chronic ailments. Relatively few of those sampled in their homes suffer the decrepitude and confinement of prolonged illness.[2] Moreover, older people tend to be aware of their health condition.

The salience of health as a basic ingredient of adjustment to old age is great, but it is responded to differentially by different strata of the older population. In terms of help desired from the community, utilization of resources,[3] and concern about health, the problem even among some who are in serious health circumstances is not paramount. Among the reasons that health is not even more prominent in the adjustment of the aged is the fact that many older people (at least in this survey) tend to be *adaptive to adverse circumstances.* Some develop a resilient cloak of indifference, acceptance, resignation, or apathy that shields them from the frustrations and limitations imposed by illness. Others ignore or otherwise sup-

---

[1] Gumpert has pointed out in this connection that by social and psychological criteria some individuals are "old" even in their twenties. Withdrawal to the shell is not necessarily a phenomenon of chronological aging.

[2] It will be recalled that about 6 per cent of the aged population are institutionalized.

[3] To be dealt with more fully in Chapter 9.

press the health problem even at the expense of poor health. One would like to know the sources of these dispositions, the differences between the aged, the younger adult, and the child in response to ill health and the comparative responses of a predominantly native-born group. Likewise, it would be of value to know if in his "private" world the aged individual is as stoic as he is in his "public" expressions. Seemingly, the greatest discrepancy between attitude or belief and behavior occurs within the upper class group.

There is a notable association between health and status and income. Employed people have complaints less frequently than the unemployed, the retired, the housewife, and the widow. Poor people suffer more frequently from ill health than do the wealthy. And there is a hint that those who possess health insurance that protects against the economic hardships of illness in old age are more willing to undertake costly medical care than those who do not own insurance. It would be of the greatest significance to have comparative national figures on this apparent tendency, taking into account those who voluntarily seek insurance protection and are, hence, probably more strongly motivated to have medical service.

One final point is worthy of mention here, namely, that the characterization of the health aspects of aging in both the spheres of physical manifestation and social consequences is not a simple age-determined phenomenon. Rather, as we have seen, the importance of health in the lives of older people rises or falls in accord with a variety of interacting factors. The influence of any one of these is conditioned or modified by the presence of others. A seriously ill person of British birth does not necessarily deny himself medical care, though his cultural disposition may sway him to ignore or deny that a problem exists. We cannot lose sight of the fact that while a cultural bent or an environmental force does exert a potent influence upon behavior and attitudes, there are sufficient instances of "deviant" cases emerging from the interplay of forces impinging on the older person to warrant caution on the part of both the scientist and practitioner. Again, generalizations about the aged, while sometimes valid and useful, require detailed specifications with all the deviations and exceptions underscored.

Chapter 9

The Use of Community Health Resources

CASE HISTORY

Miss P., aged eighty-four, presented a cheerful, care-free appearance and gave the impression of being unusual. She had a fairly youthful complexion and seemed quite vigorous despite the fact that she has a very decided limp as the result of an accident a few years back. She indicated that she had been operated upon at S. . . . Hospital and that the surgeon had done a marvelous job, making it possible for her to walk again when many felt sure that she was doomed to invalidism. She laughingly mentioned taking long walks frequently to give dolls to the children at R. . . . Settlement House. She was so thankful to be able to get around. It meant a great deal to continue living in her own home and she took pride in the fact that it was so well kept. The interviewer was impressed with the creativity that obviously had gone into decorating her little home. Although she had to live on limited social security benefits, she seemed well able to manage. She indicated that she returns periodically to the hospital, where the staff evidently shows her a good deal of affection. She boasted about the fact that she was "on exhibit" several times at hospital conferences.

It was a source of pride to Miss P. that everyone in the building in which she lived knew her and liked her. When she walked down the street, several waved at her and told her how well she looked. In the interview situation, this respondent tended to be somewhat garrulous, often lost her train of thought, and repeated herself a good deal. Also, despite the fact that she wore a hearing aid, she very frequently could not understand the interviewer's questions.

The interviewer got the impression that Miss P. was managing very nicely in her familiar surroundings even though she appeared to be somewhat senile.

WITH ADVANCING AGE many people find it increasingly necessary to call upon various community services to assist them in some aspect of their life problems, be they employment, housing, financial, or familial problems. Still others might conceivably benefit from the judicious use of a service organized to meet a specific immediate problem they are facing. But many people, for reasons we shall examine in this chapter, do not make use of any community agency, whether public or private, despite the seriousness of their need for assistance. On the other hand, some are disposed to learn about and utilize whatever organized help exists in the community.

Before presenting the survey findings regarding patterns of use of health resources, it would be well to preview some of the conclusions about community resources presented in Chapter 11. In general, we found a paucity of community agencies available to the older people of New York. Among those services providing facilities for ambulatory older persons, two factors contributed to maintaining the number of cases at a low level. First, the functional nature of the services—the agencies are not equipped to act as omnibus problem agencies. They handle only cases that fit the philosophy and policy of the agency in question. For example, a family agency would not normally undertake the care of a senile psychotic or attempt to place an older worker in a job. The latter are seen as specialized functions of other services. Second, the personnel of most agencies committed to the care of the problems of aged people are extremely limited. The proportion of the aged to the total numbers seeking agency help—apart from medical clinics—is too small to warrant any immediate or drastic increase in professional staffs. It is argued that despite the well-publicized rise in the numbers of the aged in the past few decades, the type and numerical frequency of "cases" appearing for aid at a given agency office have not greatly increased nor are they changing in nature. Many such services report that the bulk of their older clients are obtained indirectly through requests by adult children for placement of an elderly parent in a mental institution, nursing home, or home for the aged. Few older people come personally for help. Those who do appear often limit the scope of their requests to some specific problem, for example, the need for a new apartment, a medical checkup, or the desire for employment. In many instances, however, a specific request that appears to be initiated by obvious motivations is deeply embedded in a complexity of life problems, the nature and significance of which are shielded from professional view. An understanding of some of these life problems is needed to yield clues to the dispositions and resistances shown by older people to use community agency resources. At the same time a clearer understanding of these dispositions and motivations is also required to guide agency policy aimed toward giving the most effective help to those in the older age groups.

In the early phases of this study, much concern was felt about the health status of the older population. This concern is reflected in our findings. In this chapter we are therefore confining ourselves to the use of medical resources and facilities. We shall also deal to a more limited extent with the use of community recreational facilities in the following chapter. It is believed that the findings will have application beyond that in the health care and recreational fields.

In Chapter 8 we reviewed briefly the relationship of access to certain health resources—such as a private physician, regular physical checkups, and prepaid health insurance—to such factors as economic position, health status, and worry about health. At this point, it may be fruitful to extend our analysis to include an additional aspect of the problem: the actual use of health facilities of all types. First, let us establish the facts gathered thus far.

Those older people in the sample who are in the lowest socioeconomic status group report the greatest frequency of illness (nearly twice as many as in the upper group report three or more current illnesses) and the least regular use of physicians. Almost half of the low economic group have no regular physician, while less than one-fourth of the high group so report. Nearly as many in the low as in the high economic group have regular physical examinations, although undoubtedly quite different causation is involved for the two groups. About one person in six in the low status group pleaded poverty as the reason for not having a regular checkup. Finally, having health insurance seemed to be related to better health.

With these facts in mind, let us continue to examine the survey results. As an aid to the analysis, an index of the use of health resources was devised. It consists of four component questions:

1. Do you get advice on health matters from a clinic or hospital? From a private physician?
2. How often do you have such a [regular physical] checkup?
3. Do you have a regular doctor who takes care of your illnesses?
4. Have you ever gone to a clinic for medical help?

One point was given for obtaining advice on health matters, one point for having a checkup once a year or oftener, one point for having a regular physician, and one point for ever having gone to a medical clinic. The distribution of the Use of Health Resources Index scores is as follows:

Score	Number of cases	Per cent	
0	41	8	
1	73	15	Low use
2	153	30	
3	168	34	High use
4	65	13	
Total	500	100	

Fewer than one person in ten received a score of "0." Of the 73 persons scoring "1," 29 received the score for having been to a clinic, 23 for having a physician, 20 for receiving advice, and one person for a checkup at least once a year.

We hypothesized that use of health services would be influenced by health status, age, socioeconomic status, employment status, level of activity respecting use of other forms of community resources, the extent of social isolation, neurotic tendencies, and predisposing attitudes toward using health services.

FACTORS INFLUENCING USE OF HEALTH SERVICES

Although other factors do play significant roles in determining the health-directed activity of the older person in this study, the

most obvious consideration in this regard is the individual's actual health condition. In general, those who are in relatively good
health do not seek out medical services as much as do those whose
health has deteriorated. This is seen in Table 60. Whether poor
health drives the individual to seek medical services or whether
in seeking medical aid the person develops a greater desire to
continue medical care even though health improves, is a question
suggested but unanswered by this finding.

TABLE 60. USE OF HEALTH RESOURCES ACCORD-
ING TO GOOD AND POOR HEALTH
STATUS

Use of health resources	Good health	Poor health
	(Percentages)	
High	41	56
Low	59	44
Total	100	100
Number of cases	284	216

While the general fact that ill health and use of health services
are related is not surprising, since it directly reflects enlightened
self-interest, two additional facts must be noted and explored.
First, as Table 60 indicates, the correlation between health condition and use of services is by no means a perfect one. On the
contrary, considerable numbers of those in *good health* use health
services, while, concurrently, there are many in poor health who
do not seek health services that would seem warranted by their
condition.[1] The second fact is that there are additional influencing conditions that sustain as well as negate the relationship
between health and use of services. Let us now look more closely
at this relationship.

Income tends to have a controlling effect upon the use of
health resources *independently* of the effect of poor health. Although
there is a general increase in use as health status declines, this

[1] Commenting on the use of physicians in a rural New York county, Bright and
Hay report: "Contrary to what might be expected in terms of the need for medical
attention, the percentage of total persons in the old age group using a doctor did not
increase markedly." Bright, Margaret L., and Donald G. Hay, *Health Resources and
Their Use by Rural People*, 1952, p. 4.

increase is not found among those who are in the lowest status and income groups. *There is no greater use of community health resources in this economically depressed group among the poor in health as compared to those in good health.* Of the 207 persons whose incomes are less than $25 per week, not quite half are users of health services in both the poor and good health status groups. But in the higher income groups, declining health is accompanied by greater use of health services. Indeed, the poor health group having incomes between $25 and $49 per week are as active in the use of health services as are those in poor health whose incomes are $50 per week or more. Sixty-two per cent of the low use group are past the age of seventy; 74 per cent of them are women and 68 per cent of the latter are widows, the vast majority of whom are retired or are housewives who have never worked.

At this point we can assert that it is primarily among economically depressed widows that we find no corresponding rise in health activity with a decline in health status. The general finding that at the lowest income level the expected rise in health-directed activity does not occur where health is poor depends heavily on them. It is interesting that in the next highest income group, $25 to $49 per week, this expected rise does occur to a significantly greater extent than in the immediately lower income group.

Pursuing the analysis a bit further, we find that about two-thirds of this least affluent group are recipients of either Old-Age Assistance or Old-Age and Survivors Insurance. Nearly one-fourth are receiving assistance from children or other relatives. Eighty per cent of them do not own any form of health or hospitalization insurance. To sum up: at the bottom of the economic ladder we find a group comprising about one-fifth of the sample who are: (a) in poor health, (b) primarily widows, (c) not employed and receiving their income from welfare or federal benefits or from relatives, and (d) over seventy years of age. Half of this group are not obtaining the extensive medical attention their condition would seem to warrant.

From the standpoint of community health and welfare planning and health education, we have here an important challenge.

In widows, who tend to be isolated as a group and who lack the material and motivational resources to improve their health condition, the community faces a major obstacle to reducing the serious consequences of chronicity in old age. One particular segment of this group offers the greatest challenge of all: a group of formerly well-to-do widows who continue to regard themselves as members of the middle to upper class and whose behavior is similar to that of those currently in these classes. That is, on the whole, they do not overtly concern themselves with poor health but, even those who do, cannot cope with it financially. They are far below the general average of use of medical facilities of more affluent widows within the same health categories. A carefully considered preventive health and health service plan, we must conclude, *can succeed to the extent that it first recognizes the differential dispositional and behavioral characteristics of the aged population and approaches the manifestly different subgroupings in the most appropriate manner.*

What additional factors play a part in reducing efforts toward health maintenance? Are there clues that would assist in determining what types of influences, if brought properly to bear on the problem, would serve to reduce the numbers of the chronically ill persons over sixty, or at least to lead them to seek appropriate health care?

USE OF SERVICES AND ISOLATION

One such clue resides in the factor of social isolation. We find that those who are isolated from social activity feel themselves to be older, have a lower standard of living, feel a lack of affection from others, and have a tendency toward a negative self-appraisal. In what ways does isolation, with this constellation of negative feelings and opinions, contribute to poor health-maintenance? One might surmise that feelings of embitterment toward life, feelings of self-disparagement, and self-rejection would have a depressing effect on all activities, among them the health-oriented activities. Would not the extra burden of declining health itself, together with the other factors which have been cited, tend to reduce motivation to seek medical aid? Let us examine our data with a view to answering these questions.

We know that relative social isolation is related to one's economic status. Nearly two out of three persons in the lowest status group are relatively isolated. We also know that fully 50 per cent of those in the lowest status group are in poor health. Our prediction would be that those in poor health but not socially isolated would be more inclined to use health services than would be those in good health who are isolated. In Table 61 we find this supposition strikingly confirmed.

TABLE 61. USE OF HEALTH RESOURCES ACCORDING TO SOCIO-ECONOMIC STATUS AND RELATIVE ISOLATION FOR GOOD AND POOR HEALTH STATUS[a]

| | Good health | | | | Poor health | | | |
| | Isolated | | Not isolated | | Isolated | | Not isolated | |
Use of health resources	High status	Low status	High status	Low status	High status	Low status	High status	Low status
	(Percentages)							
High	40	43	37	44	44	44	76	69
Low	60	57	63	56	56	56	24	31
Total	100	100	100	100	100	100	100	100
Number of cases	53	86	83	61	32	108	34	42

[a] The total number of cases used here is 499. One respondent could not be classified on the Isolation Index.

In other words, while there is no increase in the use of resources by the poor health-isolated group over the good health-isolated group, a great increase in use occurs among the poor health-not isolated group over their good-health counterparts. This finding is all the more startling when we note that within each socio-economic status group the trend is the same. Where poor health and isolation from friends and relatives are found together, there is no more tendency to use health services regardless of one's class position than there is among those who enjoy good health.

Another bit of evidence dramatizes this finding even more. We know that more than half (53 per cent) of the relative social isolates are widows. Widowhood and isolation need not necessarily be related. In the upper economic status group, widowhood and isolation are, in fact, far less related than they are in the lower economic group. Partly this is attributable to the fact that there is considerably more social activity in general in the upper as compared to the lower status group. Ignoring the economic status factor, however, we might explore the possibility that for those who have high social status needs, the maintenance of health is essential. For when health declines, the personal mobility that one would normally possess is curtailed and, when coupled with widowhood, may result in comparative social seclusion. This would be particularly disastrous among people of

TABLE 62. WILLINGNESS TO USE MEDICAL ADVISORY CENTER AC-
CORDING TO STATUS OF FRIENDS FOR WIDOWS AND
OTHERS[a]

| Use medical advisory center | Widowed | | All others | |
	Friends dead	Friends living	Friends dead	Friends living
	(Percentages)			
Yes	55	72	63	62
No	36	22	31	29
Don't know	9	6	6	9
Total	100	100	100	100
Number of cases	101	115	109	166

[a] The total number of cases used here is 491. Nine respondents failed to answer the question of whether their friends were now living or dead.

upper socioeconomic status where social isolation brought about by such factors as widowhood and illness may curtail social relations almost as much as if one had committed some reprehensible act. In Table 62 we have a test of our question regarding isolation and use. Here, we are asking the widowed in the sample to state whether or not they would use a center for medical advice for older people if it were available in their neighborhood. Two groups are compared: those whose friends have died and those who have friends still living. The factor of friendships is employed here, since we are dealing with social relationships among peer groups. Our hypothesis would suggest that there would be a greater tendency for those widowed and having friends to be more actively disposed to maintaining their health than would widows with no friends. No prediction is made concerning the nonwidowed group.

From Table 62 we see that having living friends seems in fact to be a significant factor in elevating the positive response among the widowed. It is interesting that among the nonwidowed there is no difference in attitude toward using such a center regardless of whether friends are living or dead. The need to keep social contacts among the widowed, however, seems to dispose toward a favorable reception of a medical advisory center.

ACTIVITY LEVEL AND USE OF SERVICES

We have suggested the possibility that overall activity may have a bearing on health maintenance activities. Using the activity level index described in Chapter 7, we hypothesized that sheer degree of activity would have an effect upon the use of health resources, since the active person is more likely to go to his physician or to a clinic if he is already fairly active in other respects. The finding on this score is totally negative. By itself, activity level bears no relationship to using health facilities.

It is possible that different levels of general activity operate in independent ways with various subgroups or segments of the sample to produce this negative result. For example, we find that active men are more likely to use health services extensively than are generally inactive men.[1] Inactive women tend to use medical facilities more than do active women. This curious finding suggests that the nature of the men's activities does not preclude their caring for their health also, while the types of activities carried on by women generally may tend to reduce health activities. To be adequately tested, this hypothesis would require a larger population than is available in our sample, but from our data it would seem that homemaking activities and church or club work—activities engaged in by women more than by men—limit the time or reduce the motivation to attend clinics, see doctors, and carry on other health-connected activities. It should

[1] The data are not presented here.

be noted that the effect of one's activity level upon health-oriented action is not great and is certainly less potent than are economic position, health status, and degree of social isolation. In this connection, we see from Table 63 that regardless of the individual's level of activity, the poorer his health the greater is his health-directed behavior. Illness is a more significant galvanizer of health-oriented activity than is the individual's general activity level. More qualitative material is provided by the addition of the factor of isolation. An older person whose activity level is low, but who has friends and relatives whom he sees fairly often, is considerably more use-oriented than is his relatively socially isolated counterpart. Among the nonisolates, greater

TABLE 63. USE OF HEALTH RESOURCES ACCORDING TO ACTIVITY
LEVEL FOR GOOD AND POOR HEALTH STATUS

Use of health resources	Good health		Poor health	
	Active	Not active	Active	Not active
	(Percentages)			
High	41	40	58	52
Low	59	60	42	48
Total	100	100	100	100
Number of cases	131	153	69	147

general activity is linked with lower health activity, though the difference does not reach statistical significance. The inactive isolates are lowest in use of health resources.

These findings suggest that it is not so much the fact of activity by itself but *social activity* in particular that acts as the catalyst in regard to health. Particularly in the higher socioeconomic status group, the maintenance of social relationships demands the early institution of health care measures that will ensure an uninterrupted social life. Where general as well as social activity is low, health directed measures are not so vigorously sought. At the same time, it should be borne in mind that both poor health and greater isolation are found to be more prevalent in the lower socioeconomic group.

WORRY ABOUT HEALTH AND THE USE OF HEALTH FACILITIES

Perhaps more potent "conditioners" of actions connected with health are certain attitudes or dispositions toward oneself, toward one's health, and toward other situations in life. One of the most interesting of these "conditioners" is the degree of expressed concern about one's health. Worry about health, we noted above, was more characteristic of those in the lower economic group who have, in fact, more to worry them. It was also pointed out that worry about health did not increase to so great a degree as one might surmise with each succeeding poorer health group. Now we may ask this question: Does worry about health tend to increase or decrease the tendency to use health facilities? It might be argued that those who use facilities worry least since their problems are being cared for. The evidence, on the contrary, shows that the nonworriers are the least frequent users of health services. In fact, among those in poor health, the nonworriers do not use health services so intensively as those who do worry. Among those in good health the finding is similar, though the difference is smaller and not quite significant. Table 64 summarizes these results.

TABLE 64. USE OF HEALTH RESOURCES ACCORDING TO WORRY ABOUT HEALTH FOR GOOD AND POOR HEALTH STATUS[a]

Use of health resources	Good health		Poor health	
	Worry	Never worry	Worry	Never worry
	(Percentages)			
High	51	37	63	43
Low	49	63	37	57
Total	100	100	100	100
Number of cases	75	209	123	92

[a] The total number of cases used here is 499. One respondent did not reply to the question of health worry.

It would appear, therefore, that those who show a concern about their health status, whether it be good or poor, tend to become active in the effort to check the problem. Those who are deliberately indifferent even in the face of acknowledged deterioration of health are consistent in that they seek medical aid to a significantly lesser extent.

These results suggest that much of the motivation for seeking the means to curtail or remove health-destroying processes is tied to social forces. The isolated older person often shows strong dependency needs that are unmet. Having others about him who give him emotional support tends to make him more responsive to their urgings to seek medical care or take better care of his health. The urgings of friends and relatives may: (1) encourage a desire to resist and combat the degeneration of life processes that accompanies aging by instilling the motive to live, compete, and have social intercourse with others; and (2) lead the individual to seek medical help when illness occurs. Without the companionship of others, many older people fail to adapt to the loneliness that follows the death of spouse and peers. A life, with little meaning and no purposes and with few personal and no human resources, culminates in an increasingly contracting variety of experiences. It is not difficult to comprehend, therefore, the findings of this study in respect to this socially isolated group; namely, indifference or apathy toward health and resignation to one's fate, as seen in failure to show concern about health, is associated with failure to use health facilities. There is some likelihood also that some of those who are not concerned about health, though they might do well to seek help, are unrealistically optimistic about their condition. Finally, among men who are leading a more active life there are greater health-directed activities as well. Undoubtedly, the factors involved in bringing about negative attitudes toward life (such as poor health itself) are also involved in bringing about the isolation of the person. Our evidence indicates that where some semblance of social activity is preserved, the tendency to continue self-serving activities is heightened. The person who is encouraged to come out of his social shell, to develop some type of companionship, will be aided in a variety of ways. If these conclusions seem reminiscent of a familiar theme—that love, companionship, and interest taken by others have a buoyant effect on many people—we have illustrated the fact that basic emotional needs of the person continue throughout life and may even become somewhat more intense in the later years.[1]

[1] Murphy, Gardner, *Personality*, 1947.

HEALTH ATTITUDES AND USE OF SERVICES

Another attitudinal factor that plays a role in determining the use of health facilities is the view taken of the resources themselves. A person expressing considerable dislike for medical services, physicians, or clinics cannot be expected to utilize these facilities. For purposes of testing this assumption an index of attitudes toward medicine, hospitals, and physicians was devised from our questionnaire. It consists of scores based upon their agreement or disagreement with the following statements:

	Scored response	Number of cases	Per cent of total sample
Doctors don't take a real interest in what happens to you	Agree	95	19
The trouble with hospitals is that once you get in, you never know if you'll get out alive	Agree	120	24
Most doctors don't care how much they hurt you	Agree	63	13
Doctors tend to treat younger persons better than older persons	Agree	86	17
A person should always follow the doctor's advice	Disagree	42	8

The distribution of scores and the groupings used for analysis purposes are shown below. That a generally favorable view of physicians and hospitals is held by the aged may be seen from these figures:

	Score	Number	Combined number[a]	Per cent
Favorable	0	263	390	78
	1	127		
Unfavorable	2	68		
	3	24	109	22
	4	15		
	5	2		
Total			499	100

[a] Data were not available for one case.

We find a general but slight increase in negative attitudes with an increase in age. Thus, while those aged sixty to sixty-four have 81 per cent respondents with positive attitudes, the over-eighty group have but 68 per cent such respondents. If having a positive attitude toward physicians and hospitals is predictive of actions, then we should find a significant drop in the use of health facilities between the younger and older segments of our sample. We find this to be the case in Table 65.

TABLE 65. USE OF HEALTH FACILITIES ACCORDING TO AGE FOR POSITIVE AND NEGATIVE ATTITUDE TOWARD PHYSICIANS AND HOSPITALS[a]

Use of health facilities	Positive attitude		Negative attitude	
	Under 75 years	75 years and over	Under 75 years	75 years and over
	(Percentages)			
High	50	42	44	36
Low	50	58	56	64
Total	100	100	100	100
Number of cases	297	93	73	36

[a] The total number of cases used here is 499. One respondent did not express an attitude toward physicians and hospitals.

Where both negative attitude and older age are combined, there is considerably less use of resources than in the "younger" and positive attitude group. Undoubtedly, the situation producing this result is complex. In general, the person over seventy-five is in poorer health and poorer financial condition than his more youthful counterpart. Hence, though his need is greater, he may be able to do less about his situation. The resulting frustration may make him feel less enthusiastic about medicine and also less willing to use health facilities. That the result is not alone a function of attitude or health condition, may be seen from the fact that there is no relationship between attitude toward medicine and actual physical health status nor between attitude toward medicine and the use of resources, each taken separately. Hence, it is the factor of age that is most significant in determining use. Here we have further evidence of the general trend toward resignation with aging. Undoubtedly, many of those in the eighth decade and older feel they are beyond salvation from medical science and are putting their care in other hands.[1]

ETHNIC PATTERNS IN USE OF HEALTH SERVICES

Inasmuch as our sample encompasses a broad range of cultural backgrounds and origins, it is instructive to compare the various ethnic groups in their responses to the question of the use of health facilities. Entangled in the web of forces acting upon the individual as motives to action are the values and sentiments that are the sum and product of his life experiences. The data presented here are by no means conclusive with respect to each ethnic group or any of its members. The different groups contain within themselves combinations of old cultural traditions, customs, and attitudes regarding health mingled with the effects of New World values and attitudes. In some groups the effects of the latter are minimal and the group retains its distinctive cultural patterns. In other groups, cultural values merge with those of the American "host" culture and the effect is a pronounced divergence from those values to be found among residents of the country in question. Thus, we do not deal with "pure" groups in any sense. We can only hope in a sample survey such as this to describe some of the flavor of Old World cultural patterns as they are accepted, rejected, or modified by contact with the local culture of Kips Bay-Yorkville.

Perhaps the most graphic way to illustrate our data is to compare each ethnic subsample with the responses of the total sample as well as with one another. For this purpose, we present in Table 66 such a comparison. While the number of cases within each group is relatively small, some degree of consistency of these results can be found with the factor of concern about health, which was highly related to the use of health facilities. It will be recalled that earlier we characterized those of native American,

[1] Another related phenomenon is reported by Dr. Frederic Zeman: Residents at a home for the aged attribute many of their symptoms to "old age"; hence, they do not report illnesses until they are beyond therapeutic help. See Greenleigh, Lawrence F., *Psychological Problems of Our Aging Population*, 1952.

TABLE 66. USE OF HEALTH FACILITIES ACCORDING TO ETHNIC ORIGIN

Ethnic origin	High use of facilities	Low use of facilities	Total	Number of cases
	(Percentages)			
Czechoslovakia	62	38	100	42
Italy	56	44	100	27
Hungary	53	47	100	55
Russia, Poland	52	48	100	27
England, Wales, Scotland	48	52	100	39
United States	46	54	100	63
Germany, Austria	41	59	100	116
Ireland	33	67	100	66
Other	55	45	100	65
Total	47	53	100	500

British, Irish, and German-Austrian birth as "health optimists," while we regarded those of Russo-Polish, Czechoslovakian, and Italian origin as "health pessimists." We can now compare the relative ranking of the "optimists" and "pessimists" on their use of health services. This can be seen in Table 67.

The Czechs, who worry most if in good health and rank third in worry if in poor health, are the greatest users of services. In this connection, it may be pointed out that the Czechs are well-known for their emphasis upon physical fitness. Many of the

TABLE 67. RANKING OF ETHNIC GROUPS ACCORDING TO USE OF HEALTH FACILITIES AND ACCORDING TO WORRY ABOUT HEALTH FOR GOOD AND POOR HEALTH STATUS

	Use of health facilities Rank[a]	Worry about health: Rank order[a]	
		Good health	Poor health
Health optimists			
England, Wales, Scotland	5	8	8
United States	6	7	6
Germany, Austria	7	5	5
Ireland	8	4	7
Health pessimists			
Czechoslovakia	1	1	3
Italy	2	3	2
Hungary	3	2	4
Russia, Poland	4	6	1

[a] A rank of "1" denotes highest use or greatest worry; a rank of "8" denotes lowest use or least worry.

Sokols or fraternal clubs in Kips Bay-Yorkville are both athletic and social orders. The British-born respondents are lowest in rank in worry both in the good and poor health groups and are sixth in rank on use of services. The Italians rank second and third in the "worry" tables, and second on use of resources. The health optimists rank lowest in use and in worry if in poor health. With some exceptions, we find in general a consistency between concern over health and use of resources within each ethnic group.[1]

If any one generalization may be made in respect to these data, it must be conditioned by such factors as economic status and actual health status. Taking them into account, our generalization is this: Western European cultural traditions reflect a strong philosophical bent toward self-sufficiency and personal independence. It may be redundant to point out that this is particularly true in Britain and Ireland. Hence, unless illness strikes hard among our elderly respondents of British, Irish, and German-Austrian origin,[2] there is a tendency not to use health services. Perhaps this indicates that resistance to preventive health measures would be higher among them than among their Eastern and Southern European counterparts. Among the latter group there is a tendency to be concerned and active about health matters even when health is still good. Hence, the increase in use of facilities is not so great in their group when illness strikes. In this regard, it cannot be maintained that low economic circumstances contribute most to reducing the use of resources among the different ethnic groups. The most striking evidence is seen in the Irish-Czechoslovakian comparison. Among the Irish there is a rise of but 3 per cent in use between those in good and poor health, while there is a rise of 31 per cent in use among a comparable group of Czechs. In each group, more than three-fourths of the respondents are in the low economic group. A thorough analysis of the reasons for these ethnic differences is needed, but it is far beyond the scope of this report.

[1] *Rho* between good health worriers and poor health worriers is .47. *Rho* between good health worriers and high use is .48 while between poor health worriers and high use it is .64.

[2] This is also true of native-born Americans, among whom the West European ethic prevails.

NEUROTIC SYMPTOMS AND USE OF SERVICES

One additional factor that may play a role in determining the use of medical resources is the influence of neurotic or hypochondriac tendencies. It is of prime importance to know the extent to which older people tend to place a strain upon already overtaxed medical services even when their physical health may not require intensive or protracted care. At the same time it is instructive to gauge the breadth of the problem presented by older persons making use of medical facilities for purposes of gaining emotional support or for the social experience which "clinic going" may provide.

One way to measure the effects of the "overdisposition" to use health facilities is to determine the extent to which persons with superficial or vaguely defined symptoms, but who are otherwise in good health, make use of community facilities. Such a measurement is made possible by use of a Neurotic Symptoms Index. Although not necessarily an indicator of neuroticism, this Index provides the essential ingredients required for our measurement: the symptoms are vague, not necessarily related to actual illness and commonly associated with neurotic conditions. The Index is based upon responses to the following items:

How often are you troubled by the following difficulties:

> Nervousness (score 1 for "often" or "sometimes")
> Headaches (score 1 for "often" or "sometimes")
> Not being able to sleep (score 1 for "often")

Persons whose scores were "2" or "3" were combined to form a "high" neurotic group.

Since it is our purpose here to examine the relationship between the use of health facilities and neurotic symptoms in otherwise healthy people, it would be important to show the relationship between the possession of these symptoms and the objective health index. This is done in Table 68. We see that such symptoms are heavily displayed among those in poor health and much less so among those in good health. Since the symptoms employed in the Index may also be symptoms of physical illness, we cannot differentiate within the poor health group those persons suffering from exclusively "organic" conditions and those in whom neurotic symptoms may be independent of organic ailments. It is interesting, however, that about one-fifth of those in good health are among the high neurotic symptoms group.

TABLE 68. NEUROTIC SYMPTOMS ACCORDING TO HEALTH STATUS

Neurotic symptoms	Good health	Poor health	Total
	(Percentages)		
Low (none)	48	23	37
Medium (one)	31	32	32
High (two or three)	21	45	31
Total	100	100	100
Number of cases	284	216	500

Turning now to our central problem, we find that when health is good and as neurotic symptoms increase, use of medical resources decreases significantly (Table 69). The 15 per cent difference between the high and low neurotic symptoms groups in good health is statistically significant. Moreover, note that there are no

TABLE 69. USE OF HEALTH RESOURCES ACCORDING TO NEUROTIC SYMPTOMS FOR GOOD AND POOR HEALTH STATUS

Use of health resources	Good health Neurotic symptoms			Poor health Neurotic symptoms		
	Low	Medium	High	Low	Medium	High
	(Percentages)					
High	65	57	50	46	47	44
Low	35	43	50	54	53	56
Total	100	100	100	100	100	100
Number of cases	136	89	59	49	70	97

apparent differences among the three neurotic symptoms groups in poor health. These results lend themselves to speculations which the data cannot confirm or deny. For example, it would appear that minor, vague complaints involved in the Index are all that are experienced by some of the high symptoms-good health group. These, then, could be our hypochondriacs. In addition, there are other more seriously disturbed respondents whose symptoms are part of a more involved pattern of emotional illness. These would be the neurotics and psychotics. Finally, there are others, neither hypochondriac nor seriously disturbed, who manifest symptoms connected with minor physical ailments.

The psychological state of the individual, his self-perception, his understanding of the meaning of his symptoms, and evaluation of alternatives for dealing with it are only some of the conditions that may lead to increased use of health services. Table 70 indicates some of these complexities. Here we compare those within each health group who judge themselves to be in good or

TABLE 70. NEUROTIC SYMPTOMS ACCORDING TO HEALTH STATUS
FOR GOOD AND POOR HEALTH SELF-RATING

Neurotic symptoms	Good health self-rating		Poor health self-rating	
	Good health	Poor health	Good health	Poor health
	(Percentages)			
Low	52	24	36	22
Medium	31	47	32	26
High	17	29	32	52
Total	100	100	100	100
Number of cases	212	63	72	153

poor health according to the degree of expressed neurotic tendency. There are some having high neurotic symptoms despite good health as given either by self-estimate or objective rating. These people have symptoms that do not add up to a reportable physical problem. Included may be some of our stoic "silent sufferers." A significant increase in symptoms occurs if a person reports his health to be poor though in fact it is good according to the objective rating. The hypochondriacs and others with neurotic patterns may show up here together with some of our "social sufferers" who require an audience for complaints that are as much a cultural as a phenomenological event.

A slight (but not statistically significant) rise in symptoms is seen in the poor health-good self-rating group over those who are in good health but who rate themselves as poor or fair in health. Here again may be the "stoics" whose group values demand a negation of physical ills. Their reports of symptoms are presumably inhibited to a considerable extent, since those in equally poor health but who admit its state also express neurotic symptoms and complaints quite freely. In this final group are doubtless combinations of actual serious illness, neuroses, and cultural and class expressions of suffering.

Altogether, the patterns of use of community health services are as complex as the individuals and groups seeking their services. No one explanation encompasses the maze of motives at work. We cannot take refuge in clichés such as "hypochondriasis" or "clinic hopping" to explain health activities among the aged. Those working with or planning for the aged must expect diversity rather than uniformity if they would be responsive to the health needs of the older population.

Chapter 10

Attitudes Toward the Use of Community Facilities

CASE HISTORIES

In both the cases reported below, the men are married, in good health, and employed full time. One respondent, Mr. R., is in our high socioeconomic status group and the other, Mr. B., in the low group. Both are sixty-two years old and were born in Great Britain.

Mr. R. is described as refined in manner, living in comfortable circumstances in a well-furnished apartment. He works as the branch manager of a bank and earns about $7,500 per year. His life is somewhat prosaic, going to and from his office each day, eating his meals at home with his wife and two daughters who share the home. He has two brothers whom he sees regularly each week. Although he has a mild case of diabetes and is dieting, this does not interfere with any of his activities. He sees a physician two or three times a year for a regular checkup. He avoids medical clinics "because that's for poor people who can't afford a doctor and, besides, I like personal attention."

He enjoys his work greatly and does not look forward to the idea of retiring. Although he is financially secure now, he feels that the family should be responsible for the care of an older person who cannot help himself. In Mr. R.'s opinion: "They [older people] should live with their children. Children should take care of them after all the sacrifices they made."

Mr. R. and his wife do not go out much but content themselves with playing cards, watching television, and reading the papers. They belong to no outside organizations, but spend much time talking with family and friends. Regarding "golden age" clubs Mr. R. feels: "If you have a family and get around you don't need special clubs." Being Jewish, Mr. R. attends a local synagogue but only on major holidays, placing little emphasis on religion in his life. He feels that he is living now much as he wants, and feels that life past sixty is interesting if a man has his health and good family relations.

Mr. R.'s morale would be rated high on our scale, though he is a little regretful that he did not achieve a professional career. His main concern is to accumulate a large enough pool of savings so that he would not have to depend entirely on a retirement pension.

Mr. R. leads a well-regulated, easy life, surrounded by his family, and is in obvious good spirits. He combines comparative good health, family life, a secure position, and the comforts of an urbane middle class life.

* * * *

Mr. B. is described as unrefined but at ease, living in a small, neat apartment with modest furnishings in a rather run-down building. He drives a funeral coach for a living, earning less than $4,000 a year. He stresses his robust health and boasts of the fact that he has not been to see a physician in years, although he believes that people ought to have a regular checkup. His two brief encounters with local medical clinics were both negative experiences for him and he is averse to ever using them again. Said he: "I don't like clinics—it always makes you feel like it's charity. I don't like the regimentation of waiting and sitting around." He is violently opposed to geriatric services of any kind and somewhat cynically remarked that they "might kid you along so you won't expect too much," referring to what might be done in a center for older people.

Mr. B. and his wife live by themselves. His ambition is to buy a bungalow in the country and retire to it. He looks forward to this plan, inasmuch as he has been working since he left school at the age of fifteen. He would like to get some kind of job after "retirement," but at a "quieter" type of work. He feels an additional source of income would be needed for country life. He realizes this may be a dream, so he plans to visit his two married daughters more frequently. They live some distance away in another city.

Mr. B.'s home life is very much like that of Mr. R. His activities center about his job in the daytime and the newspaper and television set at night. He feels more like staying at home nights now than before.

Mr. B., now sixty-two, is an Elk but rarely goes to meetings at the Lodge. Also, he would not go to a club for older people because "I wouldn't want to be saddled with old people." He has numerous friends and acquaintances who drop in from time to time. He is quite satisfied with his way of life, feeling that "middle-age" is the best time of life. He is an Episcopalian and is somewhat more convinced of the importance of religion than Mr. R. His main concern is to have enough money upon retirement and an adequate pension. The bungalow, fishing, and raising chinchillas are in his thoughts. His routinized life, his health and job, home, family and friends combine to give him a pleasant, optimistic outlook on life.

ANY COMMUNITY, whether a small town or a great metropolitan center, must be aware of three basic determinants of the use of community facilities. These are:

1. *Community Needs.* A community must assess the services and facilities required to meet the problems created by the hazards of modern life—illness, unemployment, financial distress, housing dislocations, family breakdown, personality disturbances. It must attempt to answer such questions as: What proportion of the population will seek such services at any given time? Are there variations in need according to time of year (seasonal unemployment, "vacation time" delinquency, winter illness) or according to neighborhood? The adaptability of a community to its demands and requirements determine the adequacy with which these demands and requirements are resolved.

2. *Community Resources.* To be effective, community facilities must be available when and where they are required on the strength of demonstrated or *anticipated* need. Such resource problems as size, location, specialization of function, nature of staff, must be appropriately settled or the resulting conglomeration of facilities will lack the necessary integration and efficiency. Will this service meet the recognized community need? Is a new facility required or can the existing ones be adapted to new purposes? Should the facility be specialized for some one segment of the population or should it aim to serve all? These are some of the questions asked by community leaders and administrators who plan the coordination of service functions.

3. *The Disposition to Use.* When we speak of needs and resources, we often refer to certain demographic or sociological facts, such as the proportion of delinquents to the number of youth centers, the number of drug addicts to the size of the narcotics squads, the proportion of young married women to the availability of maternity or obstetrical services. While these facts are important for community planning, they depend too largely upon "averages"

or incidence "rates" based upon past experience and also too largely upon numbers in the population. Less stress is placed upon the "causes" of delinquency or narcotic addiction in planning community services. To await the outcome of definitive studies of these subjects before instituting some kind of community action would be foolhardy. Yet research upon these and other subjects can be of vital aid in directing social action.

In the field of aging, services and facilities have developed largely through the demographic and statistical process outlined above. It is the purpose of this chapter to illustrate how the study of the population in question may give additional clues to the nature of the needs and the resources to meet them. We shall concentrate our efforts upon the disposition or expressed desire of older people to use community health and recreational services and the factors influencing these dispositions.

Disposition to use a service or facility involves a multiplicity of factors that may be roughly divided into the *structural* and the *social-psychological*. The structural factors include knowledge of the existence of the service, distance from home to service, cost, and meaningfulness of the service to the group for whom it is intended, and so on. The social-psychological factors include motivations to use a service, social pressures encouraging or hindering use, and attitudes toward the types of services offered. It is with these social-psychological factors that we are concerned in this chapter. What stimulates a person to use community services and what factors inhibit use? What attitudes predispose a person to think positively of using a clinic or a recreational center and what factors provoke a negative response? These deeper lying questions are at the root of the statistical and demographic approaches to planning programs of community service.

Before turning to an examination of our survey findings, it would be well to consider a developing controversy in the area of aging relevant to our thesis. The controversy centers on the question of whether specialized services for the aged (homes for the aged, geriatric clinics, day care centers for the aged) are more acceptable to the older person as places to care for his needs, or whether services for the aged should be part of general community services available to all groups. The heart of the problem is or should be the social and psychological consequences of age-segregation. Is it a good thing for the older person and for the community? However, the issue has become clouded with certain extraneous facts and problems. One of these is the apparent success of some day center programs or old age clubs in attracting and holding a segment of the older population. A second is the rejection by most medical groups of the "geriatric clinic." Geriatrics is not considered a medical specialty by many physicians and geriatric clinics are regarded as overspecialized services. Still further is the fact that hospital and social welfare administrators are tending to become more selective in the choice of patients or clients as the problem increases in magnitude. Often, the prospect of having to provide custodial or long-range care of older persons with chronic ailments or longstanding personality disturbances results in the decision to reserve professional services for the younger, more acutely ill, or seriously disturbed person. This tendency has resulted in a movement toward age-specialized programs: mental institutions, homes for the "indigent" aged, "nursing" homes, and day care centers. We shall examine the older person's views on this subject presently.

THE DISPOSITION TO USE

Of basic importance to all these matters are the feelings and attitudes of the elderly themselves. To understand their views, we turn to an examination of our data. For purposes of our analysis, a scale of disposition to use medical resources was developed. The scale is based upon responses to the following questions:[1]

If you were suddenly taken very sick, where would you turn for help?

If this neighborhood had a medical center especially for older people, would you go there for advice on your health problems?

If this neighborhood had a medical center especially for older people, would you go there for treatment, or would you go to a center where they treated people of all ages?

[1] The scale is formed in the order presented. See Appendix 4 for an analysis of scalability.

Scores of one point were given for each of the following: any of the responses "doctor," "hospital," or "clinic" to the first item; a positive response to the second question; and a positive response to either alternative in the third question. A maximum of three points could be obtained.

Those whose scores were "0" or "1" were grouped into a "low disposition" category while the remaining two score groups were combined into a "high disposition" category. A low score would indicate that the person did not look with favor upon seeking medical aid in an advisory, therapeutic, or emergency setting, while a high score would indicate that the person was more disposed toward seeking such aid. The individual questions will be treated separately below but here we will concentrate upon the index.

Only one respondent in 14 received a score of "0" while nearly two out of five received the maximum of "3." Earlier, we surmised that people in the lower socioeconomic group would be more responsive to preventive medical facilities, while those in the upper status group would not. This was based upon the hypothesis that people of high status would tend to flout the need for medical care for fear that illness itself might endanger their social position, or would choose private rather than clinic care since the latter would be regarded as socially unacceptable. A similar type of assumption can be made using the Disposition to Use Health Services Index, since we are facing the person with theoretical services and asking for his potential behavior. As seen in Table 71, the differences between the socioeconomic groups

TABLE 71. DISPOSITION TO USE HEALTH SERVICES ACCORDING TO SOCIOECONOMIC STATUS

Disposition to use health services	High status	Low status	Total
	(Percentages)		
Favorable	60	73	68
Not favorable	40	27	32
Total	100	100	100
Number of cases	203	297	500

are in the surmised direction. While three-fifths of the upper status group are favorably disposed, a significantly greater proportion of the lower group are so disposed.

From Table 71 we might guess that those in low status are more favorably disposed because they have had more experience using community medical facilities. We find, however, that while there is a slight tendency for those who are favorably disposed to health services to actually use them more frequently than those low in disposition, the difference is small and not statistically significant. Thus, the actual experience in using existing services has little bearing on attitude toward the use of potential medical services. We might speculate concerning the possible reason for this discrepancy. A prime explanation might be found in the nature of the questions forming the index. Two of these questions specifically ask the respondent to state his preference for centers that are "especially for older people." Inasmuch as such special centers are virtually not available in any Kips Bay-Yorkville neighborhood[1] the respondents are reacting to a hypothetical, nonexistent service. Preference for the special medical services would, it might be assumed, run high among current nonusers. We find this to be true but only among those in the lower socioeconomic group. This is a fact of first importance, since it is among the ill nonusers of health services that we may expect to find the highest potential of chronic and debilitating ailments in still later years. The tendency to feel one way or the other about using local health resources is only partly dependent on one's previous experience. We must look further to find the more fundamental factors producing positive or negative feelings.

Status Factors in Attitudes Toward Using Services

Let us begin with the fact of class differences in disposition to use hypothetical health services. Are these differences the same among the good and poor in health in each status group, or is state of health the more important factor in disposition as it is in the actual use of resources? From Table 72 we see that health

---

[1] A small geriatric clinic did, in fact, exist in a relatively inaccessible part of the area during the survey period, but it was only slightly used by area residents.

status does play an important role in disposition to use resources. The poorer the health, the greater is the positive attitude within each economic class group.

It should be noted that favorable disposition in the good health group is significantly greater among those of low status than those of high status. However, this difference disappears when we consider members of both socioeconomic status groups who are in poor health. In other words, although there is a significant rise in favorable disposition for both status groups when in poor health, those in low status are still more favorably inclined than those of high status among all who are in good health. Are health values higher among low status older people than they are among

TABLE 72. DISPOSITION TO USE HEALTH SERVICES ACCORDING TO SOCIOECONOMIC STATUS FOR GOOD AND POOR HEALTH STATUS

Disposition to use health services	Good health		Poor health	
	High status	Low status	High status	Low status
	(Percentages)			
Favorable	56	67	72	79
Not favorable	44	33	28	21
Total	100	100	100	100
Number of cases	137	147	66	150

high status people? Earlier, we concluded that the reverse was true, since good health is essential to support the social activity so strongly valued among those of high social class. Is there a discrepancy of findings here? It becomes clear that no discrepancy exists when one brings into sharper focus the nature of the high disposition group.

Before doing so, let us consider the following: The person who is relatively high in the economic scale and who holds comparatively high social status in the years past sixty can be assumed, in general, to have fulfilled many of the goals and ideals of American life—material wealth, security in the later years, social recognition. Although the struggle for success does not terminate at any arbitrary age limit, by and large our high status group has attained a position in life that can be threatened most by forces over which they exercise little control—economic depression or personal incidents such as accident or illness. They wish to continue to enjoy that which their former youth and vigor made them capable of achieving. Hence, considering these factors, together with the strong need for health maintenance, their disposition to use medical facilities is quite high and particularly so in poor health. On the other hand, the upper status group is consistently more optimistic, superficially without anxiety and, it would appear, relatively inactive with respect to health matters. However, a close examination of the facts reveals that the reverse is more nearly the case. The invocation of medical powers that could halt or reverse the interloping disease is even more vigorously carried out than in the low status group *when illness actually strikes*.

The factors leading to a high disposition to use medical facilities by those in low economic and social status are equally complex, but stem from entirely different social motives. As we have seen, anxiety about one's health was prominent in this group and with good reason. One of their major life problems concerns health, although for some a degree of indifference and resignation to ill health has taken such deep hold that there exists no inclination toward self-maintenance or medical care. For the great majority, however, the test of reality and the harsher circumstances of life may make local health facilities highly desirable. Thus, even if in good health, those of lower status are substantially more positive toward using potential services than those of higher status. Within the low status group, disposition to use health services varies with a group of interrelated factors. The most resistant with respect to favorable disposition are the widows in good health, particularly those past seventy-five years of age, who are social isolates and generally inactive. This group of older women is more markedly opposed to the idea of using community health facilities than are their counterparts in the high status group.

The most favorably disposed group in the low status category are men[1] between the ages of sixty-five and seventy-five, in poor

---

[1] There is, generally, a tendency for men to be greater users of medical services than women.

health, retired or unemployed, and married. In general, men, whether married or single, are more favorable than women; the nonisolated are more favorable than the isolated; further, those younger, married, and in poor health are more favorably disposed.

The most potent factor in favorably disposing a person to utilize a medical service is, as we have seen, the status of his health. In both the high and low economic groups, if health is poor there is a significantly greater disposition to use health facilities than if health is good.

To sum up the foregoing: Among the good health group more of those in the low than in the high status group are favorably disposed. Here, as in many other areas, no differences in attitude exist between the low status and high status groups in poor health. The significance of this finding resides in the fact that it is only when a health crisis impinges upon many higher status people that a reaction sets in to correct or alleviate. Yet even this reaction does not differ markedly from the level of health consciousness found in the low status person who is in good health. The reaction is great but not so great as their command of services would suggest.

Self-Perception and Disposition to Use

If the disposition to use services is affected by health and, as we have seen, health influences one's perception of himself, then self-perception may likewise affect one's disposition. This is, in fact, the case. It will be recalled that each respondent was asked to state how he would describe himself: "old," "elderly," "middle-aged," or what other descriptive term. Taking only the 456 persons who made a direct response, we can test the supposition that self-perception with regard to aging affects the use of facilities. In Table 73, the results are presented for each economic status group.

The most striking aspect of this table is the fact that disposition is less favorable if the individual regards himself as old or elderly. Statistically speaking, this decrease is reliable only for those in the high economic status group. A careful study of this table in the light of the finding reported below that favorable disposition is related to actual age suggests the following interpretation: Those who identify with youth or whose social self is youth-directed but whose health is failing are highly disposed to retain this self-image and to protect their social selves and thus have a favorable disposition to use health services. This defense is found to a noticeably greater extent among those of higher social status. Those in the higher status group who regard themselves as elderly or old (only 35 per cent of the upper status group) are far less favorably disposed to use health services. In effect, to be regarded as old relegates the individual to a lower status which he either must or does, in fact, accept. The need to preserve youth is

TABLE 73. DISPOSITION TO USE HEALTH SERVICES ACCORDING TO SOCIOECONOMIC STATUS FOR YOUNG AND OLD AGE SELF-ESTIMATES[a]

| | Age self-estimate | | | |
| | Middle-aged or young | | Old or elderly | |
Disposition to use health services	High status	Low status	High status	Low status
	(Percentages)			
Favorable	67	78	55	70
Not favorable	33	22	45	30
Total	100	100	100	100
Number of cases	119	125	65	147

[a] The total number of cases used here is 456. There were 33 persons who said they "don't think of age" and 11 did not respond to the question.

removed and, to a significant extent, disposition to use services is lessened. It is not that the individual adopts an "aged" outlook but simply that pressure to conform to upper middle class values is reduced. This view is strikingly reinforced by Table 74. Here we see that among those who retain the age self-evaluation of young or middle-aged there is a uniformly high favorable disposition at all chronological age levels. However, among those who regard themselves as old or elderly, there is apparently a desperate need for health service in the preretirement years. With advancing age, the "pressure" declines until over the age of seventy-five, when disposition to use health services is fairly low. Especially of interest is the wide difference in disposition between those over seventy-five who regard themselves as old and those over seventy-five who regard themselves as young. Clearly this result should caution the service planner that objective health condition and self-regarding attitudes are of fundamental importance in raising or lowering the threshold of favorable response to some community program "for the aged."

TABLE 74. DISPOSITION TO USE HEALTH SERVICES ACCORDING TO AGE FOR YOUNG AND OLD AGE SELF-ESTIMATES[a]

Disposition to use health services	Age self-estimate					
	Middle-aged or young Age (in years)			Old or elderly Age (in years)		
	60 to 64	65 to 74	75 and over	60 to 64	65 to 74	75 and over
	(Percentages)					
Favorable	72	72	74	87	67	55
Not favorable	28	28	26	13	33	45
Total	100	100	100	100	100	100
Number of cases	78	127	39	32	99	81

[a] The total number of cases used here is 456. There were 33 persons who said they "don't think of age" and 11 did not respond to the question.

Interestingly, favorable attitudes decrease generally with increasing age in both good and poor health status groups, as shown in Table 75. Those over seventy-five in poor health are no more favorably disposed than those in good health under sixty-five. Increasing age tends to make people less interested in health and medicine, although this interest is conditioned by the individual's state of health. Those over seventy-five are the most critical of the profession and the most skeptical of its practices. Whether this negative tendency is a cultural phenomenon for those born more than seven decades ago or whether it may be due to accumulated harsh experiences in the later years, or a general "crustiness" toward professional services, is a question about which we can only speculate since our numbers are too few for an adequate test. Social planners are, however, hereby forewarned that the older client is not overly enthusiastic about utilizing services (for example, medical services), the more so if preventive health measures for those still in good physical condition is the aim.

TABLE 75. DISPOSITION TO USE HEALTH SERVICES ACCORDING
TO AGE FOR GOOD AND POOR HEALTH STATUS

Disposition to use health services	Good health Age (in years)			Poor health Age (in years)		
	60 to 64	65 to 74	75 and over	60 to 64	65 to 74	75 and over
	(Percentages)					
Favorable	68	61	51	84	78	71
Not favorable	32	39	49	16	22	29
Total	100	100	100	100	100	100
Number of cases	72	151	61	45	103	68

Another significant factor determining the attitude toward
health services is the person's attitude toward the aged generally.
Previously, we indicated that a general youth orientation was
linked to the actions one would take to preserve youthfulness.
Attitude toward the aged was obtained through the employment
of an index based upon agreement or disagreement with the
following statements:

	Agree	Disagree	Don't know	Total
			(Percentages)	
Older people should dress more conservatively than younger people	73	16	11	100
Older people ought to go around with friends their own age rather than with younger people	55	38	7	100
You can't expect older people to accept new ways of doing things	42	48	10	100
It's undignified for older people to be interested in the opposite sex	27	53	20	100

One point was given for each "agree" response.

The index may be described as an "age conservatism" index.
Those with scores of "0" or "1" are "low" conservatives or youth-
oriented, those with scores of "2" are "medium" conservatives,

and those with scores "3" or "4" are "high" conservatives or age-oriented.

It is apparent from a glance at Table 76 that age conservatism is positively related to favorable disposition to use medical facilities. The more conventional the thinking about the behavior of older people, the more positive feeling there is about the use of facilities.[1] A tendency, small but consistent, exists for more men than women to be favorably disposed even in the youth-oriented group. Thus, while men rise from 60 per cent to 81 per cent favorable (with greater conservatism) on the question dealing with willingness to use a medical advisory center, among women the increase is from 54 per cent to 66 per cent favorable.

TABLE 76. DISPOSITION TO USE HEALTH SERV-
ICES ACCORDING TO AGE CONSERVA-
TISM

Disposition to use health services	Age conservatism		
	Low	Medium	High
	(Percentages)		
Favorable	63	68	78
Not favorable	37	32	22
Total	100	100	100
Number of cases	180	146	174

Attitude toward the aged similarly affects use-dispositions in each economic group and to about the same extent.

A deeper understanding of the meaning of conservative attitudes comes from an examination of the data relating health and attitudes toward the aged. Within the good health group, no increase in favorable disposition to use health services occurs with increasing conservatism. However, within the poor health group there is an increase in favorable disposition to use medical services (from 69 per cent to 81 per cent). A youth orientation toward the aging process leads (for nearly a third of those who are low in conservatism) to a decreased tendency to seek medical care *despite the fact that they are in poor health*. For these people, the preservation

[1] This apparent discrepancy between this and our previous finding that a youthful age self-estimate is related to favorable disposition is dealt with below.

of youthfulness obscures the need for medical care to a significant extent. At the same time, poor health is at least one factor that "causes" some older people to feel their aging. There are more age-conservatives in the poor health than in the good health group. In general, the acceptance of the aging process, for whatever variety of reasons or motives, is closely associated with the ills with which the older group are afflicted. But it is a two-edged sword: one develops medical complaints because one grows older at the same time that the medical complaints make one feel older.

Further evidence of the fact that self-attitudes, chronological aging, and difficulties arising from confused group identifications are present can be seen in the following analysis.

The disposition to use health services is not uniformly affected by either an age-conservative or a youth-oriented outlook, nor by the facts of age alone. Indeed, the less conservative group are more favorably disposed *only if they are in fact chronologically youthful*. The critical age seems to occur between seventy and seventy-five. On the other hand, among those who are conservative in attitude toward age, there is a high disposition to use services regardless of age. Age-conservatism is a factor in high use. At the same time, chronological age is a factor in high use among those who have youth-oriented attitudes.

Clearly, the conditions of life, the *Weltanschauung* of the individual, and the multiplicity of factors that are associated with six decades or more of personal life history must all be taken into account in explaining disposition to use health resources. There is no simple theory or explanatory principle that can account for the behavior of the older person. To look exclusively at immediate life problems fails to get to the core of the individual, his perspectives, values, and deeply embedded attitudes. Research and social planning for the aged must reflect the same appreciation of complex dynamic processes that has contributed so greatly to our understanding of children, youth, and middle-aged adults.

AGE-SPECIALIZED SERVICES

We have noted that in the past ten years a lively controversy has arisen among both professionals and administrators over the wisdom of providing special or geriatric service agencies for older persons. Some have argued that services for the aged ought to be an integral part of general service agency functions without any special treatment accorded the older group. Protagonists of the specialization point of view reason that older people form a "natural" subcultural group and tend to seek one another out for friends, social affairs, and work associates.[1] The argument runs that, since they have so much in common, it is best to retain the natural character of their associations and provide services that take advantage of this fact. Those opposed to age segregation contend that the health problems of the aging are no different from those at younger age levels, though the problems may occur more frequently or become more chronic.[2] It has been contended that the cultural isolation of the aged tends to induce a sense of minority status with its attendant facets of self-hate, self-consciousness, and defensiveness.[3] Moreover, many feel that age specialization serves to reinforce many of the prevailing stereotypes of the aged[4] or to evoke a militant reaction to the enforcement of age-determined associations. The arguments on both sides of the issue have been growing more intense, since agency planning and community service organizations are seeking clearcut guidelines to initiate programs.

Our survey findings throw some light on this subject. Let us first look at the responses to two medically oriented questions and then at the responses to a socially oriented question.

Are the Aged Disposed to Use Specialized Services?

The following question was asked: "If this neighborhood had a medical center especially for older people, would you go there for

[1] "Today we see . . . natural grouping by age . . . in our factories. Within each work-clique there tends to be an age grouping. . . . While there is some interrelationship between the work-groups and the age-groups, there appears to be a natural gravitation of age to age, youth to youth, middle age to middle age. . . . This 'age to age' phenomenon appears to be a natural expression of man's insecurity, longing for understanding. Empathy springs from similarity of experience and pressures." New York State Joint Legislative Committee on Problems of the Aging, *Growing with the Years*, 1954, p. 10.

[2] Bortz, Edward L., "Geriatrics as a Specialty," 1953.

[3] Barron, Milton L., "Minority Group Characteristics of the Aged in American Society," 1953.

[4] For a discussion of age-stereotypes see Tuckman, Jacob, and Irving D. Lorge, " 'When Aging Begins' and Stereotypes About Aging," 1953.

advice on your health problems?" In response, 316 persons (63 per cent) said "Yes"; 145 (29 per cent) said "No"; 39 (8 per cent) did not know. Clearly there is a generally favorable attitude toward the idea of using such a specialized center. Note in the phrasing of the question that a positive response implies that the person aligns himself with "older people."[1] On the other hand, a negative response may stem from any number of reasons, only one of which may be that the respondent regards himself as younger.

Who are the positive and who the negative respondents to this question? From what we have seen previously some of the key considerations are likely to be class status, health, the degree of

TABLE 77. ATTITUDE TOWARD USE OF AN ADVISEMENT CENTER FOR OLDER PERSONS ACCORDING TO SOCIO-ECONOMIC STATUS

Attitude toward use of advise-ment center for older persons	High status	Low status
	(Percentages)	
Yes	51	72
No	40	21
Don't know or no answer	9	7
Total	100	100
Number of cases	203	297

isolation, and attitudes toward the aged. First, with respect to social and economic status, it is evident from Table 77 that lower status position is related to the disposition to use an age-related medical advisory service.

If we now examine the data within each socioeconomic status group, we find that health plays a significant role in shifting the disposition pattern. Table 78 shows that each economic group has a rise in positive attitude when health is poor.[2] Deteriorating

[1] It is also quite conceivable that a "yes" response is more indicative of a positive attitude toward using a medical service, and the question of self-identification may or may not enter as a factor.

[2] The low status difference is significant, although the high status difference is not. This latter finding may merely reflect the relatively few instances of persons of high status in poor health.

health tends to make some older people look more favorably upon a specialized advisory medical service, particularly among those of lower status. More than three-fourths of those in poor health and of low status are positively disposed toward such a center.

Refining and sharpening these differences further, we explored the possibility that social isolation played a role in producing them. By itself, however, isolation does not provide any predictive value with respect to the question of disposition. Just as many of the isolated as the nonisolated are favorably inclined toward the center for older people. Perhaps, therefore, it is not at all a

TABLE 78. ATTITUDE TOWARD USE OF AN ADVISEMENT CENTER FOR OLDER PERSONS ACCORDING TO SOCIOECONOMIC STATUS FOR GOOD AND POOR HEALTH STATUS

Attitude toward use of advise-ment center for older persons	Good health		Poor health	
	High status	Low status	High status	Low status
	(Percentages)			
Yes	47	65	58	78
No	41	27	39	17
Don't know or no answer	12	8	3	5
Total	100	100	100	100
Number of cases	137	147	66	150

matter of isolation but one of the meaning of the use of age-specialized health service that is at issue here.

Among widows, where relative isolation tends to be frequent, it might be assumed that those of high status would be resistant to the center concept if in good health but would be highly favorable if health were poor. Table 79 shows this assumption to be incorrect. For while a minor rise in favorable attitude is noted among low status widows, no such rise—indeed a slight decline—in favorable attitude occurs among the high status widows. High status widows may demonstrate here their previously noted resistance to the acceptance of the aging process. Even among those in poor health, no rise in favorable attitude occurs. Although the numbers are too few to be definitive, there is a suggestion here

TABLE 79. ATTITUDE OF WIDOWS TOWARD USE OF AN ADVISE-
MENT CENTER FOR OLDER PERSONS ACCORDING TO
SOCIOECONOMIC STATUS FOR GOOD AND POOR
HEALTH STATUS[a]

Attitude toward use of advise-ment center for older persons	Good health		Poor health	
	High status	Low status	High status	Low status
	(Percentages)			
Yes	48	72	44	77
No	37	22	53	17
Don't know or no answer	15	6	3	6
Total	100	100	100	100
Number of cases	*52*	*69*	*30*	*69*

[a] The total number of cases used here is 220. This includes both widows and widowers.

that disposition is more favorable among married persons in poor health of both economic groups.

We have already seen that in general those who reject the conservative view of aging are less favorably disposed toward the use of community health services. We should now be confident in predicting that on the question of an old age service there would be an even more marked variance from those who are age-conservatives or "age-oriented." Table 80 confirms this prediction: a significant increase in favorable attitude does occur among those having more conservative beliefs. Perhaps among these age-

TABLE 80. ATTITUDE TOWARD USE OF AN
ADVISEMENT CENTER FOR OLDER
PERSONS ACCORDING TO AGE CON-
SERVATISM

Attitude toward use of advise-ment center for older persons	Age conservatism		
	High	Middle	Low
	(Percentages)		
Yes	71	62	57
No	22	34	32
Don't know or no answer	7	4	11
Total	100	100	100
Number of cases	*174*	*146*	*180*

conservative respondents the acceptability of the advisement center was determined to a considerable extent by its special nature. Hence, we can only conclude at this point that preference for a geriatric medical facility among age conservatives is suggested by our data.

Other factors also play a role in limiting favorable opinions concerning an old age advisory center. Women, particularly widows among the high social and economic status group, are considerably more resistant than are men. A significant decrease in amenability occurs among the high status group over seventy-five but is not matched in the lower status group where favorable attitudes continue. These findings are consistent with the previously noted status-related influences on health activities.

One possible explanation of the relatively high degree of unfavorable attitudes toward an old age center among the high status group is the fact that members of this group could more readily turn to their own private physicians for medical care. Our data indicate, however, that regardless of whether one has a private physician or not, there is no increase or decrease in favorable attitudes. Similarly, even among those who state that they never seek medical advice, about half are favorably disposed toward an advisement center.

Responses to the question of using a neighborhood health advisory center were also analyzed for ethnic variations. The differences cited previously between Northern and Western European as compared with Southern and Eastern European groups continue with few exceptions. With declining health the proportionate increase in favorable disposition is more marked among the Southern and Eastern European groups than among the Northern and Western European groups. Thus, a cultural factor in the acceptability of an advisory service appears to exert some influence.

The Geriatric Center

The second medically oriented question presented the individual with a choice that more directly tests his preference for specialized versus integrated services: "If this neighborhood had a medical center especially for older people, would you go there for treatment, or would you go to a center where they treated people of all ages?" As Table 81 indicates, 39 per cent of respondents would prefer a special geriatric center. Another 21 per cent would prefer a general treatment center where age was not a factor. Twenty-two per cent reject both types of center and the remaining group (almost one in five) did not know where they stood or would not answer.

This question provides a clear choice between acceptance or rejection of the geriatric concept. Unlike the question of medical advice, here we find that health plays almost no role in influencing attitudes. A slightly higher proportion[1] of high status respondents prefer the geriatric center if they are in poor health.

TABLE 81. ATTITUDES TOWARD TYPES OF MEDI-
CAL CENTER

Preferred service	Per cent	Number of case
Age specialized	39	196
Age integrated	21	107
Neither	22	109
Don't know or no answer	18	88
Total	100	500

Socioeconomic status itself operates to elevate the number of high status persons who reject both types of center. Almost twice as many high status as low status people in each health group reject both types of center.[2] These findings are presented in Table 82.

Of significance in this finding is the fact that between one-third and two-fifths of the group, depending upon status position, are favorably disposed toward a specialized or geriatric medical service center. This is neither an overwhelming endorsement of age-specialized service nor conclusive evidence of opposition to such a service. It simply indicates a *differential responsiveness of the*

[1] Statistically not significant.
[2] There is a slight tendency for preference for a geriatric center among those over seventy-five.

older population to the concept of age-specialized services, at least in the field of health. The fact that favorable attitudes are widely distributed (there are no age, sex, religious, ethnic, or class differences other than those already mentioned) indicates that the decision is a highly personal one with many factors simultaneously affecting it.

That self-regarding attitudes are responsible for some of the preferences can be drawn from the fact that among men, a systematic increase in preference for a geriatric center occurs with increasingly conservative attitudes toward aging. The man who feels that older people should dress more conservatively or avoid interest in the opposite sex also tends to feel that it is better to go

TABLE 82. ATTITUDE TOWARD TYPE OF MEDICAL CENTER ACCORDING TO SOCIOECONOMIC STATUS FOR GOOD AND POOR HEALTH STATUS

	Good health		Poor health	
Preferred service	High status	Low status	High status	Low status
	(Percentages)			
Age specialized	33	41	44	41
Age integrated	20	21	20	23
Neither	33	18	26	15
Don't know or no answer	14	20	10	21
Total	100	100	100	100
Number of cases	137	147	66	150

to a special center for the aged. No such trend occurs among women, possibly because as we noted in our discussion of morale many of them tend to feel their aging to a somewhat lesser degree.

A measure of the consistency of attitudes toward using special medical facilities for the older person may be obtained by comparing responses on the question of using an advisory center for older people with those concerning the use of special or general treatment centers. Such a comparison is shown in Table 83.

Of those who would use an advisory center, more than twice as many would prefer a geriatric treatment center to one available to all age groups. It is also clear that three-fourths of those favoring an advisory center also favor some kind of neighborhood treatment center. Those who do not favor an advisory center generally do not favor any type of treatment center. It may be concluded that at least some of those preferring a geriatric treatment facility are responding to the age aspect. For some, perhaps, this may be the determining consideration. For others, although they make a choice, their preference may not indicate a wholly favorable attitude toward one or the other type of center. Thus, about two-fifths of the sample expressed a preference for a geriatric center but about half of that group may have made their choice primarily because the center would be exclusively for older people.

TABLE 83. ATTITUDE TOWARD TYPE OF MEDICAL CENTER AC-
CORDING TO USE OF AN ADVISEMENT CENTER FOR
OLDER PERSONS

	Use of advisement center		
Preferred service	Yes	No	Don't know or no answer
	(Percentages)		
Age specialized	55	13	10
Age integrated	26	13	18
Neither	5	57	26
Don't know or no answer	14	17	46
Total	100	100	100
Number of cases	316	145	39

The high degree of rejection of both types of center by those of higher social and economic status (and this is most marked in those occupying the highest status category) undoubtedly reflects a preference for private physicians[1] on the one hand and the rejection of the use of clinic or neighborhood medical facilities on the other. It is interesting to note, however, that 57 of the 74 persons in the upper status group who would prefer a center for older people have private physicians of their own.

[1] Fifty-five of the 65 persons of upper status preferring neither center have private physicians.

One of the arresting side-issues is the relationship of one's actual experience with using medical clinic facilities and responses to the question on disposition to use a medical center. It is well known that favorable contact with an object, person, or group tends to reduce tension toward related objects, persons, or groups. Our data are suggestive of a similar phenomenon. Those who have had no contact with clinics are significantly more resistant to any form of medical center. As indicated in Table 84, in both

TABLE 84. ATTITUDE TOWARD USE OF A MEDICAL CENTER ACCORDING TO SOCIOECONOMIC STATUS FOR PERSONS WITH AND WITHOUT CLINIC EXPERIENCE[a]

| | Clinic experience | | No clinic experience | |
Would use	High status	Low status	High status	Low status
	(Percentages)			
Some center	76	85	59	71
No center	24	15	41	29
Total	100	100	100	100
Number of cases	63	186	121	91

[a] The total number of cases used here is 461. There were 39 respondents who answered "don't know" to the question of attitude toward use of a medical center.

socioeconomic groups, experience with clinics is closely associated with willingness to use some type of medical center service.

It is, of course, quite possible that it is not experience with clinics that makes for a more positive attitude toward a center, but that whatever factors determine actual use of clinics also determine favorable attitudes toward possible use of a new medical center. At least to some extent, nevertheless, older people who have had some experience in the use of clinic facilities seem more highly disposed to use a center for medical treatment.

Age-Specialized Social Clubs

The third item relating to age specialization deals with responses to the following question: "If you had a choice of joining a social club made up of people mostly younger than you, or one with people mostly around your own age, which would you prefer to join?" The distribution of responses was as follows:

	Number of cases	Per cent
Would join club for younger people	77	16
Would join club for all ages	85	17
Would join club for people own age	171	34
Would not join any club	162	32
No answer	5	1
Total	500	100

About one-third of the sample indicated a preference for an older person's club. An additional 16 per cent stated a preference for a nonspecialized club. The fact that a person would prefer to join a club of younger people indicates that the person does not care for an "aged" social group and that he goes to the opposite extreme to avoid it. About one-third of the sample would not join any club. It is possible that among the reasons for not desiring membership in any club may be that social clubs carry the connotation "for older people only" and that this in turn is rejected. The nonjoiner's reasons must remain indeterminate since they were not probed. On the question of age specialization, then, we can assert that about one person in three prefers a social club made up mostly of older people.

Earlier we discussed the view that people of high social status tend to have pronounced needs for both active social lives as well

TABLE 85. ATTITUDE TOWARD JOINING A SO-
CIAL CLUB ACCORDING TO SOCIO-
ECONOMIC STATUS

Attitude toward joining a social club	High status	Low status
	(Percentages)	
Would join club for younger persons	25	9
Would join club for all ages	14	19
Would join club for persons of own age	36	33
Would not join any club	24	38
No answer	1	1
Total	100	100
Number of cases	203	297

as contact with younger people and more youthful activities. These tendencies appear again when we examine their choices regarding the type of social club they would join. From Table 85 we see that nearly three times as many high as low status individuals would join a club of mostly younger people. Although in both status groups about a third choose a club for older people, the disposition not to join any club is significantly greater in the low status than in the high status group. Not only are greater social needs expressed by the high status group,[1] but these needs are seen as being satisfied by either "young set" or general clubs

TABLE 86. ATTITUDE TOWARD JOINING A SOCIAL CLUB ACCORD-
ING TO DISPOSITION TO USE HEALTH SERVICES

| | Disposition to use health services | |
Attitude toward joining a social club	Favorable	Unfavorable
	(Percentag'···	
Would join club for younger persons	16	15
Would join club for all ages	19	12
Would join club for persons of own age	40	21
Would not join any club	24	51
No answer	1	1
Total	100	100
Number of cases	342	158

at least as often as by clubs for older people. Social needs we have generally found to be greater for those of higher social position at all ages past sixty.

Since joining a social club or going to a medical center requires a certain heightened degree of motivation or activity level, it might be hypothesized that where a disposition to use medical services is high a favorable attitude toward joining a club would appear. That this is clearly the case is seen in Table 86. Even more remarkable is the preponderant choice of a club for mostly older people by those whose disposition to use medical facilities is high. Equally interesting is the fact that *there are no class status differences in these tendencies.* Even among those in the high status group, where the disposition to use services is low, those who do

[1] A clear-cut demonstration of this fact is found in the data concerning visiting of friends. In the high status group, 45 per cent are high-frequency visitors while in the low status group only 32 per cent are high-frequency visitors. This difference is significant statistically.

favor their use prefer a center for older people. In the low status group about two-thirds of those only weakly disposed to using health services also would not join a social club, while among those who favor using such facilities, fewer than one-third would not join a club. It would seem that the basic factor operating here is not so much status as a desire to participate in activity outside the home, be it health or social in character.[1]

Concerning the individual's level of activity as an index of his desire to join clubs, a low general level of activity and a desire not to join clubs are significantly related only among those in the low status group. The nonjoiner is likely to be the homebound, nonuser as well. It is interesting that in the high status group, with its strong social affiliation needs, the joining tendency is high regardless of the level of overall activity. Of greatest importance, however, is the fact that, as shown in Table 87, among the high status people, if the individual is already socially isolated he tends twice as frequently as his nonisolated counterpart not to desire to join any kind of club. Even among the relative social isolates, however, only a third would not join.

Certainly, from all that has been reported in this chapter, one could not reasonably conclude that many of the older people in our sample are lacking in spirit or are not vigorously self-interested. Their positive feelings toward medical services, while for various reasons not matched by corresponding actions, are generally not the responses of the demoralized group they are often pictured to be. In the field of health, where the course of action is clearly understood, favorable attitudes toward the use of facilities are prominent. In the social sphere, joining activity is not so greatly favored. Social needs can be met through other forms of activity and where these needs are low, "club work" is anathema.

On the question of age-specialized as opposed to general service centers, it is not possible to generalize for the sample as a whole. There is a wide divergence of feeling and opinion among aged persons on this question. Social and psychological factors involv-

[1] In a society in which a premium is placed upon "getting out and doing things," even the activity involved in leaving home to attend to some chronic ailment at a medical clinic provides some degree of social value as well.

ing the self-image and acceptance of one's own aging are intimately tied to the choice of "geriatric" or "golden age" centers or services. The evidence clearly points to a major principle: *If programs of services for older people are effectively to reach those who are*

TABLE 87. ATTITUDE TOWARD JOINING A SOCIAL CLUB ACCORDING TO RELATIVE SOCIAL ISOLATION FOR HIGH AND LOW SOCIOECONOMIC STATUS[a]

Attitude toward joining a social club	High status		Low status	
	Isolated	Not isolated	Isolated	Not isolated
	(Percentages)			
Would join club for younger persons	21	28	9	9
Would join club for all ages	11	16	16	25
Would join club for persons of own age	33	39	33	33
Would not join any club	33	16	41	33
No answer	2	1	1	
Total	100	100	100	100
Number of cases	*85*	*117*	*194*	*103*

[a] The total number of cases used here is 499. One person could not be classified on the Isolation Index.

inclined to use them, such services must be as diverse and embedded in as many organizational contexts as there are preferences, attitude patterns, and values regarding aging among the older population. Geriatric health centers or age-specialized recreational or activity centers or age-defined casework agencies will attract only certain sections of the aged population. Failure to recognize the effects of self-perception and attitudes toward aging can mean that only a fraction of those in need of service will respond. The principle stated above is especially important in the field of health education. Diabetes control programs, for example, aimed to help the older person would seem to be handicapped if a frontal campaign is made upon the aged.

Diversity of approach appears to be the keystone of widespread acceptability and use in both service and educational programs.

PART IV

TRENDS AND PROGRAMS

Part IV:

Trends and Programs

ONE APPROACH toward determining the needs and problems of a given group in the population is to assess the meaning of these problems to the community, that is, to explore the ways in which the community has mobilized itself to meet them. This type of approach was adopted as a complementary method to the cross-sectional survey of the aged population of the Kips Bay-Yorkville Health District reported upon in the previous sections. Its purpose was to assess the extent to which the community was organized to deal with the problems of older people. By using both a sample survey as well as a resources survey, it was anticipated that a more nearly complete picture of the needs and problems of the aged would emerge—a picture as seen by the aged individual himself and one as seen by professionals and program administrators whose interests are to promote community welfare. The term "experience survey" describes the essential nature of this aspect of the study—a survey of knowledge accumulated in the course of work in aiding older persons in distress.

Systematic information concerning services and programs was obtained through informal interviews with administrators and staffs of health and welfare agencies in New York City. These discussions centered upon the kinds of situations about which aged persons sought professional help and the specific work done by these community resources. It was possible to focus and to concretize discussion by exploring ways in which a proposed counseling center designed specifically to serve the aged might fit into the existing network of health and welfare services of New York City. Even this approach had the shortcoming of being somewhat academic. Professionals, long hardened to the frustrations of having numerous unmet needs in their communities, pointed out that the acid test in exploring new resources for the aged would lie in the actual experiences in making referrals: "Will X agency accept Mr. Brown with his kind of problem?" The key to success in social agency work is frequently not what the agency itself can do with or for a client but whether referrals for services offered by other agencies can be accepted.

As is generally true throughout the nation,[1] it was found very early in this survey that *there are very few health or welfare agencies whose programs are specifically designed to assist older people.* There are a wide variety of health and welfare services open to all age groups. Traditionally, homes for the aged and hospitals for the chronically ill have been the major community resources geared to the needs of older people in need of professional help. In recent years recreational centers for the aged have developed rapidly, but otherwise there have been few new resources.

With respect to already established services open to the general community, our interviews with administrators of health and welfare agencies in New York City reveal that, by and large, older people make much less use of such community facilities than do other segments of the population. Is this failure to utilize facilities due to the older person's lack of awareness of their existence? Is he pessimistic about how much help he can expect from them? Does he lack the motivation to employ these resources even if he is fully cognizant of them? Are agencies themselves reluctant or unable to offer programs which will draw in aged clients? These are problems which require closer study.

The lack of community services for the aged and the apparent reluctance of the older person to use what services already exist should not, however, be taken to mean that no need exists. On the contrary, the survey of 500 aged individuals reported in this volume gives evidence that many older people are faced with pressing problems, some of which are not amenable to solution by

---

[1] See: The President's Commission on the Health Needs of the Nation, *Building America's Health*, vol. 2, 1952; U. S. Department of Health, Education, and Welfare, *Man and His Years*, 1951; Governor's Conference on the Problems of the Aging, Sacramento, California, *Proceedings*, 1951; Brunot, Helen H., *Old Age in New York City*, 1944.

way of the traditional services for the aged. In other areas throughout the nation, governors' conferences and health and welfare councils testify to the growing community concern that the needs of older people, although starkly real among large numbers, are not being met.[1]

On the basis of the knowledge we have accumulated, we can only speculate as to the causes for this lag between the acknowledged needs of the aged and the development of services to meet them. Certainly, the increasing proportion of aged individuals in the population is a contributing factor. Not to be overlooked is the fact that most of the available health and welfare funds, both governmental and philanthropic, are already heavily invested in ongoing programs involving the maintenance of extensive physical plants and of organizations serving primarily the needs of children, parents, young adults, and those in their middle years. In view of the limited financial resources available, in most agencies the community is then faced with what amounts to a choice between maintaining these services at the expense of possible new services for the aged, or curtailing existing services for the general population in order to meet the needs of older people. Most social planners would agree that the amount of funds available for health and welfare needs is not a fixed amount but varies according to economic trends and the prevailing orientation of governmental administrations. Within this context, in any given period the social planner has to weigh the needs and demands of various segments of the community in terms of available financial resources.

Aside from financial problems, many professional workers frankly admit to being perplexed over any attempt to meet the needs of a group for whom there are so many serious problems coming at a point so near the end of the life span. These members of the professional community wonder about the advisability of investing resources in such a group when so many unfulfilled

---

[1] The following are some of the states that have recently issued carefully documented reports on problems of the aged: California, Colorado, Connecticut, Florida, Illinois, Maine, Massachusetts, Michigan, Minnesota, New Jersey, New Mexico, New York, North Carolina, Oregon, Pennsylvania, Rhode Island, Vermont, West Virginia, and Wisconsin. At this writing, the report of the Council of State Governments on problems of older people further documents the case.

requirements are reported among younger people. The implicit philosophy contained in the views held is that community services for youth and younger adults should have precedence over services for those who are in the "decline of life." The adage that "youth must be served" is a real and operative, if not a conscious ideology in the structure of existing community resources.

Decisions to favor one group and to deny another are, indeed, difficult to make. The very presence of these "choice points," however, indicates that "problems and needs of the aged" are more than a matter of the distress experienced by individual aged persons. These are community problems and needs as well, and they affect the entire fabric of community welfare.

Chapter 11

Trends in Services for the Aged in New York City

PLANNING FOR AN AMBULATORY AGED POPULATION

ONE OF THE COMMON MISUNDERSTANDINGS about the older population of our country is the belief that a concomitant of old age is ill health, invalidism, and childlike dependency.[1] Indeed, if one were to scan the resources available for older people one could easily gain the impression that the major social need in planning for this group lies in the area of custodial care and hospitalization. Actually, while the needs of seriously ill aged persons are most pressing, this group encompasses only a small proportion of the aged population of the United States.

It is gratifying to note that most aged people in our country are in a physical condition enabling them to pursue the most varied kinds of activities. The vitality of individuals who have reached their sixties and seventies has astounded many of the physicians who are responsible for their care. It is interesting to note that of the population over the age of sixty-five about 69 per cent live in their own independent homes and evidently manage to care for their needs without any kind of custodial supervision. One physician well known for his pioneering work in geriatrics made the significant comment that our concept of old age was distorted, in that people in their sixties could be considered at the very prime of life and should be thought of as capable of making a substantial contribution on through their seventies and even early eighties.

---

[1] This belief is exposed as being unfounded in the report of the President's Commission on the Health Needs of the Nation previously cited. Our own findings fully concur with those of the Commission.

One major finding of our survey of resources for older people in New York City is that these resources (the few that exist) are geared not toward that large ambulatory section of the population but rather toward the most severely ill, the most dependent, and the most disturbed group. Services are not geared toward preventive work with the aged. Services are not geared toward assisting the aging person at a point when debilitating and demoralizing influences begin creating havoc with his body and with his personality.

Much evidence can be mustered to support the proposition that it is economically unsound, as well as morally unprincipled, for our society to neglect the aging group. There is statistical evidence to show that individuals in their sixties or early seventies are vulnerable to such diseases as cancer, cardiovascular diseases, arthritis, and other conditions to which man is heir.[1] The adage "A stitch in time saves nine" is applicable. Incipient conditions find more fertile ground for development among the aged than in the younger, more resilient population segments. Yet, diseases can be detected in the early stages and managed or controlled by modern medicine, almost as well among the aged as among those who are younger. Similarly, preventive measures in the field of mental health could probably counteract the alarming trend which has led to the flooding of mental hospitals with aged patients.[2] Signs and symptoms of senility and personality deterioration among older people have often been attributed to the functional consequences of rejection and isolation. Yet little has been done to pin down this supposition or to organize programs to counter these social and psychological factors.

As compared to the rest of the population, the use of community facilities to improve the mental health status of the aged of New York City is insignificant. The harsh reality of the situation here is that mental hygiene clinics, guidance centers, and

[1] U. S. Department of Health, Education, and Welfare, *Fact Book on Aging*, 1952; Perrott, G. St. J., and others, *Illness and Health Services in an Aging Population*, 1952; President's Commission on the Health Needs of the Nation, *Building America's Health*, 1952; Monroe, Robert T., *Diseases in Old Age*, 1951.

[2] Stevenson, George S., "A Guide to a Community Committee on the Mental Health of the Aged," 1953.

private practitioners in the fields of psychiatry, psychology, and counseling are not geared to help those aged persons who are beginning to show maladjustment, neurotic disturbance, incipient senility, behavior disorder, and psychosis.[1] This is all the more unfortunate, since, as one writer has said, ours is a culture that systematically "insults" the aged person.[2] The older person is pressured out of the labor force, is often faced with diminished financial resources and a lowered standard of living, with a continuous reduction of social ties because of the death of peers and loved ones, and with the emotional impact of waning physical vitality in a culture emphasizing youthful beauty and youthful vigor.

This fact of having health and welfare services geared to the nonambulatory section of the aging population presents a grave problem to the social planner. Can existing resources be influenced to encompass within their framework this long-neglected group? Can prejudices, misunderstandings, commitments to other pressing community needs, and the lack of a preventive orientation be counteracted by an educational process? Does sound social planning preclude the establishment of specialized services for the aged which can do a preventive rather than merely a palliative job?

Social planners in New York City have been faced with the problem that has arisen as a result of the increase of welfare and health organizations geared to deal with segmental problems of the community. These problems had previously been neglected by the more traditional services. The sprouting of these organizations presents both a boon and a liability. On the credit side is the feature that a flexible democratic process in the health and welfare community permits new problems to be attacked vigorously and brought to public attention. Thus, in the last decade, we have become aware of the need for resources for such groups as those suffering from cerebral palsy, infantile paralysis, multiple sclerosis, cancer, heart disease, alcoholism, mental re-

[1] A recently opened private psychiatric service at low cost handles patients up to the age of fifty, for example.

[2] Havighurst, Robert J., "Social and Psychological Needs of the Aging," 1952.

tardation, mental illness, and so forth. Public response to aid these unfortunates more than justifies the existence of organized efforts in their behalf. On the debit side, the growth of such organizations without sound social planning has meant that there has been some duplication in service, and elaborate administrative and capital expenses have gone into the establishment of new agencies and resources which might have been used to adapt the programs of existing agencies to meet new needs. For the layman, constantly plagued by the appeal of numerous fund drives for his charitable contributions, the morass of appeals has been most confusing. Some programs in need of voluntary contributions have not attained the funds they require, while others have been oversubscribed on the basis of superior fund-raising techniques. The area of aging has been among those "poor country cousin" problems having no central source of organization or funds.

Social planning in the field of problems of the aged is now at the point where a vital contribution can be made to community welfare. The relative newness of the problem and the absence of elaborate organizational groups to meet the needs of this section of the population makes possible the development of services along sound scientific lines rather than on the basis of emotional appeal. The responsibility of the social planner is to assist existing governmental and voluntary agencies to face the problems of the aged and to help them develop preventive, diagnostic, or therapeutic programs within their own networks. New services for the aged should be established only in areas that do not lend themselves to the intervention of the traditional services. It is economically unwise to embark upon social experiments in the field of health and welfare services without prior establishment of pilot test programs to determine their usefulness. This is a technique employed widely in industry and is particularly appropriate to the field of social planning.

SERVICE FOR WHOM?

A number of individuals have expressed the fear that if one were to follow through on all the recommendations of social planners, health experts, and "do gooders" we would have a society in which every individual would be propped up by another whose main function would be limited to the support of this dependent person. It is true that most of our ambulatory aged persons have managed quite well prior to achieving the status of a "senior citizen" and can be expected to continue without developing problems of such serious proportions that an intervening hand is needed.[1] Nevertheless, for those older people who do or will require services, the community should be, but is not, fully ready.[2]

Throughout the history of this country, there has always been controversy about the establishment of new public services. Thus, government-supported public schools, well-baby stations in health departments, and the development of a social security system all met considerable opposition before being accepted as necessary public enterprises. There is no doubt that with time will come the demand upon those responsible for developing community services to plan new types of resources, or to expand existing ones, for the aged. By sheer weight of numbers the aged group is making its presence felt. About three million persons, or one in 25, were sixty-five years and older in 1900. By 1950 those sixty-five years and older totaled almost 12.5 million or about one in 12 in the population. The number in this group passed the 13 million mark in 1952 and is currently increasing at the rate of about 400,000 a year.

This quantitative change also has implications in terms of the new kinds of problems that arise. There is the problem of a large group for whom there is no adequate place in the labor force. There is the question of pressing health problems for this group, and also adequate housing and residential and custodial care.

What is needed is creativity on the part of social planners so that these new problems can be met both in ways that have proved successful and in new ways that have been devised with

---

[1] Riesman makes the point that the autonomous person does not "really" age, at least in a deleterious way. See Riesman, David, "Some Clinical and Cultural Aspects of Aging," 1954.

[2] Nor, as indicated previously, fully willing to offer assistance.

imagination by those who have worked directly with the aged.[1] In the sections that follow, an attempt is made to evaluate the existing resources for the aged and to indicate areas in which new or expanded services are indicated.

EMPLOYMENT

In 1952 only 24.5 per cent of the population over the age of sixty-five received income as wage-earners. It has been estimated that by 1975 the proportion of employed men over sixty-five will have dropped from 70 per cent in 1890 to only 35 per cent of the total. It is well known that many aged individuals are dropped from the labor force at this age because of mandatory retirement systems. Others who are unemployed for other reasons (health, seasonal employment, and so on) find it extremely difficult to secure employment once they are out of a job. Many experts have indicated that this policy is both unfair to the older person and unsound from an economic standpoint.[2] Several studies have pointed up the fact that retirement, rather than being something to which workers look forward, is something that many put off as long as possible. A study of garment workers in New York revealed that "industrial workers approaching retirement have a deep resistance to retirement" and that the reasons for this attitude were cultural, economic, psychological, and social. The authors of the study noted:

> Often, only through work does the individual develop his meaningful social contacts, express his creative interests, make his contribution to society, and achieve status in the community. In a real sense, therefore, for many workers, and especially for the men and women in this study, work is more than earning a living. It is a way of life.[3]

[1] Some cogent remarks on the need for new concepts and ideas in dealing with the problems of the aged have been made by British social and medical scientists who have surveyed needs and resources in England. See: Nuffield Foundation, *Old People*, 1947; and Sheldon, J. H., *The Social Medicine of Old Age*, 1948.

[2] Kuh, Clifford, "Employment of the Older Worker—A Challenge to Industry and Public Health," 1952; Barkin, Solomon, "Jobs for Older Workers," 1952; *Proceedings* of the Governor's Conference on the Problems of the Aging, Sacramento, California, 1951.

[3] Tuckman, Jacob, and Irving Lorge, *Retirement and the Industrial Worker:* Prospect and Reality. Teachers College, Columbia University, New York, 1953, p. 90.

The New York City Mayor's Advisory Committee for the Aged found that 41 per cent of teachers and other city employees who have retired on pensions appeared dissatisfied with retirement. Inadequate income and the desire to work were considered chief problems by the Committee.[1]

Where does a person over sixty go when he wants to find a job? For most people in the population, employment can be obtained through such sources as personal contact, commercial employment agencies, newspaper advertisements, and federal or state-supported employment services. Unless he has a marketable skill (and in many instances even if he is highly skilled), the older worker finds many of these avenues increasingly closed to him. A recent government report states:

> Once out of a job, older workers face an especial obstacle to finding other jobs in the face of the prevalence of formal and informal hiring age restrictions. Many studies have been made of job orders, want ads, and the employment practices of individual industries. All such studies show a high rate of age specifications and requirements and discrimination against the older worker. Such age limits in hiring significantly reduce the chances of success of older workers in competition for new employment and . . . cause him to undergo much longer periods of unemployment than the younger worker. A very substantial percentage of industries have taken to practicing a maximum hiring age limit, ranging from age 35 for women in some occupations to age 65 in others, with employers most frequently specifying ages below 45.[2]

In New York City there are few employment services that will extend a sympathetic hand to the older worker.[3] Several agencies which are noncommercial and receive support from philanthropic organizations or from foundations have embarked upon cam-

---

[1] Bunzel, Joseph H., and Louis Gare, "Some Factors in Satisfaction with Retirement," 1953.

[2] *Retirement Policies and the Railroad Retirement System:* Report of the Joint Committee on Railroad Retirement Legislation. Part 2, "Economic Problems of an Aging Population." 83d Congress, 1st Sess. Senate Report 6, Government Printing Office, Washington, 1953.

[3] A compendium of services and resources for the aged of New York City is to be found in the *Directory of Social and Health Agencies: 1954–1955* prepared by the Welfare and Health Council of New York.

paigns to find jobs for older workers.[1] While these agencies have not operated on a large scale, their work has demonstrated the feasibility of carrying on public campaigns for the older worker. These campaigns sometimes overlap activities of other organizations, such as those devoted to finding jobs for the handicapped. There is room, however, for much wider activity in this area.

One of the problems of the older worker is changing his job orientation when opportunities narrow down and exclude him. There is evidence to show that older workers in the labor force tend to concentrate in the more marginal, lower paid jobs.[2] The function of private and public employment agencies in this regard is to provide counseling which will enable the older worker to assess his abilities in the light of current labor market requirements and existing practices respecting the employment of older workers. Toward this end, the State of New York has enlarged its staff to handle more cases of unemployed older persons.

For the aging person who is forced out of his customary employment because of health factors, such as a cardiac condition, arthritis, diabetes, and other illnesses or disabilities, there is the problem of helping him obtain training along other lines. Unfortunately, rehabilitation work involves considerable investment of professional time and often the older person is not deemed a suitable subject. It is argued that even if he were to be rehabilitated, and this is an increasingly risky matter with increasing age, the social barriers against him would make his finding a job in a new field very unlikely.

RECREATION

Planning suitable recreational facilities for all sections of the population is a job that is indeed challenging. Unfortunately, our culture is one that makes it easier for individuals to be passive observers of other people's activities rather than active participants. The tremendous growth of television as a medium of

---

[1] It is to be noted that to most if not all employment agencies an "older worker" is a man past forty-five and the age is even younger in the case of a woman.

[2] Lehman, Harvey C., "Gainful Occupations Engaged in Most Often by Men and Women of Age 65 and Over," 1954.

entertainment has increased the fear of some that our nation will gradually consist of people who will have little in the way of resources for self-education and stimulation and instead will become passive on-lookers.

When one thinks in terms of recreation resources for older people, the problem becomes even more complex because of the nature of this group. Our aged population tends to be more socially isolated than younger segments. A number of studies have indicated that there is a falling off of group activity in the later years and an unwholesome tendency for older people to be crowded out of the stream of life once they give up economic activity.[1] After spending a lifetime narrowly devoted to the business of earning a living, the older person feels confused and perplexed when suddenly confronted with nothing but leisure time. All previous living habits have to be altered to face this new situation. For many aged individuals, retirement involves confronting a great void with the very real potentiality of demoralization and debilitation.

Recreation for the aged individual must provide new gratifications to replace those that accrue to the wage-earner who receives material rewards for his efforts. Some older persons need a substitute for a routine, and organized recreational efforts can help them find this. The day centers run by the Department of Welfare in New York City and other voluntary agencies help to fill the void faced by the displaced aged worker and his widowed or isolated spouse. Recent reports indicate that there are some 5,000 individuals participating in the activities of such centers. While this is a small number in view of the 750,000 persons who are sixty-five years of age and over in the city, there is no doubt that this kind of program will expand rapidly in the years to come.[2] It has proved its effectiveness and every institution that has attempted to embark on such a program has noted the tremendous growth that takes place within the first few years.

[1] See for example: Cavan, Ruth S., and others, *Personal Adjustment in Old Age*, 1949; Havighurst, Robert J., and Ruth Albrecht, *Older People*, 1953; and Tuckman, Jacob, and Irving Lorge, *Retirement and the Industrial Worker*, 1953.

[2] The Council of State Governments estimates that not more than 5 per cent of older persons in any community are members of a "golden age" club.

It is apparent that for some aged people day centers do not provide an answer because of attitudes and feelings that preclude their participation in activities with other older people. Numbers of persons do not wish to associate with their contemporaries because of an inability to accept aging or because of a fear of becoming isolated from the younger section of the population. Others in this group resist contact with recreation centers because they view the activities as better befitting children or doddering seniles than mature individuals. Deeply ingrained prejudices against such activities as painting, singing, dancing, craftwork stem from a lifetime in which these interests have not had a part in the individual's life. It is important to recall that many of today's aged spent most of their work life laboring 60 and 70-hour work-weeks before the change in the national pattern which began to take place in the 1930's and 1940's. Such individuals had little if any time at all to cultivate or engage in leisure-time activities.

There are a number of older persons who do not join day centers because they resist associating with other aged individuals of different socioeconomic status or different ethnic group membership or, possibly, different religious affiliation. Breaking down such barriers is not always feasible when one realizes that deep-seated social prejudices, sustained over a lifetime, are not easily removed. One might venture the opinion that as the nation continues to accept the diminution of social barriers and learns to utilize its expanding leisure time more creatively, so will the aged group reflect these changes.

All health and welfare institutions that have contact with elderly individuals can play a role in redirecting their energies toward gratifying pursuits that are intrinsically congenial to the older person's outlook.[1] Those who counsel the aged must themselves be creative in helping the older person find a spark within himself that can lead to the development of pursuits to replace the satisfactions derived from gainful employment or keeping a home and rearing children.

---

[1] Elon H. Moore in "Professors in Retirement," 1951, makes the point that in choosing activities for retirement "one man's meat is another man's poison."

Aside from the recreation day centers mentioned above, interest is beginning to develop in such places as libraries, churches, and homes for the aged in recreational programs for their members.

INCOME MAINTENANCE

Expressed simply, the situation is this: Many of our aged population live far below a standard that is regarded as minimal by both public and private agencies. In February, 1956, there were 8.1 million people receiving Old-Age and Survivors Insurance, representing about 57 per cent of the population over the age of sixty-five. As noted above, benefits for retired workers are generally well below even subsistence levels. There were in this period 5.9 million individuals receiving Old-Age Assistance, or about 43 per cent of the population over sixty-five, and their benefits averaged $880 per year per person.[1] It has been estimated that in 1954 an elderly retired couple in New York City required an annual budget of about $2,137. Estimated annual budgets for single persons ranged from $1,488 to $1,618. These budget standards, designed to be a measure of cost of living requirements, were based on "a representative list of annual purchases sufficient to maintain current standards of adequate consumption at low cost."[2] It is estimated that about seven million aged persons in the United States live on a budget decidedly below a minimum standard of living. The ramifications of such decline in living standard are far-reaching. Limited income often leads to neglect of one's health by failure to seek medical attention. It also severely limits the possibility of engaging in satisfying recreational, social, or cultural activities. Additionally, there is the psychological element of sharply reduced status in the community and, at the same time, adjustment to a penny-pinching life after decades of more comfortable existence.

During 1955 the number of persons receiving Old-Age Assistance from the New York City Department of Welfare fluctuated around 50,000. This represents a substantial part of the public

[1] *Social Security Bulletin*, vol. 19, May, 1956, p. 1.

[2] *Fact Book on the Aged in New York City.* Welfare and Health Council of New York City, Appendix Table 15, p. 80, 1954.

assistance caseload of the Welfare Department. The average grant was a little less than $68 per month,[1] an amount that falls short of the previously cited estimated standard budgets for elderly persons in New York City. As can be seen, the grants do not reach a level commensurate with a standard of living necessary for proper maintenance. It must be remembered that in order to satisfy eligibility requirements for Welfare Department assistance, individuals must demonstrate need on the basis of having no income or resources beyond an amount necessary for final burial arrangements. It has been suggested that public welfare agencies encourage part-time income-producing activity for older people, such as baby sitting, craft work, and bookbinding, so that their standard of living may be raised.

Several outstanding trends in New York City seem to be developing. First, the proportionate number of older persons who will require Old-Age Assistance will slowly decline as the cumulative effects of federal Social Security benefits, union and employer pension plans, and other private resources make themselves felt. The drain on municipal funds, however, is likely to continue for a long period. For together with an increase in the absolute numbers of older needy people, there will be increases in the living costs and medical expenses of many "remnant" older groups. Those over sixty-five in New York City are rapidly approaching one million in number. It has been predicted that older people will constitute a growing proportion of the city's permanent residents through the years.

Recent increases in Social Security benefits are likely to reduce the pressure upon the city for financial assistance. At the same time, the growth and popularity of welfare funds and pensions, while they do not provide for adequate living, are often supplementing Old-Age and Survivors Insurance funds and the assistance of children.

The support of elderly parents by their adult children presents a mixed picture in New York City. Although many children continue to support or contribute to the support of needy parents, many others either will not or cannot give them adequate assist-

[1] *Monthly Statistical Bulletins*, Department of Welfare, New York City, 1955.

ance. On the question of support the following figures emerge from research reported here and elsewhere. In the Kips Bay-Yorkville survey sample, all respondents were asked: "Do the young people in your family usually take care of the older people?" The replies were as follows:

	Per cent
Yes	48
No	18
Do not have family	28
"Don't know," No answer	6
Total	100

By contrast, when the relatives and friends of our respondents were asked to name the source they thought older people should depend on mainly for support, the results were:

	Per cent
The government	35
Themselves	29
Their children	29
Other relatives	1
Other	6
Total	100

Only 23 per cent of the group felt that the government was doing enough for older people. The largest single problem reported by the associates of their older friends or relations was the problem of finances.

While the desire to care for older parents or relatives is fairly high, this desire does not extend into the area of financial support. The government is felt to be the central source for assistance. Since depression days, some states have reinstituted laws requiring financial support of indigent parents by adult children. In New York children are held legally responsible by state law for the care of indigent parents. The current situation is such that in order to become eligible for public assistance some older people must authorize the Department of Welfare to institute court proceedings for nonsupport against their children. Although it does have the effect of coercing adult children to make some sort of contribution, there is a view gaining considerable support that enforcing this legal responsibility often has a deleterious effect upon family relationships.

HEALTH SERVICES FOR THE AGED

It is generally recognized that health problems are more frequent and more serious in the later years than at any other time. With the rapid growth of the aged population and an expected continuation of this trend, it is obvious that existing health services will have to be expanded to meet this need. The alternative will be a growing crisis in the distribution of medical services. For the hospital administrator, there is concern with the problem of keeping hospital beds open for emergency medical needs. There are sufficiently large numbers of chronically ill aged individuals requiring a combination of medical and custodial care to overwhelm the hospitals of New York City.[1]

Hospital administrators have emphasized the fact that in order to keep hospital space available for the entire population, the intake of aged patients has to be carefully screened. One administrator has expressed the opinion that city hospitals are carrying a disproportionate share of the aged population. It is felt that this is unfortunate because city hospitals are all working up to capacity and are not able to embark upon experimental programs that seem indicated for the aged population. A program in the health maintenance of older people, essentially a feature of preventive medicine, could have a long range positive effect in reducing the need for hospital admissions. A recent report notes:

> Nearly 25 per cent of the persons well at age 60 will develop within the ensuing five years a chronic ailment for which they probably will seek or need medical treatment, and, in many cases, will continue to require care throughout their remaining lifetime. The

[1] Nevertheless, as seen in Part III, the ambulatory sample does not present a picture of dire medical need. There is no question, however, that it is a medically vulnerable group.

percentage increases to about 40 at age 70, 57 at age 80, and 90 at 90, although with advancing age the absolute numbers of persons subject to the risk of developing a chronic disease decreases in accordance with the age composition of the population.[1]

It would appear that local voluntary hospitals will have to take the initiative in this field. Substantial evidence has emerged to show that adjustment to retirement or widowhood and health status are closely related. The need for an advanced type of social medicine involving treatment of the whole person seems to be accepted. A number of investigations have pointed to the need for intensive study of incipient personal and health problems.[2] Centers attuned to the needs of the aged would do much to uncover conditions that tend to create debilitation and sickness in old age. There is a need for diagnostic services, such as laboratory, x-ray, and other special tests. Many of these services can be found in a variety of settings in the community but have not yet been fully mobilized on behalf of the older person.[3]

The following types of services need to be expanded and modified to help meet the needs of the aged.

Home Care

In New York City there has been a trend toward developing home care programs within all city and some voluntary hospitals. The value of home care rests in the fact that the home is a familiar setting, unlike the strange atmosphere of the hospital, and the patient does not have to isolate himself from those he loves and from the setting which is most natural to him. It is even possible to treat a patient in the home during the terminal phase of his illness. At the same time, such a program allows for the maximum use of hospital bed space for acutely ill persons. Home care is at

[1] Perrott, G. St. J., and others, *Illness and Health Services in an Aging Population.* U. S. Public Health Service Publication no. 170, Government Printing Office, Washington, 1952, p. 35.

[2] See: Galdston, Iago, *The Meaning of Social Medicine,* 1954; Simmons, Leo W., and Wolff, Harold G., *Social Science in Medicine,* 1954; Wolff, Harold G., *Stress and Disease,* 1953.

[3] Nearly all hospitals in New York City are finding substantial reductions in outpatient services. It has been suggested that experimental units at moderate cost be set up to help develop a specialized geriatric service.

once good medical practice, good for the patient and economically sound. One pioneering hospital has found that such a program calls for a great deal of flexibility. Heretofore, the average hospital patient's stay was rather cyclical in character. He would require specialized care after surgery or a serious heart seizure, for example, but subsequently his status in the hospital became one of boarder rather than patient. Involved was excessive use of hospital beds and resultant higher administrative costs for a single illness. Whereas in a hospital all kinds of housekeeping and dietary services have to be mobilized for a patient, these are just as available to him in his own home. A home care unit has to be organized to allocate physicians, nurses, housekeepers, and attendants for home visits. It is also possible to recruit other services for the home (for example, dentist, physiotherapist). In this way, it is possible for hospitals to cover a much wider population than if restricted to the traditional type of hospital care.

Geriatric Clinics

There have been several attempts to establish geriatric clinics in New York City, most of which have not been very successful. Many physicians have expressed opposition to the clinics on the ground that there are no diseases peculiar to old age. Nevertheless, the continued interest in geriatric clinics throughout the country has made it probable that pioneering attempts will continue in this direction. The reason for this, as expressed by one proponent of the program, is that the aged get shunted around in hospital clinics, which are disease-oriented rather than patient-oriented. It is felt that physicians and clinics are overburdened. The aged are seen as constantly "grousing," and it is alleged that little satisfaction is derived by physicians from the palliative work that is done with them. Since many aged persons already feel isolated and rejected, they are keenly sensitive to any indication of a lack of concern for them at clinics. The proponents of geriatric clinics hold that the total needs of elderly patients can best be met in settings especially geared for their needs. It is felt that physicians require special sensitivity to the older person's need for warmth, friendliness, and feeling of self-worth. Some physicians have found that friendly talks with the aged seem to have as beneficial an effect as the prescription of some remedy.

It is interesting to note that the lack of success of one geriatric clinic in New York City was attributed to the fact that older patients resisted using the clinic. They felt that the service offered was a segregated one and reflected prejudice against them. They were not prepared for the idea of a specialized clinic for older people and saw it basically as a way for the hospital to provide inferior service for them. It was recognized that an educational campaign might have helped to overcome such resistance. Until the desires and feelings of older people themselves are tapped to determine the lines that acceptable services must take, abortive experiments in geriatrics are bound to continue.[1]

Rehabilitation Centers

While most rehabilitation centers have been oriented toward the younger section of the population, there has been widespread interest in the problems of the disabled aged. Two leaders in this field expressed the opinion that in the field of geriatrics there has not yet been established anywhere the kind of team approach, successful in other age groups, that is necessary to meet the problems of the aged.[2] They were opposed to medical settings in which the practice of medicine was not geared to the particularized needs of the aged. For one proposed establishment, they felt that a medical-surgical unit and a vocational advisory unit should work hand in hand toward the goal of restoring the elderly patient to an employable state. While aware that this undertaking had much futility connected with it since there were sociological barriers to the employment of the aged, they believed that demonstration programs were nevertheless required to show the feasibility of restoring the employment potential of older persons. Until the establishment of the geriatric rehabilitation unit at the Goldwater Memorial Hospital in New York City, there was no large-scale effort to deal with the problems of the disabled aged

[1] A noteworthy exception is the Charles Silver Memorial Clinic of Beth-Israel Hospital (a voluntary institution) offering a modern geriatric service in a new facility.

[2] In this regard, see Switzer, Mary E., and Howard A. Rusk, "Keeping Older People Fit for Participation," 1952.

in the city. A number of other plans are being contemplated by city and voluntary agencies, including a geriatric rehabilitation center at Kingston Avenue Hospital under municipal auspices.

Nursing Services

Nursing services must be considered a necessary part of the complement of services for the aged residents of any urban area. Since chronic diseases are more prevalent among the aged than among any portion of the population, medical care in the home is required by this group in order to maintain their independence. Public health nurses are constantly called upon by physicians of the community to visit homes where patients require bedside nursing care, help with diets, isolation of communicable diseases, and general health education. Public health nursing is becoming more and more recognized in New York City as a major asset to total patient care. There are a number of major agencies providing this type of service, such as the Visiting Nurse Service of New York and Public Health Nursing Service of the Department of Health. A recent report indicated that nursing care to the home-bound elderly is increasing at a fast rate. Unfortunately, however, elderly persons often are not aware of the existence of these services.

Homes and Institutions for the Chronically Ill

In New York City there are a variety of voluntary, municipal, and proprietary programs to meet the needs of the chronically ill. Public and private chronic disease hospitals are, unfortunately, under tremendous pressure to admit new patients and are constantly faced with the problem of inadequate bed space. Very often families find it necessary to place individuals in private nursing homes that are operated as business ventures. A large number of alleged abuses in the latter field have led to the demand for closer regulation by governmental bodies. It is fairly common knowledge in the community that nursing homes are both extremely expensive and, on the whole, limited in the services they offer. There are 77 private nursing homes in New York City with an aggregate of fewer than 3,000 beds.[1] The least expensive homes average about $40 per week for care, and these have long waiting lists. Most homes are much more expensive and are beyond the means of low and middle income families. Families in need of special care for the chronically ill have, in the past, been able to receive assistance from a special counseling service of the United Hospital Fund but this was discontinued in 1953. The experience of this service was that the problem of care for the chronically ill was one of the major health problems in New York City. Many homes and hospitals for the chronically ill refuse to accept cancer, tuberculosis, or mental illness cases, particularly if they occur in aged persons.

MENTAL HEALTH

The problems of mental health that occur in the later years are dramatically illustrated by reports issued by the Department of Mental Hygiene of the State of New York for the year ending March 31, 1952. Of the 15,044 first admissions to state hospitals, 6,320, or 42 per cent, were aged sixty years or over, compared with 41 per cent during the previous year. The median age increased from 52.1 to 53.4 years. The increase in the number of elderly admissions has been a noteworthy characteristic for several decades, according to this report.[2]

Interviews with key informants in this field present a fairly uniform picture of the problem of mental illness among the aged population. It is agreed that many aged persons are placed in state mental hospitals because of the lack of middle-range community facilities for their care. Mild symptoms of deterioration, such as loss of memory, forgetfulness, inappropriate behavior, which are manifestations of beginning senile processes, often lead to the institutionalization of the older person. A recent survey in California[3] similarly indicated that over one-third of the patients

[1] As of the spring of 1954.

[2] On a national level it has been estimated that while the population over sixty-five has quadrupled since 1900, persons over sixty-five admitted to mental institutions have increased tenfold.

[3] Governor's Conference on Problems of the Aging, Sacramento, California, *Proceedings*, 1951, p. 131.

aged sixty and over who were admitted to state hospitals were not psychotic and did not need the special care of a mental hospital. Another 20 per cent had such mild symptoms that they could have been cared for elsewhere if suitable facilities existed.

A number of factors contribute to the aggravation of mental health problems of an aged population in an urban area. Such processes as the onset of cerebral arteriosclerosis and the loss of faculties of hearing and vision are but part of the picture. Psychological collapse is often precipitated by the emotional stress accompanying loss of employment, death of a spouse and loved ones, isolation from community life, and an awareness of declining physical vigor.[1] Since research in social psychiatry is in its incipient stage, substantial work remains to be done in tracing the link between adverse sociological conditions affecting particular segments of the population and corresponding high incidence of emotional disorders. There is no doubt that many aged are propelled into unwholesome social environments and a high incidence of mental illness results.

The need is quite apparent for preventive measures to enable this vulnerable portion of the population to continue functioning. The fields of psychiatry, psychiatric social work, psychology, and allied professions have been unable to adapt some of their most progressive techniques, developed in the course of aiding the younger population, to meet the needs of the older group. Indeed, there is a good deal of skepticism about the ability of these professions to help older people to live within their culture with less friction and unhappiness than now occurs. It is amazing to find that little work is being done with retired aged persons to help them redirect themselves in a period of great stress. Also, very little is being done to help a very large group of widows, some of whom react badly to the death of their spouse and their own retirement from the role of homemaker. There is need for diagnoses of conditions involving psychosis, cerebral arteriosclerosis, senility, neurotic adjustment, and situationally derived distress.

---

[1] See: Stern, Karl, "Problems Encountered in an Old Age Counselling Center," 1950; and Adams, G. F., and A. T. Welford, "Some Social and Psychological Problems of Ageing," 1953.

Just as is the case with physical deterioration, incipient mental disorder, if not corrected at a proper time, can lead rapidly to the need for institutionalization.

While there are a variety of mental hygiene clinics available to all segments of the population, very few hospital outpatient departments are able to invest resources and time for psychotherapeutic work with aged patients.

Family casework agencies in New York City have developed highly professional services for dealing with maladjusted individuals in diverse counseling situations involving parent-child relationships, marital problems, and other social dislocations. While the problems of the aged have been of concern to these agencies for many years, a very small portion of their caseloads are devoted to this group. The most common use of such service as does deal with the aged involves the counseling of adult children who are concerned about living arrangements for their parents. *The elderly person very rarely presents himself to a social agency for assistance in problems of adjustment to his circumstances.* At the present time a number of family agencies in New York City are grappling with this problem and are attempting to determine ways in which the problems of the ambulatory, so-called normal aged can be handled within the framework of their agencies.[1] A good deal of community interpretation remains to be done so that older persons will understand the nature of these services and will avail themselves of them.

The experience of Dr. Alexander Leighton in attempting to set up a mental hygiene clinic in a rural area in Nova Scotia points up the kinds of barriers that may arise in attempting to expand mental hygiene facilities for the aged:

> A psychiatric clinic cannot simply "set up shop" and get to work treating patients. If it is to be effective in any sense, the staff inevitably must become concerned with local social structure because the problems appearing at the clinic must be solved in this context. . . .[2]

[1] The Community Service Society of New York has just embarked upon a program of research and evaluation of its work with the aged.

[2] Leighton, Alexander H., *The Stirling County Study:* A Research Program in Social Factors Related to Psychiatric Health. Second Annual Report, June, 1952. Ithaca, N. Y., p. 14.

Skills utilized in work with younger people in the population must be adapted to take into account the particular problems, circumstances, and sentiments of the older people involved. Otherwise, a so-called "professional definition" of the older person's problem may be far off the mark.

HOUSING AND LIVING ARRANGEMENTS

It has been estimated that 94 per cent of the aged live in non-institutional households and that at least 69 per cent live in *their own* households. Approximately 6 per cent live in institutions, and about 13 per cent of the men and 28 per cent of the women live with relatives. Nine per cent of the men and 19 per cent of the women live alone or with nonrelatives.[1] It is quite clear from these figures that our aged population dwells in the community and is not heavily institutionalized as many laymen would believe.

It appears to be generally recognized that the aged in an urban area like New York City tend more to occupy substandard housing than other elements of the population because of the lowered standard of living of many aged people.[2] Since World War II some protection has been afforded the older person by rent control legislation but relocation to better housing has not been possible for older persons, because of the continuing shortage of housing and the prohibitive rental rates of new housing. For many of the aged, this means continued living in circumstances not conducive to good health. Many elderly people live in tenement "walk-ups" despite the fact that they suffer from cardiac conditions. There is the impression also that aged people in New York City tend to occupy "Old Law" tenements constructed before the enactment of the Tenement House Act in 1901. They live in cold-water flats, railroad-type apartments, and in apartments that have outside toilet facilities. The liberalization of the (World War II) rent control law in New York State permitting

[1] Joint Committee on Railroad Retirement Legislation, *Op. cit.*, p. 31.

[2] For an estimate of national housing conditions as they apply to the aged, see American Public Health Association, Committee on the Hygiene of Housing, *Housing an Aging Population*, 1953. In addition, 1950 Census data show that a significantly greater number of persons over sixty-five who are heads of households, live in dwellings classified as dilapidated or with inadequate plumbing facilities.

landlords to increase rents in controlled housing has created a particular hardship for the aged.

If he is without housing, the recipient of Old-Age Assistance or Old-Age and Survivors Insurance benefits is very often compelled to take a furnished room. This has certain negative psychological ramifications, since many older persons desire to maintain independent apartments in which they can keep furniture and other articles with which they have lived through the years and which have sentimental value for them. Nor does living with strangers or with an extended family always come easily.[1]

Until recently, elderly persons were almost completely neglected in plans for public housing. Recently, however, a new program has been instituted to ease the situation. On November 26, 1951, the New York State Housing Commissioner announced that in the future 5 per cent of the dwelling units in each state-aided public housing project would be set aside for the aged. These facilities would be especially designed for safety and convenience. To reduce the possibility of accidents, bathrooms would have nonslip floors and square bathtubs with seats and handgrips in the walls to facilitate getting in and out of tubs; thresholds would be eliminated to lessen the danger of tripping; electric instead of gas stoves would be installed to prevent asphyxiation due to negligence. To simplify housekeeping, shelves and cabinets would be placed at low, easy-to-reach levels and windows would have "mechanical operators" for easy and safe opening and closing. Apartments would face the sunny side of the project and more heat would be provided in these apartments than in others.[2] These kinds of living arrangements are just beginning to be available to aged citizens of New York City but, unfortunately, the number of apartments is still extremely limited. It is significant, however, that such specialized housing will be incorporated in all new state-supported projects of this type. A major gap in this planning is that there is no provision for the unattached older person.

[1] See Burgess, Ernest W., "Family Living in the Later Decades," 1952.
[2] See American Institute of Architects, "Buildings for the Handicapped and/or Aged," 1952.

The older person is often insecure about his status in the community and can be intimidated to the point where he is unwilling to press complaints to rectify unwholesome housing circumstances. Because many aged persons live in substandard housing, it is necessary for law enforcement agencies to intervene more vigorously in their behalf when facilities are not kept up to par by negligent landlords.

Residential Care

It is in the field of residential care that the most creativity has been displayed by social planners. Traditionally, the social welfare community's main concern has been the provision of care for the aged in congregate homes. In New York City there are a great many homes for the aged organized along both sectarian and nonsectarian lines. There are homes for the aged sponsored by fraternal organizations, lodges, veterans groups, trade union groups, as well as homes supported by municipal agencies. Organizationally sponsored residential care facilities are desirable, since they house residents who have homogeneous background and who are, therefore, more likely to be congenial. It is universally true in New York City, however, that admission to homes is desired by more people than can be accepted. Waiting lists run from two to five years. A very important improvement in service in the past few years has been the establishment of centralized application units within the welfare federations of the three major religious groups in New York.

There is a wide range of professional practice in the various homes for the aged, some of which provide the latest in medical care, social service, rehabilitation, and recreation. At the other extreme are homes operated by lay managers, some of which provide purely custodial care with little effort to individualize their programs. These latter are in the tradition of the institutional "poor house." Among the more professionally oriented agencies, there is growing concern about the kinds of aged persons who can best use their facilities. There is increasing emphasis upon accepting physically ill people requiring a protected environment, or individuals who, because of emotional problems, cannot maintain an independent residence. The more advanced homes for the aged are showing some reluctance to accept the well, ambulatory aged. This is a reflection of the recognition that a home for the aged is perforce an abnormal setting tending to impose serious limitations on the independence of residents, thereby creating a major social dislocation. Skilled social workers are finding that the initial request for placement in a home for the aged often reflects a frantic, unrealistic attempt to meet problems that can be resolved by less drastic methods.

Several homes for the aged have embarked on new programs whereby their services are extended to those waiting for admission to the home. Persons requiring immediate counseling help, physical care, or opportunity to socialize with their contemporaries have been allowed to make use of a number of services of the home. The experience of some of these programs has been that once the aged person is given assurance that he can be taken into the home if his situation becomes difficult to cope with, he develops sufficient self-confidence to continue living outside the home for a much longer period of time. Just as the home care program of the hospitals has been a way to reduce excessive use of hospital beds, so the nonresident aid programs of homes for the aged have been a way of keeping space available in the homes for those who really need it.

Among the aged who cannot continue independent living arrangements are those who could benefit most from a noninstitutional setting. Some social agencies in New York City do provide residential care for aged individuals and couples more akin to residence living than that which a home for the aged would provide. Such establishments provide private rooms and cafeteria services while at the same time allowing the older person a wide latitude in his choice of a life routine. There is need for study of the use of such services and exploration of their modifications. There has also been a very promising trend in New York City leading to the development of foster care and boarding-home living arrangements. Both public and voluntary agencies have been experimenting along these lines. A good deal of care is required in arranging for foster home living for an older person. Just as in the case of the placement of children in foster homes, this requires a skillful matching of individual needs with a family setting congenial to him. The advantage of this kind of living is that it allows the older person to exercise considerable independence in his life regime, while concurrently affording him the protection of an agency that will supervise his living in areas he can no longer handle himself.

MISCELLANEOUS RESOURCES FOR THE AGED

Very few areas of our society are untouched by the growing social problems of the aged. For instance, the president of the Travelers Aid Society took note of the fact that more and more aged people were becoming clients of her organization:

> Compulsory retirement of men at 65 years of age, and women at 60, is forcing many aged workers to become "runaways." Upset by lack of employment and by the turmoil of modern life which adds to their insecurity, these men and women leave home and begin wandering toward where they hope they will be wanted.[1]

Similarly, groups offering free legal services are finding that aged persons are making more use of their facilities. A growing trend has been the utilization of children's summer camps for the benefit of older persons during periods just before and just after the usual vacation period when children are not using these facilities. Camping experience for the older adult is taking hold and is an example of the kind of creativity that is needed to meet the problems of the aged from various angles. Sheltered workshops are another example of good social adaptation. Recently some of these organizations have begun to think in terms of extending their services to cardiac patients as well as to other disabled segments of the population. Unfortunately, it is still difficult for an older person to receive employment in a sheltered workshop.

In the field of adult education, there is growing realization in New York that public education facilities can be adapted to those aged persons who wish to use this period of their lives for

[1] *New York Times*, May 2, 1953, p. 64.

exploration of new areas of thought and interest. There is still very little being done in the adaptation of public school facilities for the use of aged persons, but it is anticipated that the time is not far off when adult education activities for the benefit of the aged will be part of public school programs.

Noteworthy is the fact that some professions have not yet begun any kind of community activity for the benefit of aged persons in the community. In the field of dentistry, for instance, facilities are inadequate for aged persons who require dentures. Many recipients of Old-Age Assistance or beneficiaries under Old-Age and Survivors Insurance simply must forgo proper dentures inasmuch as they are so difficult to obtain. Similarly, older people have financial difficulty in securing hearing aids and eyeglasses. These facts are particularly disturbing because loss of hearing and vision and the feeling of being unsightly for the lack of teeth often lead to the older person's increased isolation from the community.[1]

CONCLUSION

As with the weather, everyone speaks about problems of the aged but few do anything about them. Many excellent recommendations have been made by a variety of state organizations for social planning for the aged and serious attempts have been made to carry out certain of these recommendations. Far more remains to be done, however, to make even a modest impact on the complex problems prevalent. There is need for planning by both public and private agencies in areas of health, hospital care, and welfare services. Ingenuity, innovation, and creativity are needed to devise new ways to meet a problem having numerous facets. Within our society are the basic ingredients to create a more wholesome atmosphere for older people. Social scientists, community planners, and practitioners in the fields of medicine, social work, political science, psychology, and others must be brought together for a coordinated approach to the total problem. The progress being made, as indicated by this report, is far below the current and anticipated needs.

[1] Recently Dr. J. H. Sheldon, the British gerontologist, suggested that glasses, hearing aids, and good shoes are of prime importance but are often overlooked.

Chapter 12

Some Programmatic
Interpretations

OUR CONSIDERATION OF THE PROBLEMS OF AGING began with the
assertion that a proper understanding of aging can best proceed
from the premise that "the aged" are not a homogeneous population. Even a casual review of the findings of this study cannot but
bring home emphatically the validity of this assertion. In this
final chapter we shall explore the ramifications of this point of
view, together with the survey results, toward enlarging the perspectives that guide community organizations and programs for
older people.

WHO ARE THE AGED?

Let us begin with an apparent contradiction. As individuals
age, particularly past the seventh decade of life, a process tending
toward greater homogeneity may be seen in which the factors
that normally differentiate a population tend to weaken in their
influence or even disappear. This development toward greater
homogeneity, however, is never fully completed. Although men
and women in their eighties tend to look and act more like one
another than is the case at earlier ages, although the retired college professor and farmer may have a similar interest in gardening, although widows and widowers have much in common, and
the well-to-do and the poor may have similar concerns over
health—with all these similarities, the process never reaches the
point at which all differences disappear.

The sixties are usually the most crucial years for the older
person. The crises he must face are manifold and have been

treated here and elsewhere.[1] During this period, physiological and psychological changes are taking place that are closely related to the individual's functioning in society. The view others take of him and his own image of himself are undergoing marked transformations. Gradually, he settles into new social roles: grandparent, retiree, widow, "the old man." Expectations of others concerning his behavior become more fixed; in turn, he develops "the characteristics of the aged."

It is the contention of the authors that although a trend toward homogeneity does in fact occur, it tends to be exaggerated by both the public at large and the professional community seeking to serve older individuals. Differences in levels of functioning are overlooked; differences in background and experiences are ignored; class and cultural values are not considered; and a host of individual problems and needs are submerged under the all-inclusive categorization of the individual as "aged." Tuckman and Lorge find that most of their subjects who are not themselves old "believe that a specific chronologic age rather than other criteria of aging determine when old age begins and a worker becomes old."[2] In a further study these writers assert:

> It is evident from this study that the use of chronologic age as a criterion of aging must be abandoned and more adequate objective criteria developed if the erroneous notions and stereotypes about old people and the older worker are to be broken down.[3]

Exactly the same type of definition based on chronologic age may be found in regard to adolescence, however inadequate it may be.

In regard to community services for the aged, Brunot wrote:

> The first requisite to a more intelligent and humane community program of services aimed to benefit aged persons is a recognition of their individuality as persons. No program based on the implied or

[1] See: Havighurst, Robert J., and Ruth Albrecht, *Older People*, 1953; Cavan, Ruth S., and others, *Personal Adjustment in Old Age*, 1949; Tibbitts, Clark, editor, "Social Contribution by the Aging," 1952.

[2] Tuckman, Jacob, and Irving Lorge, "When Does Old Age Begin and a Worker Become Old?" *Journal of Gerontology*, vol. 8, October, 1953, p. 488.

[3] *Ibid*, " 'When Aging Begins' and Stereotypes About Aging," p. 491.

explicit assumption that all persons over the age of 60 are alike in personality, problems or needs, can possibly contribute effectively in service to the half million aged members of our community.[1]

Older people must be differentiated both as individuals and members of particular groups from which they derive certain attitudes, values, beliefs, customs, and modes of behavior. An understanding of class membership, sex roles, cultural origins, familial structures, living standards, and the like can only provide the background for a more thorough understanding of the individual. Certainly, attempts to understand a particular child or adolescent based solely upon a comprehension of "childhood" or "adolescence" would be shallow indeed. To understand "old people"—and this is a more complex task than has been generally recognized—is only a beginning. Community services for the aged must eventually come to grips with the individual himself. The test of their usefulness will not reside solely in the number served but also in the degree to which the services rendered reached the "total person," complete with strivings, needs, motives, attitudes, and individualized problems.

NO COMMUNITY SERVICES FOR SOME?

No agency or institution expects its facilities to be deluged with requests for service, although over a period of many years it may serve the vast majority of the populace at some time. The simple fact is that not everyone is in need of service. So, too, with the aged. In reciting the list of critical situations he will face as he gets older, we may think that, surely, every old person will soon be rapping at the doors of all available professional services. In fact, it would appear that it is a minority who use community services at all. Those with acute or chronic complaints, whether of a social or medical nature, use the services available to all again and again.[2] Aside, however, from those who might be benefited by attendance at a health or social welfare center, many

[1] Brunot, Helen H., *Old Age in New York City*. Welfare Council of New York City, 1944, p. 124.

[2] See Buell, Bradley, *Community Planning for Human Services*. Columbia University Press, New York, 1952.

older people manage to cope with and adjust to adverse conditions without resort to professional aid. The authors would venture the opinion that if such personal abilities were not available, increase in the use of current professional facilities for the aged would inundate every agency.

We expressed the view in Chapter 8 that older people, particularly those in the lower socioeconomic group, seem to be able to adapt to adversity. It is to be remembered that in this study we are dealing with a population, 70 per cent of which migrated to this country and survived wars, depressions, and other hazards to live past their sixtieth birthday. Undoubtedly, most of our group have struggled through their lives meeting and enduring a variety of hardships. In one way or another they adapted to these hardships. While the adjustment level of those of lower status is relatively poor, it is to their credit that so many were able to cope successfully with their problems. Service planning for the aged must bear in mind two "guiding principles":

1. Many people are able to rise to the challenge of aging and to adjust, despite great difficulties.
2. The aged cannot be treated as a homogeneous, undifferentiated population.

In the remainder of this chapter, we shall attempt to point out the kinds of services that appear to be needed, with attention given also to what we have learned from our sample of older people. The recommendations do not necessarily call for the establishment of new agencies or new institutions. In many instances, some kind of programmatic modification would meet the need.

WITH REGARD TO HEALTH

It is evident from the present study that a more precise definition of those segments of the population to be served is required if those most in need are to respond. In Chapter 10 we saw that willingness to use community health services was dependent upon a number of factors, the most fundamental of which were the social and economic status of the individual, his state of health, and the degree of his social isolation. Considering the various rationalizations that are created by the high status person to maintain the illusion of youth, programs in the health field for those people should emphasize less "noxious" health practices, such as a thorough routine checkup by a private physician or health clinic. On the basis of the discrepancy between actual and estimated health ratings, it may be predicted with some degree of certainty that delay in seeking medical care in this group would be fairly common. Hence, regular examinations would note the presence of existing or potential health dangers without arousing undue anxiety.

Among people of low status, the most pressing problems in the field of health are to make inroads into the belief that it is illegitimate to visit a physician except when one is ill, to make contact with the social isolate, and to provide both advisory and treatment services in age-specialized as well as in nonspecialized settings. The experience of the Adult Counseling Services of New York City seems to be that initial resistance to medical examinations can be overcome if the medical service forms part of a more general attempt to give casework or psychological guidance to the person. Health examinations are often the acceptable springboard from which counseling can start. It may be that latent anxiety about health among older people makes medical care a problem. Our evidence makes it apparent that no one type of medical facility will be adequate to serve the needs of all older people requiring care. Some feel a specialized or geriatric service is more likely to take greater pains with them because of their age. Others feel a geriatric service classifies them and this stigmatizes them as a group with which they do not closely identify.

There is some evidence presented here that it may be the "neighborhood" character of a service that will attract older people. Considerable numbers of our sample gave as their reason for older people not using nearby recreation centers the fact that people do not like to go alone or be among strangers. Since recreational facilities are often created to serve particular communities or neighborhoods of large urban centers, it would seem logical that medical facilities that are part of indigenous neighborhood services would prove popular. The local district health center, recreation service, or day center as well as welfare and casework agencies might experiment with medical services. Particularly in areas in which homogeneous ethnic groups are definable by neighborhoods, the local nature of the service under auspices of leading citizens, nationality or religious groups are more likely to be successful than would generalized and less personal services. In responding to the question of which hospital they would select if it became necessary, the majority indicated the hospital with which they were most familiar. Either it was in the neighborhood or the individual had used it previously. Little attention was paid to such factors as the strength of different medical services, diagnostic or therapeutic facilities, or even the reputation of the institution.

We have noted in this study the great impact of poor health upon individual adjustment. The great challenge to medical and welfare services for the aged is to reduce the gap between individual apathy and professional reluctance, on the one hand, and the high incidence of chronic diseases, enforced retirement, and institutionalization, on the other, brought on by these conditions. The major problem is to have all services remove the individual at least one step from his present status: systematic therapeutic care for the hospitalized chronically ill person to reduce the custodial inpatient population; outpatient care or protected homes for the ill as dictated by the degree and nature of illness; boarding or foster home care for the person in homes for the aged; independent living arrangements for those "on placement" or being rehabilitated; and preventive medical, social, and psychological service for the ambulatory well older person with or without "problems." A periodic revaluation of each person's situation may reveal sources of progress as well as stagnation in the services rendered.

There is a vast field for varied efforts in the field of preventive and rehabilitative medicine for older people. There is a need for centers where elderly people can receive an assessment of their health status. As suggested by a recent California report[1] these

[1] Governor's Conference on the Problems of the Aging, Sacramento, California, *Proceedings*, 1951.

centers can be located at existing inpatient or outpatient departments of hospitals, private medical clinics, at health departments,
or within industrial medical services. In New York City such
centers could be located within the municipal Health Department, which has already had successful experience operating
cancer detection units. Such an assessment setting would require
the use of skilled staff members, that is, physicians, nurses, social
workers, psychiatrists, and psychologists to ascertain potential
areas of trouble in the older person. Early detection of serious
problems could be useful to physicians, social agencies, and those
community organizations concerned with helping the aged.

The problem of the aged as faced by hospitals is, indeed, a very
complex and serious one. A citywide planning commission bringing together voluntary and governmental services would be a
step toward evaluating problems and responsibilities for the care
of an aging population. The development of piecemeal services
for the chronically ill has long been viewed by social planners as
inadequate to meet the overall need.

There is need for research-oriented medical services in which
the individual can receive comprehensive treatment in dealing
both with specific diseases and with such conditions as are faced
by retirees, widows, and others for whom aging is a critical
occurrence.[1]

There is need for the development of standard home care and
homemaking services by a variety of agencies. Included among
such needed services are experiments in the social and psychological rehabilitation of bedbound and homebound patients. Restrictions on professional consultation and guidance to the ambulatory aged have limited the possibility of restoring these
immobilized older persons to useful activity.

There is also a great need for a medically oriented setting to
help establish retirement practices on the basis of the individual's
capacity to continue gainful employment. Industry requires assessment centers of this kind, quite aside from scientific studies of
employability criteria.

[1] See Shock, Nathan W., *Trends in Gerontology*, 1951.

MENTAL HEALTH

In the previous chapter we noted the disproportionately high admissions of elderly patients to mental hospitals. We took note also that many aged individuals, though not exhibiting behavior that would demand hospitalization, are institutionalized nevertheless for lack of any middle-range services that are prepared and/or equipped to be of assistance. From the standpoint of mental health, the aging are a vulnerable group but, partly because of the great general demand upon mental health facilities, there is less done in the way of preventive and therapeutic work among the aged than among other age groups.

Experimental services which locate early problems of emotional disturbance among older people are sorely needed in the New York City community. A service that will provide early diagnosis and referral of aged persons to long-range treatment facilities would be useful in cutting down the number of admissions to mental hospitals.

A systematic campaign must be carried on to open the doors of mental hygiene clinics associated with hospitals so that preventive psychiatric treatment can be made available to older persons.

There is a need for less drastic solutions for the care of the senile aged who, currently, are being institutionalized in state mental hospitals.[1] Residential care in protected settings or in foster homes remains to be explored to a far greater degree as possible alternatives.

It might prove worthwhile for family casework agencies to conduct vigorous public relations campaigns to encourage aged persons with deep-seated personal problems to make use of their services. Help with problems of retirement, widowhood, marital relations, relationships with adult children should be included among the services within the province of such agencies.

Greater use of clinical psychologists by health and welfare institutions to detect the early stages of senility and behavioral disturbances is also now to be highly recommended.

[1] See Group for the Advancement of Psychiatry, *The Problem of the Aged Patient in the Public Psychiatric Hospital*, 1950.

RESTORING SOCIAL ROLES: THE EMPLOYMENT PROBLEM

The significance of a meaningful and useful life role has been amply demonstrated in our findings. The person who has nothing to occupy himself and his time is faced with a situation conducive to mental disorders. He wants to be recognized, to feel achievement, to be needed and valued, to receive affection. An individual's sense of worth, his personal dignity, is dependent in large measure upon the importance of his social roles. To those faced with the responsibilities of marriage, child-rearing, or simply of making a living, the prospect of not having something useful to do is remote indeed. If a person is thrown out of work by hard times, he tends to blame himself for not having enough foresight, intelligence, or ability to keep a job. He suffers from a loss of self-respect and feels himself socially inadequate. Employment restores his dignity, strengthens his belief in himself, and reclaims a useful role for himself in society. The situation of the older retired or unemployed person illustrates our point. Our respondents do not give age, declining efficiency, or incompetence as the reasons for their present status. Health or the retirement age was the cause of retirement. It is of first importance to know how many of those retired (though their terminal average wage was under $40 per week) and those still working were or are very satisfied with their jobs. To hold a position past sixty signifies the individual's skill, experience, wisdom, or indispensability. For this reason, the economic practices that ban employment past a given age require drastic revision, or perhaps should be abolished entirely. It will be recalled that voluntary retirement usually occurs about the age of seventy. Even if economic pressures require mandatory retirement, it would appear that the age should be advanced at least five years in the interests of the social and emotional health of the older population.

Program-wise, because of the vital role of employment in the adjustment of single people, retirees, and the widowed, new explorations are badly needed into such areas as: gradual retirement, retiree workshops in unused portions of industrial plants, state-sponsored retail outlets, sheltered workshops, and part-time positions at jobs the person might not have considered in his earlier days. In addition, both private and public sponsorship is required for the vocational retraining of the able older worker for jobs commensurate with his ability. Up to this time, vocational rehabilitation is provided only for persons salvageable for the labor market following handicapping accident or illness. Employment opportunities through retraining for capable older persons should be provided where industry has closed its doors to their regular jobs.

Vocational guidance and vocational training services must work hand in hand with employment agencies to place older workers. Ingenuity of the highest order is required to remove the negative stereotypes of older workers from the public mind as well as to ease the path to reemployment.[1]

Those who have examined the proceedings of the Arden House Conference on Criteria for Retirement[2] and have studied the results of this and other researches on aging cannot but conclude that voluntary, prepared retirement should replace arbitrary age requirements for the termination of employment. Externally imposed role transformations are normally resisted. In the case of the older person, particularly the individual who faces a life situation that does not offer a productive, routinized, and ego-satisfying substitute for employment, retirement or unemployment or the threat of these is as devastating to his self-image and social adjustment as would be a mandatory rule that he change sexes at a given age. Particularly for the male provider, who is often so closely identified with his job, employment offers an anchorage. A carpenter who retires is a "retired carpenter," not simply a retired man. His occupation is his identity.[3] The preeminent position of the need for adequate, role-saving, and gratifying work for those who can do even part of a day's labor

---

[1] See Breckinridge, Elizabeth L., *Effective Use of Older Workers*, 1953. Also, for an account of an interesting study of problems connected with the employment of older workers, see Welfare Council of Metropolitan Chicago, *Community Services for Older People*, 1952.

[2] Mathiasen, Geneva, editor, *Criteria for Retirement*, 1953.

[3] In this connection, it is noteworthy that baby sitting, the restoration of a familiar role, is becoming widely adopted as a legitimate part-time occupation for older widows or retired women who no longer have family responsibilities of their own.

should place employment planning and services at the top of the priority list of community undertakings.

There is a need for agencies devoted to securing part-time employment for older workers. Most agencies do not attempt to find a part-time job for individuals. One agency, sponsored by a philanthropic organization, has recently begun to touch this need. This is a service especially needed by those individuals receiving Old-Age and Survivors Insurance under our Social Security system. Many recipients of OASI benefits find it necessary to secure work providing additional income in amounts not exceeding the ceiling on current income specified as a condition for continued eligibility.

For widowed women, there is a need for a service that will provide occasional jobs, such as baby sitting, serving as companions for bed-ridden persons, and occasional light housekeeping tasks. Many widows have never been in the labor force and have never acquired skills in any other line.[1] These kinds of jobs frequently coincide with their experience as homemakers.

There is need for more employment agencies which will be able to pursue aggressively the problem of ferreting out jobs for older workers. A good deal of community contact work is necessary for this. A selling job has to be carried on to overcome the resistance that exists in many industries regarding the hiring of older workers.

There is a need for miscellaneous organizations which will utilize the business and crafts skills of older persons. There is ample opportunity in New York City for the organization of cooperatives in which the skills of experienced individuals along many lines can be organized. There is also a potentially useful place for craftshops where the products of older people can be put on public sale.

Social agencies and health organizations can help older workers obtain jobs by providing services that will enable the older worker to take stock of his skills as well as his health status. Potential employers need help to obtain adequate pictures of

---

[1] For problems of older women attempting to enter the labor force, see Miller, Frieda S., "Older Workers and Older Women," 1951.

what jobs in their plants are medically suitable or can be adapted for older people[1] and what positions would be best handled by a younger person. There are few resources for making such estimates at the present time.

FINANCIAL PROBLEMS

Another problem that is interrelated with employment status in old age is that of income maintenance. Loss or reduction of employment, whatever the reason, is accompanied by reduced income for most people. If accompanied by poor health, the problem becomes even more vexing. Adjustment to reduced income is not simply a matter of adjustment to a material change in living standards, for psychological factors are also involved in the adjustive process. The individual's sense of self-esteem is intimately tied to the life image of himself that he bears. A marked change in a personal way of life may be so painful to accept that serious personality disturbances ensue. Efforts to mitigate economic insecurity in the later years are, accordingly, of great importance in enhancing adjustment in old age. From the long range point of view, it is important now to plan ways and means of providing for adequate income in old age to forestall individual as well as community dislocations in the future.

Current benefits under Old-Age and Survivors Insurance and Old-Age Assistance are grossly inadequate. These need to be raised by legislative action. Widowed women under the age of sixty-five should be made eligible for survivors' benefits if they are not employable. As now constituted, OASI recipients are denied survivor's benefits until they reach the age of sixty-five.

Expansion of private pension planning in industry seems to be much needed.

Modification of eligibility requirements for public assistance seems to be in order. Legal requirements that compel parents to seek financial support from adult children by instituting court action against them should be liberalized to take into account individual family problems.

[1] See Abrams, Albert J., "Job Engineering and Job Re-assignment for the Older Worker in American Industry," 1954.

Public welfare workers require further training as to the social and psychological aspects of applications for Old-Age Assistance as well as those involving eligibility. The painful experiences encountered by older people approaching public assistance agencies can be ameliorated by sound social work practices. The work of the social investigator is a difficult one; yet he can help the older person find stability in later years. As one recent report stated:

> The public assistance worker not only performs the social work function of bringing economic benefits to those who need them but also, in the process of doing so, brings reassurance and support to those he serves. . . . But it seems a fairly safe assumption that for most people in our traditionally self-reliant culture the recognition and confession of need for public aid generates anxiety and related uncomfortable feelings. The public assistance worker, by the very reason of his official status, can do much to allay this anxiety.[1]

HOUSING

As we have suggested earlier, some older persons apparently prefer to maintain an independent residence; others probably find that some type of communal living more adequately fills their particular needs. Whatever the choice may be, there is an opportunity for creative planning in the area of housing the aged, particularly in the case of noninstitutionalized accommodations. As the planning and construction of new buildings under public and private auspices continue, it would not be amiss to take into consideration the needs of some portions of the older population for whom special problems exist.

There is need for rapid expansion of public housing facilities to meet the needs of single aged persons of low income and of couples who cannot obtain suitable apartments because of the continuing housing shortage. Small units in low cost cooperative developments could be provided by organizations such as lodges, trade unions, fraternal orders, civic organizations to meet the needs of those aged individuals who have income from pensions

[1] Wickenden, Elizabeth, *The Needs of Older People, and Public Welfare Services to Meet Them.* American Public Welfare Association, Chicago, 1953, p. 68.

and social security adequate to enable investment in such co-operatives. The Upholsterers' International Union of the American Federation of Labor recently developed plans to build a $5,000,000 village in Florida for their retiring members; pensioners will be able to obtain cottages for rentals between $42 and $50 per month. While such a program gives promise of work that can be done along these lines, it does not necessarily mean that whole communities for the aged need be set up. To be given serious consideration is the fact that such an arrangement tends to segregate and isolate the aged from their younger contemporaries. It is yet to be demonstrated that age separation is sufficiently acceptable to older people themselves to warrant the promulgation of "retirement cities."

For that large group of aged residing in substandard tenement housing in New York City, there is need for a concerted drive on the part of the City Department of Buildings and Housing to ensure that facilities such as heat, hot water, garbage disposal, lighting, and maintenance of hallways are kept up to at least minimum standard. There is need for the involvement of community organizations to intercede on the behalf of aged persons who are suffering as a result of neglect by landlords.

There is room in New York City for the development of a housing bureau which will make available to aged persons information concerning available furnished rooms and apartments. There is need for an investigation of facilities of this kind for older people by a central housing resource which will assure them minimum protection.

Continued expansion is desirable of middle-range facilities such as residences, hotel-type facilities, foster homes, and boarding homes to meet the needs of aged persons who cannot continue living alone in the community but who, nevertheless, need not enter homes for the aged.

There is need in the field of homes for the aged to clarify admissions policies regarding the kind of person who could best use a home for the aged. There is a tendency even in the most advanced types of homes for the aged to accept people who, with outside support, can continue living in the community.

Finally, there is needed in the community a diagnostic service that will aid aged persons and their adult children to make decisions about suitable living arrangements based on a thorough physical and psychological evaluation of the older person's condition.

LEISURE-TIME ACTIVITY PROGRAMS: NECESSITIES OR DIVERSIONS

Based upon the findings of the study and also upon direct observation of a variety of recreational or activity centers and "clubs" for older people, two major interpretations follow.

First, for some older people, notably those who are socially isolated, whose central life role has terminated (for example, widowed housewives or retired people) and who are socially dependent, activity programs not only would provide interesting leisure-time activities but also would be essential to sustain or restore interest in life itself.

Second, for a considerable number of others, activity programs are recreational and diversionary. The individual does not root his existence in them, nor is he void of other pursuits that claim his time and energy. It is the *raison d'etre* of countless fraternal societies, athletic clubs, church organizations, and the like. It provides an escape from boredom or burdensome personal problems, an opportunity to do something different and have new experiences, a chance to meet others, to "socialize," to exchange small talk, to be involved in diversionary projects that excite latent interests or dormant talents.

Recognition of these two types of need patterns will go far to dispel the illusion that activity programs "create" adjustment, an allegation not borne out by our findings. In the case of the first type of service indicated above, casework and psychological or psychiatric facilities coupled with activity programs would go further to restore unity to the individual's life so that he does not remain abjectly dependent upon the synthetic values involved in being busy "doin' nothin'." Perhaps programs that produce salable or utilitarian commodities would enhance the process of restoring ego strength to these people.

In the second type of service—the diversionary—great value may be had in permitting the individual to indulge his fancies, do as he pleases, and create for personal pleasure. There is room for personal development for everyone, and if in the process the satisfactions derived are psychologically hygienic or if the individual discovers a flair for some activity that will prove useful as he becomes older, these programs will have more than justified themselves.

The location and age composition of social or recreational services should be guided by the knowledge that resistance to one or the other is high and that diversified resources of both types are required. Localization to the familiar within the neighborhood would seem most appropriate.

There is a need for the development of recreational programs within settings that are very familiar to the aged person and from which he tends to be somewhat isolated as he grows older. Trade unions might well adapt their meeting halls to serve also as centers for their retired members. This would afford the older person contact with younger members of the union as well as give him a familiar setting to which he could go.

Churches could open up their meeting-place facilities for their older members at times that did not conflict with other church affairs. Day care center facilities in a church setting would provide the natural setting for older people to meet socially. Ethnic organizations could do likewise in their meeting halls. Similarly, veterans organizations could adapt their meeting halls to the needs of their World War I members who are now nearing or past retirement age. Recreation that takes place in a setting in which the older person has actively participated through the middle years is easier to come to than one that is located in a setting completely alien to him. Numbers of older people when approached as to why they do not participate in day centers in their area have given as a reason the fact that they do not wish to be a stranger in a group. This is an understandable sentiment. The use of indigenous neighborhood or local community facilities would serve to minimize this source of resistance.

Recreational activities for aged individuals along interest lines are also in order. It is notable that many aged individuals join such cultish groups as those interested in vegetarianism, occult science and astrology, as well as the more familiar hobby clubs, discussion or music groups, because joining a group around an interest seems easier than joining for the avowed purpose of seeking social companionship. Focusing group activities on special interests such as carpentry, crafts, astronomy, or stamp collecting would appeal to those aged persons having special skills, knowledge, or interests. Others requiring a more rounded kind of social experience, however, may not be happy in joining such activity programs. Some studies have shown that older people who have affiliations that bring them into contact with others seem better adjusted than those who are socially isolated.[1] If individuals can be brought into contact with one another around a common interest, at least they will have the opportunity to pursue their interest in an atmosphere conducive to social exchange.

Political clubs, trade unions, literary societies, and similar groups might develop programs within their overall operations that could be carried on by retired and widowed individuals. Trade unions could use the retired members to conduct classes in the history of the unions, to run consumer services, and to help administer buildings. Political organizations can use older individuals to edit newspapers, plan meetings, and manage fundraising affairs. There is ample room for involving retired individuals in nonremunerative but nevertheless socially useful activity.

Such media of communications as television and radio should be utilized to stimulate older individuals into more creative activity. Just as there are programs geared to the needs of housewives, children of preschool age, adolescents, there is no reason why programs should not be produced which would open up new interests on the part of the retired, the widowed, and the aged generally.

COUNSELING AND GUIDANCE

This study was undertaken as a survey of problems and resources in the field of aging. As we have wound our way through

[1] See: Pressey, S. L., and Elizabeth M. Simcoe, "Case Study Comparisons of Successful and Problem Old People," 1950; and Albrecht, Ruth, "Social Roles in the Prevention of Senility," 1951.

the complex interrelations of health and social status, self-image, attitudes toward aging, and so forth, we gradually narrowed our focus to certain individual instances of definable problems. In the last analysis, it is the individual older person with whom we are concerned, although we need much information concerning the frequency of his problems or patterns of adjustment in the aged population at large.

Community services, although mindful of the general problems of the aged, must deal with the individual and the special significance to him of what may be a general problem. It is relatively rare, however, to find service agencies dealing directly with the older person and his problems. Many such services form part of the general orientation of family casework services where the focus is on conflicted family situations involving older people. Occasionally, one finds an agency devoting part of its time in long-term psychiatric or mental hygiene work with complex personality problems of older people.

It would appear, from an examination of the types of adjustment problems faced by older people that there is great need for consultation or guidance centers. Two main interrelated varieties of factors lead to this conclusion. The first is the fact of societal "insults" to the aged,[1] such as loss of status and roles. The individual interprets his problem, however, not as a matter of status or of feelings of deprivation but as the need for a job, better living arrangements, or increased financial support. Hence, some means must be found to help the individual face frankly the realities of aging and to choose an intelligent course of conduct to follow. Moreover, in those instances where mere counseling fails because the individual's ability to sustain a proper or an independent course of action is impaired, some types of intervention may be required to guide him along the indicated path. Professional counseling for the aged should involve a multiplicity of interlocking services—medical, social work, psychological, public health, and psychiatric—to provide a broad base for making

[1] Developed by Havighurst and Albrecht; see Havighurst, Robert J., and Ruth Albrecht, *Older People*, 1953. See also Havighurst, Robert J., "Social and Psychological Needs of the Aging," 1952.

decisions concerning individual cases. This does not necessarily mean that broad new facilities need be developed or that years of special training would be required, but that present services and professional skills should be adapted to meet the requirements of the aged.

Although it runs counter to established professional practices, some consideration should be given to sustaining long-range supportive professional contacts with older people whose dependency needs may be so great that attempts to give strength to the ego through a therapeutic relationship prove fruitless. Such supportive relationships encourage dependency but, considering the relatively hopeless dependent needs suffered by some isolated and friendless old people, a portion of professional time might usefully be spent in indulging them.

Our data concerning the depressed morale of friendless lower status people would suggest that group counseling or group therapy programs would be very helpful as supportive or therapeutic measures.

It would seem from the survey of professional services and from the study of the sample that counseling services embedded in the context of local civic clubs, fraternal orders, churches, and recreational centers should prove highly effective. This is not to imply that centralized services should not be attempted. On the contrary, central services that provide multi-disciplinary functions should also prove to be successful in serving older people.

The question of age-specialized versus general services cannot be simply solved. On all questions dealing with a choice of one or the other type of service, a considerable divergence of opinion and feelings appears. Both types of service centers are required to serve those who would reject a program if one or the other repels him.

The suggestions made here are not meant to be a comprehensive program of planning for the aged. Rather, they are cited as examples of ways in which a community, on a groundwork of study, can plan ways of assisting its older members either through modification of present services or through experimentation with and inauguration of new services. The specifics of plans and actions undertaken by any given community will depend, of course, on what unique needs are discovered and what resources are available.

There have been three thoughts implicit in all these suggestions. One is that community services must be *planned* if optimal effectiveness is to be achieved. Second, services must reach the *whole individual*. The individual should not be compartmentalized into "problems," nor should the individual be lost in the mass of the group. Third, the older individual can, with help, cope with his problems. The day is long past when services for the aged can be considered exclusively in terms of homes for the aged (or in *any* exclusive term, for that matter). A great number, perhaps the vast majority of the aged, are not so much in need of *care* as in need of help in caring for themselves, and this should be an important goal for services. All these concepts are well-known and entirely familiar to welfare and health planners and practitioners, but because of their importance they bear repetition.

SOCIAL SCIENCE AND SOCIAL ACTION

It has been an implicit hope in preparing this report to convey the close working relationship between social scientific research and its application in a field of social action. While the present study involves a survey of a community problem through examination of a special population segment and the resources serving them, adaptation or variations of the social research methods employed can be directed toward a host of problems related to the development or the study of programs and services. Basic research into the problems of aging is continuing to be the subject of careful study. At the same time, practical action programs are developing nationwide. Many social scientists concerned with "action research" stand ready to lend theoretical as well as practical guidance and to conduct research as well as evaluate ongoing programs. Social research as a tool in the hands of practitioners can lend great weight to decisions concerning proper courses of action in the development, modification, and evaluation of services and programs not only in the field of aging but wherever and for whomever services are being rendered.

APPENDICES

Appendix 1

Sampling Procedure

A MINIMUM AGE OF SIXTY YEARS was fixed for purposes of the survey, since it was felt that both objectively and subjectively old age might be said to commence during the seventh decade of life. The sample was drawn so that its sex distribution would reflect the known proportions of men and women over sixty in the population. Since it was expected that the proposed service would be used more by people of relatively low socioeconomic status than of middle or high status, it was decided to draw 60 per cent of the sample from the low group, 30 per cent from the middle, and 10 per cent from the high status group. The sample, therefore, does not follow the actual socioeconomic status distribution in the population of the Kips Bay-Yorkville Health District.

In order to derive a population sample meeting the criteria set out, the preliminary problem was to divide the total area into socioeconomic subdistricts. There are, in Kips Bay-Yorkville, 409 city blocks, 50 of which are nonresidential. There remain, therefore, 359 blocks from which a sample may be selected. By rental groups the blocks may be divided as follows:

TABLE A

Rental group	Average rent per month	Number of blocks	Per cent
A	$170 and over	68	19
B	90 to $169	87	24
C	40 to 89	117	33
D	30 to 39	57	16
E	20 to 29	30	8

267

It may be noted from the table above that the proportion of high rental blocks (Groups A and B) is far greater in the District than the proportion desired for sampling purposes. Similarly, there are proportionately fewer lower socioeconomic status blocks. It was decided, therefore, that sampling in the A and B blocks would be proportionately restricted and that sampling in D and E blocks would be intensive. However, inasmuch as the population concentrations in D and E blocks are heavy, any sample blocks selected in that area would yield considerably larger numbers of aged respondents than would similar numbers in the A and B districts. That this supposition was correct may be seen from the following table which indicates the numbers of blocks selected for the sample in each of the five average rental groups together with the proportions of subjects desired from each rental group. For purposes of the selection of sample blocks, rental Groups A and B were considered to be the high socioeconomic group, C the middle socioeconomic group, and rental groups D and E the low socioeconomic group.

TABLE B

Rental group	Number of sample blocks required	Number of respondents
High (A, B)	16	55
Middle (C)	18	148
Low (D, E)	19	297

Thus, it required but one more block to obtain 297 low status respondents than to obtain 148 middle status respondents, and but three more blocks than to obtain only 55 high status respondents. These results reflect, in part, the greater difficulty in obtaining middle and high status respondents.

In order to obtain as random a group of aged respondents as would be possible after deliberately restricting the socioeconomic status proportions of the sample, a random number method for selection of sample blocks was followed.

To obtain our 500 respondents only the initial 53 sample blocks were used and the following procedure employed. Starting at a specified point on each sample block, every household was counted and every seventh household listed in advance of the interview. Households adjoining the listed seventh household were also listed as alternates and were utilized for sampling purposes when the seventh household member was not available or not eligible. All necessary information for the selection of the respondent was obtained during this listing procedure, and where possible the permission was obtained of each person over the age of sixty to arrange for an appointment for an interviewer. In households having more than one person sixty years of age or over, the respondent was selected by randomization from an age-ordered list of eligible persons in the household.

Altogether, contacts were made with 665 persons over the age of sixty. Of this number, 165 refused outright to be interviewed, agreed to be interviewed but refused at the scheduled time of the appointment, or could not be found or had died subsequent to the original contact. As seen in the following table, the refusal rate was highest in the upper socioeconomic group and declined with socioeconomic status.

TABLE C

Socioeconomic status	Number of contacts	Number interviewed	Refusal rate—percentage
High	81	55	32
Middle	208	148	29
Low	376	297	21

Appendix 2

Field Survey Questionnaire

To CONSERVE SPACE, the format of the interview schedule has been altered here. As actually used, each question was followed by the relevant response categories and an IBM code, and the interviewer's task was to circle the appropriate code for the response made. Precoding of questions is not shown here except in cases where the response categories are not self-evident. Similarly, charts and spaces provided for the interviewer to record responses to uncoded questions are not shown. Material printed in upper case represents instructions to the interviewer or codes which were not to be read aloud to the respondent.

INTERVIEWER CODE:⎯⎯⎯⎯⎯⎯⎯⎯⎯

DATE OF INTERVIEW:⎯⎯⎯⎯⎯⎯⎯⎯

COMMUNITY STUDY: KIPS BAY-YORKVILLE
NOVEMBER 1952

R'S ADDRESS:⎯⎯⎯⎯⎯⎯⎯⎯⎯⎯⎯⎯⎯⎯⎯⎯⎯⎯⎯⎯⎯

APARTMENT NUMBER:⎯⎯⎯⎯⎯⎯⎯   FLOOR:⎯⎯⎯⎯⎯⎯

RECORD OF CALLS AND CALLBACKS

CALLS	DATE AND TIME OF EACH CALL	WHAT HAPPENED
I		
2		
3		
4		
5		
6		

HOUSEHOLD COMPOSITION

NAME OR IDENTIFICATION *	SEX	AGE	NO. FROM OLDEST TO YOUNGEST	RELATION † TO R
1				
2				
3				
4				
5				
6				
7				
8				

* Circle R's number. If more than 1 person in the household is 60 or over, select respondent indicated on card.

† Write "H" beside relationship of head of house.

1. We'd like to know how you feel about living here in New York. How good or bad would you say New York is as a place to live? Would you say very good, fairly good, not so good, or very bad?

2. Now, how about this neighborhood? Do you like it very much, fairly much, not so much, or not at all?

3A. How long have you been living in this apartment (house)?
_____ or _____
YEARS   MONTHS

B. Is this your own apartment (home) or do you rent here?
_____ RENTED APARTMENT
_____ FURNISHED ROOM
_____ ROOM IN NON-RELATIVE'S HOUSE
_____ ROOM IN RELATIVE'S HOUSE
_____ OWN COOP. APARTMENT
_____ HOTEL ROOM
_____ RESIDENCE CLUB
_____ BOARDING HOUSE
_____ OTHER: _____

4A. Would you tell me who is living in the household with you?
(CHECK AGAINST FACE SHEET, FILLING IN AS REQUIRED.)

B. What is your age? (CHECK AGAINST FACE SHEET)

C. Are you now single? married? widowed? divorced? separated?
(CIRCLE ONE)

_____ SINGLE (NEVER MARRIED)   (ASK Q. 5)

_____ MARRIED:

How old is your husband (wife)?_____YEARS

Is this your first marriage?

_____YES (SKIP TO Q. 6)

_____NO: How long have you been married this
time? _____ YEARS (SKIP TO Q. 6)

_____ WIDOWED: How long have you been widowed?

_____ YEARS (ASK Q. 5)

_____ DIVORCED: How long have you been divorced?

_____ YEARS (ASK Q. 5)

_____ SEPARATED: How long have you been separated?

_____ YEARS (SKIP TO Q. 6)

5.   (OMIT THIS QUESTION FOR THOSE WHO ARE NOW MARRIED) Do you
think you might like to marry (again)?

6.   (OMIT THIS QUESTION FOR THOSE WHO HAVE NEVER BEEN MARRIED.
IF R HAS BEEN MARRIED MORE THAN ONCE, ASK ABOUT PRESENT
MARRIAGE). If you were asked to rate your (present) marriage as
to happiness, would you say it was happier than most other
marriages, or not so happy as most?

_____ HAPPIER

_____ SAME

_____ NOT SO HAPPY

_____ DK

Now we'd like to ask you some questions about your health.

7.   Concerning your health *now*, would you say your health is excellent, good, fair, poor, or very poor?

8.   Would you say it has been the same over the past five years? Has
it been getting better? Or has it been getting worse?

9.   Do you think your health is better or worse than that of other
people your age? (CHECK ONE)

_____ BETTER

_____ WORSE

_____ SAME

10A. Is there any particular physical or health problem that bothers you at present?

_____ NO (SKIP TO Q. 11)

_____ YES: B. What is the trouble?

C. How long ago did it start?

		YES	NO
IF R VOLUNTEERS	D. Is it being taken care of by a doctor?	YES	NO
MORE THAN ONE	E. Does it keep you in the house?	"	"
HEALTH PROBLEM,	F. Does it keep you from doing things?	"	"
ENTER RESPONSES	G. Does it keep you from seeing people?	"	"
AT END OF MEDI-	H. Does it keep you from your work?	"	"
CAL CHART	I. How long has it kept you in bed (during the past year)?		

_____ or _____ or _____
MONTHS   WEEKS   DAYS

11. ASK EACH QUESTION APPEARING IN THE MEDICAL CHART BELOW. FOR EACH HEALTH PROBLEM WHICH THE RESPONDENT SAYS BOTHERS HIM, ASK FOLLOW-UP PROBES I, II, III, IV.

I. How long ago did it start?

II. Is (was) it taken care of by a doctor?

III. Does it keep you: A. in the house?

B. from doing things?

C. from seeing people?

D. from your work?

IV. How long has it kept you in bed during the past year?

ASK EACH OF THESE QUESTIONS:

a) Do you have any trouble with your teeth?

_____ all or most missing

_____ false teeth

_____ OTHER

b) Are you hard of hearing?

c) Is your sight bad enough to keep you from reading?

d) Do you have cataracts?

e) Do you have glaucoma?

f) Do you have asthma?

g) Do you have heart trouble? IF YES:

_____ Did a doctor say it was coronary occlusion?

_____ Did a doctor say it was angina pectoris?

_____ Did a doctor say it was rheumatic heart?

h) Do you have high blood pressure?

i) Do you have a stomach ulcer?

j) Do you have gall bladder trouble?

k) Do you have cirrhosis of the liver?
l) MEN ONLY: Do you have prostate trouble?
m) WOMEN ONLY: Do you have female trouble? IF YES:
       _____ bleeding or spotting?
       _____ vaginal discharge?
n) Do you have kidney trouble (nephritis)?
o) Do you have bladder trouble?
p) Do you have diabetes?
q) Has a doctor said you have arthritis? IF YES: Where?
r) Have you lost the use of any part of your body?
      IF YES: Was it: _____ total loss?
                            _____ partial loss?
        Was it due to: _____ paralysis?
                            _____ amputation?
                            _____ fracture?

12. Since the time you were about 50, have you had any serious ailment (operation, accident or illness) which bothers you at all now? What bothers you now about it?
(IF CHRONIC, INDICATE. THEN ASK PROBES I–IV AND ENTER DETAILS IN CHART.)

13. Is there anything (else) you've been letting go which might better be treated by a doctor? What is it?
(IF CHRONIC, INDICATE. THEN ASK PROBES I–IV AND ENTER DETAILS IN CHART.)

14. We've been talking about your health. How much of the time does your health worry you—all the time, most of the time, only sometimes, or never?

15. How often are you troubled by *nervousness?* Would you say often, sometimes, or never?
REPEAT FOR EACH OF THE FOLLOWING: headaches
                                     not being able to sleep
                                     upset stomach
                                     constipation

16. How often do you find yourself *being lonesome?* Would you say often, sometimes, or never?
REPEAT FOR EACH OF THE FOLLOWING: day-dreaming about the
                                         past
                                     being absent-minded
                                     having thoughts of death

17A. Were there any periods in your life in which you were so worried, nervous, or emotionally upset that you could not carry on your usual activities?

       IF YES: B. How long ago?
              C. How long did it last?
              D. Did you have it taken care of by a doctor?

ASK ONLY THOSE ITEMS WHICH HAVE NOT ALREADY BEEN DISCUSSED: RESPONSES: YES—NO (APPLIES ONLY TO QUESTIONS 18–26).

18. Do you usually get up tired and exhausted?

19. Have you thought of committing suicide any time during the past 10 years?

20. Is it always hard for you to make up your mind?

21. In general, do people treat you fairly?

22. Do you have periods of deep sadness that last a long time?

23. Did a doctor ever say you had cancer?

24. Has any member of your immediate family, living or dead, ever had cancer?

       IF "YES": RELATIONSHIP _____

25. Was any part of your body ever paralyzed?

26. Do you have any enemies who want to harm you?

27. Do you drink alcoholic beverages regularly, occasionally, rarely, or never?

28. If you had more time or money to get yourself in the best physical shape possible, what physical problem would you attend to first? (ACCEPT ALL MENTIONED)

29. If you were suddenly taken very sick, where would you turn for help? (CHECK ALL MENTIONED)

          _____ PRIVATE DOCTOR (ASK: Anyone else?)
          _____ FRIEND
          _____ RELATIVE
          _____ NEIGHBOR
          _____ DRUGGIST
          _____ CLERGYMAN
          _____ CLINIC OR HOSPITAL
          _____ POLICE
          _____ OTHER (SPECIFY)

30. What class of people would you say uses free city clinics most—the upper class, middle class, working class, or lower class?

31. Would you say an older person gets more attention when he (she) is sick, or that everybody keeps away from sick older people?

    ASK ONLY IF APPLICABLE: How is (was) it in your case?

32. Do you get advice on health matters from:

    _____ Private doctor
    _____ Friend
    _____ Relative
    _____ Neighbor
    CHECK AS   _____ Druggist
    MANY AS   _____ Clergyman
    APPLY   _____ Clinic or hospital
    _____ Police
    _____ Books
    _____ Other (SPECIFY)
    _____ DON'T GET ANY ADVICE

33. If this neighborhood had a medical center especially for older people, would you go there for advice on your health problems?

34. Do you take any medicines regularly?

    _____ NO
    _____ YES: Which ones?

35. How often do you use home remedies when something is wrong with you—most of the time, sometimes, rarely, or never?

36A. Do you think it's a good idea to have a regular thorough check-up by a doctor even if there's nothing wrong?

    _____ NO (SKIP TO Q. 37)
    _____ YES (ASK Q. 36B)

   B. How often do you have such a check-up?

    _____ ONCE EACH YEAR
    _____ TWICE EACH YEAR
    _____ SELDOM/NEVER (SKIP TO Q. 36D)

   C. Do you usually have this check-up done by a private doctor or at a clinic?

   D. IF R "SELDOM" OR "NEVER" GETS CHECK-UP: Why don't you have a physical check-up (more often) even though you think it's a good idea?

37. Do you have a regular physician who usually takes care of your illness?

    _____ NO: Why is that? (Why don't you have a regular physician?) (CHECK ALL MENTIONED)

        _____ NOT ENOUGH MONEY

        _____ DON'T LIKE DOCTORS

        _____ I'M NEVER SICK ENOUGH

        _____ PREFER CLINICS

        _____ OTHER (SPECIFY)

    _____ YES

38. Have you ever heard of the following free health services:

    Visiting nurse

    Registered nurse service

    Free housekeeping service

    Free medical clinics

39A. Have you ever gone to a clinic for medical help?

    _____ NO (SKIP TO Q. 40)

    _____ YES (ASK PROBES B–E, AND ENTER ANSWERS IN CHART BELOW):

  B. What hospital?

  C. Which clinic?

  D. Were you satisfied or dissatisfied?

  E. IF "DISSATISFIED": What made you dissatisfied?

40A. If you needed medical treatment and had your choice, would you rather go to a private physician or to a hospital clinic?

  B. Why would you choose _____ (REPEAT R'S CHOICE)? (CHECK ALL MENTIONED)

        _____ CHEAPER

        _____ MORE INDIVIDUAL ATTENTION

        _____ DON'T LIKE CLINIC ATMOSPHERE

        _____ WANT MY OWN PERSONAL DOCTOR

        _____ MORE SERVICES AVAILABLE

        _____ MORE COURTEOUS

        _____ MORE CONFIDENCE IN

        _____ LESS WAITING

        _____ OTHER

41. Do you have any kind of health insurance or do you belong to a medical plan—like Blue Cross?

    _____ NO

    _____ YES: Which one?

42. If this neighborhood had a medical center especially for older people, would you go there for treatment, or would you go to a center where they treated people of all ages?

43. Here are some things people have told us about the way they feel toward doctors and hospitals. Do you agree more or disagree more?
    a) Doctors don't take a real interest in what happens to you.
    b) The trouble with hospitals is that once you get in, you never know if you'll get out alive.
    c) Most doctors don't care how much they hurt you.
    d) Doctors tend to treat younger people better than older people.
    e) A person should always follow the doctor's advice.
    f) Doctors hardly ever tell you the *whole* truth about your health.

We've talked about doctors and health. Now let's talk about your work.

44. What do you do for a living now? (CHECK ONE AND CONTINUE WITH SECTION INDICATED)

R IS EMPLOYED AT PRESENT:

```
_____ EMPLOYED BY OTHERS,
          FULL TIME
_____ EMPLOYED BY OTHERS,
          PART TIME
_____ EMPLOYED BY OTHERS,
          OCCASIONAL OR SEA-
          SONAL
ASK Q. EM 1–8 (YELLOW PAGES)
```

R IS NOT NOW EMPLOYED:

```
_____ UNEMPLOYED, SEEKING
          FULL TIME WORK
_____ UNEMPLOYED, SEEKING
          PART TIME WORK
_____ TEMPORARILY OUT OF
          LABOR FORCE BUT
          PLANS TO RETURN
ASK Q. U/TEM 1–9 (WHITE
          PAGES)
```

```
_____ SELF-EMPLOYED
ASK Q. SE 1–8 (GREEN PAGES)
```

```
_____ RETIRED
ASK Q. RE 1–11 (BLUE PAGES)
```

```
_____ HOUSEWIFE
ASK Q. W 1–5 (PINK PAGES)
```

EM 1. TYPE OF WORK (SPECIFY OPERATION):

   INDUSTRY:

   NUMBER OF PERSONS SUPERVISED:

EM 2. Would you mind telling me how much you earn at this work?

EM 3. How long have you held this job?

EM 4. Is this work your regular (usual) occupation?
   _____ YES
   _____ NO: What is your regular occupation? (SPECIFY TYPE OF
      WORK AND INDUSTRY)

EM 5. How much do you enjoy the work you are now doing? Very much, fairly much, not so much, not at all?

EM 6. What do you think you will probably do in the next five years in regard to your work—do you think you'll continue working where you are, stop working and retire, or something else?
   _____ WILL CONTINUE WORKING
   _____ WILL RETIRE, COMPULSORY
   _____ WILL RETIRE, OPTIONAL
   _____ OTHER (SPECIFY)

EM 7. Do you look forward to the time when you will retire, or do you dislike the idea?

EM 8. Now, I wonder if you would mind telling me which two of these things is most important to you in your work?
   (CHECK TWO) _____ Mixing with people on the job
   _____ Gives you a feeling of being useful
   _____ The respect it brings from others
   _____ New things happening on the job
   _____ The money it brings in
   _____ The work itself

IF R IS A WOMAN WHO IS OR HAS BEEN MARRIED, SKIP TO SECTION W (PINK PAGES). OTHERWISE, SKIP TO Q. 45.

SE 1. TYPE OF BUSINESS (OCCUPATION): _____

   INDUSTRY:_____ NO. OF PERSONS
   SUPERVISED:_____

SE 2. Would you mind telling me about how much you clear per week at this business?

SE 3. How long have you been in this business: _____ or _____

                                                YEARS   MONTHS

SE 4. Is running this business your regular occupation?

    _____ YES

    _____ NO: What was your regular (usual) occupation? (SPECIFY TYPE OF WORK; INDUSTRY; SELF-EMPLOYED OR WORKING FOR SOMEONE ELSE)

SE 5. How much do you enjoy the work you are now doing? Very much, fairly much, not so much, not at all?

SE 6. What do you expect to do in the next five years in regard to working—do you think you'll continue what you're doing, stop working and retire, or do something else?

SE 7. Do you look forward to the time when you will retire, or do you dislike the idea?

SE 8. Now, I wonder if you would mind telling me which two of these things is most important to you in your work?

    (CHECK TWO)   _____ Mixing with people

                               _____ Gives you a feeling of being useful

                               _____ The respect that it brings from others

                               _____ New things happening on the job

                               _____ The money it brings in

                               _____ The work itself

> IF R IS A WOMAN WHO IS OR HAS BEEN MARRIED, SKIP TO SECTION W (PINK PAGES). OTHERWISE, SKIP TO Q. 45.

U/TEM 1. TYPE OF WORK (LAST JOB HELD): _____

                                                 (SPECIFY OPERATION)

                                                 NO. OF PERSONS

        INDUSTRY: _____ SUPERVISED:_____

        WAS R: _____ SELF-EMPLOYED

                _____ WORKING FOR OTHERS, FULL TIME

                _____ WORKING FOR OTHERS, PART TIME

                _____ WORKING FOR OTHERS, OCCASIONAL OR SEASONAL

U/TEM 2. Would you mind telling me how much you used to earn at this work (just before you retired)?

U/TEM 3. How long did you have (that job) (that business)?

_____ or _____
   YEARS   MONTHS

U/TEM 4. Was this your regular (usual) occupation?

_____ YES

_____ NO: What was your regular (usual) occupation? (SPECIFY TYPE OF WORK; INDUSTRY; NUMBER OF PERSONS SUPERVISED; WHETHER SELF-EMPLOYED OR WORKING FOR OTHERS)

U/TEM 5. How long has it been since you stopped working?

_____ or _____
   YEARS   MONTHS

U/TEM 6. How much did you enjoy the work you did on your last job (in your last business)? Very much, fairly much, not so much, or not at all?

DO NOT ASK Q. 7 & 8 OF THOSE WHO ARE PERMANENTLY INCAPACITATED.

U/TEM 7. What do you think you will probably do in the next five years in regard to your work? Do you think you'll get another job, or will you stop looking and retire? or something else?

U/TEM 8. Do you look forward to the time when you will retire, or do you dislike the idea?

U/TEM 9. Now I wonder if you would mind telling me which two of these things was most important to you when you were working?

(CHECK TWO) _____ Mixing with people on the job

_____ Gave you a feeling of being useful

_____ The respect it brings from others

_____ New things happening on the job

_____ The money it brings in

_____ The work itself

IF R IS A WOMAN WHO IS OR HAS BEEN MARRIED, SKIP TO SECTION W (PINK PAGES). OTHERWISE, SKIP TO Q. 45.

RE   1. TYPE OF WORK (LAST JOB HELD):_____

                                      (SPECIFY OPERATION)

                                      NO. OF PERSONS

      INDUSTRY:_____   SUPERVISED:_____

      SELF-EMPLOYED:_____; or WORKING FOR OTHERS_____

RE   2. Would you mind telling me how much you used to earn at this work (business) just before you retired?

RE   3. Was this job (business) your regular occupation?

      _____ YES

      _____ NO: What was your regular occupation? (SPECIFY TYPE OF WORK AND INDUSTRY)

RE   4. How long has it been since you stopped working?

      _____ or _____

       YEARS   MONTHS

RE   5. How old were you when you stopped working regularly?

      _____ YEARS

RE   6. Did you stop working all at once, or gradually by working fewer and fewer hours?

RE   7. How did you happen to stop working when you did? (CHECK ALL MENTIONED)

             _____ RETIRED BY COMPANY ON REACHING RETIREMENT AGE

             _____ UNABLE TO FIND WORK AT REGULAR OCCUPATION OR TRADE

             _____ WANTED TO ENJOY LEISURE

             _____ HEALTH; TOO ILL TO WORK

             _____ HEALTH; OTHER HEALTH REASON

             _____ DID NOT ENJOY THE WORK

             _____ FELT THAT OTHERS EXPECTED YOU TO RETIRE

             _____ SOME OTHER REASON: What?

RE   8. How much did you enjoy the work you did on your last job (in your last business)?—very much, fairly much, not so much, not at all?

RE   9. As you think back, did you look forward to retirement, or did you dislike the idea?

RE 10. Would you say that being retired turned out better or worse than you expected?

             _____ BETTER

             _____ ABOUT AS EXPECTED

             _____ WORSE

RE 11. Now I wonder if you would mind telling me which two of these things were most important to you when you were working? (CHECK TWO) _____ Mixing with people on the job
_____ Gave you a feeling of being useful
_____ The respect that it brought from others
_____ New things happening on the job
_____ The money it brought in
_____ The work itself

IF R IS A WOMAN WHO IS OR HAS BEEN MARRIED, GO TO SECTION W (PINK PAGES). OTHERWISE, SKIP TO Q. 45

_____ IF R HAS NEVER BEEN MARRIED, CHECK HERE AND SKIP TO Q. 45.

W 1. What does (did) your husband do for a living (most of his life)?

HUSBAND IS (WAS) EMPLOYED:

_____ WORKING FOR OTHERS, FULL TIME
_____ WORKING FOR OTHERS, PART TIME
_____ WORKING FOR OTHERS, OCCASIONAL
_____ SELF-EMPLOYED

ASK Q. W2 & W3, THEN SKIP TO Q. 45

HUSBAND IS (WAS) UNEMPLOYED OR OUT OF LABOR FORCE:

_____ UNEMPLOYED, SEEKING FULL TIME WORK
_____ UNEMPLOYED, SEEKING PART TIME WORK
_____ TEMPORARILY OUT OF LABOR FORCE BUT PLANNING TO RETURN
_____ RETIRED

ASK Q. W2 THROUGH W5

W 2. INDICATE HUSBAND'S CUSTOMARY OCCUPATION: _____ (SPECIFY OPERATION)
INDUSTRY: _____

W 3. About how much does he earn now (did he earn) at that kind of work?

> OMIT Q. W4–5 FOR WOMEN WHOSE HUSBANDS ARE PRES-
> ENTLY EMPLOYED, OR WERE EMPLOYED AT TIME OF
> DEATH, SEPARATION, OR DIVORCE

W 4. Just before your husband stopped working, did he work for someone else, or did he have his own business (office)?

W 5. How old was your husband when he stopped working? ＿＿＿＿＿＿
YEARS

> ASK EVERYBODY

45. What are all the sources from which you get your present income?
＿＿＿＿＿ HUSBAND'S (WIFE'S) EARNINGS
＿＿＿＿＿ CHILDREN OR OTHER RELATIVES (SPECIFY RELATIONSHIP)
＿＿＿＿＿ SOCIAL SECURITY (OLD AGE AND SURVIVOR'S INSURANCE)
＿＿＿＿＿ PENSION FROM PRIVATE INDUSTRY, UNION, GOV'T AGENCY
＿＿＿＿＿ OLD AGE ASSISTANCE (PUBLIC WELFARE), RELIEF
＿＿＿＿＿ SAVINGS
＿＿＿＿＿ BONDS OR INVESTMENTS
＿＿＿＿＿ INCOME FROM PROPERTY
＿＿＿＿＿ INSURANCE ANNUITIES
＿＿＿＿＿ OTHER (SPECIFY)
＿＿＿＿＿ DK

46. Considering all sources, about how much would you say your
total income comes to?

47A. Is your standard of living better today—that is, are you better off
now—or is it worse than during most of your lifetime?
＿＿＿＿＿ BETTER TODAY
＿＿＿＿＿ WORSE TODAY
＿＿＿＿＿ SAME
＿＿＿＿＿ EVERYBODY'S WORSE OFF TODAY

B. Would you say it is better, or worse, than the standard of living of
most of your friends and acquaintances?
＿＿＿＿＿ BETTER
＿＿＿＿＿ WORSE
＿＿＿＿＿ SAME

48. Which one of these groups would you say you belong to? Would
you say you are in the upper class, middle class, working class, or
lower class?

49. By the way, what did your father do for a living most of his life?
    FATHER'S USUAL OCCUPATION: (SPECIFY SKILL LEVEL)

50. If there was an office or bureau which dealt only with the employment needs and problems of older people, how do you think it could help? RECORD COMMENTS FULLY.

I have some questions here about the sort of things you do for social life and relaxation now, and the sort of things you did when you were about 50 years old.

51. By the way, can you think back to the time when you were about 50. Where were you living at that time?
    _____ SAME PLACE AS PRESENT RESIDENCE
    _____ ELSEWHERE IN METROPOLITAN AREA
    _____ OTHER COMMUNITY: Where?

52. Which of the following activities do you do fairly regularly now?
    (READ CHECKLIST. IF R DOES NONE OF THESE ACTIVITIES FAIRLY REGULARLY, CHECK HERE _____ AND SKIP TO Q. 53)
    _____ R DOES AT LEAST ONE OF CHECKLIST ACTIVITIES FAIRLY
              REGULARLY. ASK FOR EACH THAT HE DOES: Do you do it more now, or did you do it more when you were 50?

    ACTIVITY CHECKLIST:
    Reading
    Listening to radio/TV
    Work on hobbies
    Just sit and think about things
    Write letters
    Go to park
    Spend time at library
    Go to movies
    Take rides or walks
    Visit with friends
    Attend classes at school/center
    Engage in religious activities, such as church work
    Play cards
    Go shopping
    Go to a bar for a couple of drinks
    WOMEN ONLY: Sew, knit, crochet

53. About how many hours a day, on the average, do you listen to the radio or watch television?

54. About how many hours a day, on the average, do you spend reading?

Now I have a few questions about your group or community activities.

55A. Do you do any of the following things at the present time? (READ ITEMS BELOW. IF R DOES NONE, CHECK HERE _____ AND SKIP TO Q. 56)
Do you go around with a certain bunch of close friends who visit each other or do things together?
Do you belong to a labor union?
Do you belong to some other club or organization? IF "YES" ENTER NAME OR TYPE:
(ASK B, C, D BELOW FOR EACH ORGANIZATION)

   B. Do you attend most of the meetings or gatherings, some of them, hardly any of them, or none of them?

   C. Is this group or organization for men only, women only, or both men and women?

   D. Did you do any of these things when you were about 50?

56A. Do you attend any sort of club or center *for older people only?*
    _____ NO: B. Do you know if there is such a group around here?
    _____ YES: C. What is the name of the group?
          D. Where is it located?
          E. How often do you go there—very often, often, very occasionally or rarely or never?
          F. How did you find out about it:
(CHECK ALL   _____ FRIEND(S)
MENTIONED)   _____ RELATIVE(S)
            _____ ANOTHER CLUB
            _____ WELFARE DEPARTMENT
            _____ HOSPITAL
            _____ OTHER (SPECIFY)

57A. On the whole, would you say you get out and around as much as you used to when you were 50?

   B. If you had a choice of joining a social club made up of people mostly younger than you, or one with people mostly around your own age, which would you prefer to join? (CHECK ONE)
          _____ CLUB WITH YOUNGER PEOPLE MAINLY
          _____ CLUB FOR ALL AGES
          _____ CLUB FOR PEOPLE YOUR OWN AGE
          _____ WOULD NOT JOIN ANY

58. Even if there are recreation centers nearby, older people seldom go. What do you think keeps them from going to those clubs and centers?

(CHECK AS   _____ TRANSPORTATION PROBLEMS

MANY AS ARE   _____ DON'T WANT TO GO ALONE

MENTIONED)   _____ DON'T WANT TO BE WITH YOUNG ONLY

                    _____ DON'T WANT TO BE A STRANGER

                    _____ DON'T LIKE BIG CLUBS

                    _____ DON'T LIKE TO GO OUT

                    _____ TOO MUCH TROUBLE

                    _____ OTHER (SPECIFY)

59. If there was a center which dealt only with the needs of older people, what do you think they should deal with? (PROBE: Can you think of anything else)?

(CHECK AS   _____ EMPLOYMENT PROBLEMS

MANY AS ARE   _____ HOUSING PROBLEMS

MENTIONED)   _____ RECREATION

                    _____ HELP TO MEET NEW FRIENDS

                    _____ FAMILY

                    _____ FINANCIAL

                    _____ HEALTH PROBLEMS

                    _____ LEGAL PROBLEMS (WHERE YOU NEED A LAWYER)

                    _____ EDUCATION

                    _____ OTHER (SPECIFY)

60A. (OMIT FOR THOSE WHO HAVE NEVER BEEN MARRIED). How many living children do you have?

                    _____ NONE (SKIP TO Q. 61A)

                    _____ ONE

                    _____ TWO

                    _____ THREE

                    _____ FOUR OR MORE

B. How often do you see them?

(ASK ABOUT   _____ AT LEAST ONCE A WEEK

ONE SEEN MOST _____ EVERY TWO OR THREE WEEKS

FREQUENTLY)   _____ ABOUT ONCE A MONTH

                    _____ LESS FREQUENTLY

61A. About how many close relatives do you have who live here in the New York area?

                    _____ NONE (SKIP TO Q. 62A)

                    _____ ONE

                    _____ TWO

                    _____ THREE

                    _____ FOUR OR MORE

B. How often do you see them?
(ASK ABOUT   _____ AT LEAST ONCE A WEEK
ONE SEEN MOST _____ EVERY TWO OR THREE WEEKS
FREQUENTLY)   _____ ABOUT ONCE A MONTH
               _____ LESS FREQUENTLY

62A. Do the young people in your family usually take care of the older people? (IF NECESSARY: I mean just in general).

B. Now about your friends—would you say that most of your *close* friends are living, only some of them, or almost none?

63. Do you have any close friends here in New York whom you occasionally talk over personal matters with?
_____ YES: About how many? _____
_____ NO: Do you have *any* friends in New York—people you see from time to time in a friendly way?
                _____ NO: (SKIP TO Q. 66)
                _____ YES: About how many? _____

64. Now, think of the friend that you know best here in New York. How often do you get to see that friend?
               _____ AT LEAST ONCE A WEEK
               _____ EVERY TWO OR THREE WEEKS
               _____ ABOUT ONCE A MONTH
               _____ LESS FREQUENTLY

65A. Have you made any *new* friends here in New York in *recent years*?
_____ NO
_____ YES: B. Think of the closest new friend you have made in recent years. How long have you known this friend?
             C. Is this person a man or a woman?
             D. Is he (she) about your age or younger, or older than you?
             E. How did you happen to meet this friend?
             _____ THROUGH WORK
             _____ THROUGH A CLUB
             _____ THROUGH ANOTHER FRIEND
             _____ THROUGH A RELATIVE
             _____ WE WERE NEIGHBORS
             _____ OTHER (SPECIFY)

66. How often do you find yourself wishing you would meet (more) new friends?
               _____ OFTEN
               _____ SOMETIMES
               _____ HARDLY EVER

67. In general, would you say that most people are easy to get along with, fairly hard to get along with, or very hard to get along with?

68. Did you have a chance to vote in the recent presidential election? IF "YES": For whom did you vote?

69A. We'd like to know how you think of yourself as far as age goes— do you think of yourself as:

        _____ middle-aged (SKIP TO Q. 69E)

        _____ elderly

        _____ old

        _____ or what? (SPECIFY):

  B. About how old were you when you first began to think of yourself as (elderly) (old)? (USE R's OWN WAY OF SAYING OLD)

  C. Did you come to think of yourself as (elderly) (old) very gradually, fairly gradually, or rather suddenly?

        _____ VERY GRADUALLY (SKIP TO Q. 69E)

        _____ FAIRLY GRADUALLY (SKIP TO Q. 69E)

        _____ RATHER SUDDENLY (ASK Q. 69D & 69E)

  D. What happened that made you feel that way?

  E. Would you say that you feel older or younger than most people your age?

70. On the whole, how satisfied would you say you are with your way of life today? Would you say—very satisfied, fairly satisfied, or not very satisfied?

71A. Are any of these things unsatisfactory to you at present? (PROBE: Anything else)?

        _____ food

        _____ living quarters

        _____ spending money

        _____ NONE OF THE ABOVE

  B. In building houses or apartments, can you think of anything special the builders might do to make them more comfortable for older people?

IF "YES": What?

72. Do you find any of the following things annoying?

  a) Being interrupted when you are busy at something?

  b) Having persons get into your personal belongings and disturbing them?

  c) Having someone rearrange things around the house that you are used to having a certain way?

73. As you get older, would you say things seem to be better or worse than you thought they would be?

         _____ BETTER
         _____ WORSE
         _____ SAME

74A. Do you think people treat you differently because you are older?

  B. Do you feel you are a lot of trouble, or only a little trouble to others?

         _____ A LOT OF TROUBLE
         _____ A LITTLE TROUBLE
         _____ NO TROUBLE

75. Which of these things would you say you've *worked hardest at* in your life?

(CHECK ONE)   _____ trying to get ahead in life
                 _____ trying to make your future secure
                 _____ trying to find happiness in life
                 _____ trying to live an upright life with nothing to regret
                 _____ trying to be a good citizen to the community

76. In general, how well would you say you've lived up to what you expected of yourself—very well, fairly well, or not so well?

77. How much do you plan ahead the things you will be doing next week or the week after—would you say you make many plans, a few plans, or almost none?

78. All in all, how much unhappiness would you say you find in life today?—almost none; some, but not very much; a good deal?

79. How much do you regret the chances you missed during your life to do a better job of living—not at all, somewhat, or a good deal?

80. How often do you find yourself feeling bitter about the way things turned out for you?—often, sometimes, or hardly ever?

81. How often do you feel that there's just no point in living—often, sometimes, or hardly ever?

82. Here are some opinions people have expressed about older people or about people in general. Do you agree or disagree with the following statements?

1) Older people should dress more conservatively than younger people.

2) Older people ought to go around with friends their own age rather than with younger people.

3) In spite of what some people say, the life of the average man is getting worse, not better.

4) It's undignified for older people to be interested in the opposite sex.

5) You can't expect older people to accept new ways of doing things.

6) Older people ought to be treated with more respect.

7) Older people ought to get together into organizations to try to get social benefits for themselves.

8) You've got to expect lots of aches and pains when you get older.

9) There's little use writing to public officials because they aren't really interested in the problems of the average man.

10) It's hardly fair for young folks to bring children into the world with the way things look for the future.

11) Nowadays a person has to live pretty much for today and let tomorrow take care of itself.

12) Things just keep getting worse and worse for me as I get older.

13) Most people lose respect for a man who no longer works.

14) Generally speaking, retirement is bad for a person.

15) A rich old man is better off than a poor young man.

16) A young woman whose husband is dead is worse off than an old woman still married.

17) I often get the feeling that my life today is not very useful.

18) These days a person doesn't really know whom he can count on.

19) I don't receive as much love and affection as when I was younger.

20) I miss not having a more active sex life.

That's about all now. I just want to go through these factual questions to see if there's anything we haven't yet covered.

83. In what year were you born? 18_____.

84. In what country were you born?
    IF "U.S.A.", SKIP TO Q. 86.

85. How old were you when you came to this country? _____ YEARS

86. In what country was your father born?

87. What nationality descent do you consider yourself? (IF R SAYS "AMERICAN" PROBE FOR ETHNIC GROUP)

88. What other languages besides English do you use rather often?

89. How many years of school did you *complete?*

90. (OMIT FOR THOSE WHO HAVE NEVER BEEN MARRIED). How many years of school did your husband (wife) have? (CIRCLE LAST GRADE COMPLETED)

91. How important is religion in your life?
    _____ Most important thing in my life
    _____ Very important
    _____ Important
    _____ Not so important
    _____ Of no importance

92. How often do you attend religious services?
    _____ at least once a week
    _____ two to three times a month
    _____ at least once a month
    _____ three or four times a year
    _____ only holidays
    _____ Rarely/Never

93. What is your religion?
    _____ JEWISH
    _____ CATHOLIC
    _____ PROTESTANT
    _____ NONE: What was your parents' religion?
    _____
    _____ OTHER

94A. Would you please tell me how you felt about this interview? Did you find it interesting?

  B. Were there any questions that particularly bothered you, or that you thought were hard to answer?
     IF "YES": Which ones?

TO BE FILLED IN BY INTERVIEWER; DO NOT ASK RESPONDENT

R'S RACE:

_____ White

_____ Negro

_____ Puerto Rican, white

_____ Puerto Rican, Negro

_____ Other

_____ Unknown

R'S GROOMING:

_____ Very neat and clean

_____ Fairly neat

_____ Not neat

_____ Untidy

R SHOWED: (CHECK ONE)

_____ Apathy

_____ Mild inattention

_____ Mild interest

_____ High interest

R WAS: (CHECK AS MANY AS APPLY)

_____ Suspicious or guarded

_____ Forgetful or confused

_____ Silly, inappropriate remarks and behavior

_____ Indecisive in answering questions

_____ Hostile

_____ Friendly and/or cooperative

R'S COORDINATION AND STRENGTH: (CHECK ONE)

_____ Very weak and feeble

_____ Weak and a bit unsteady

_____ Not weak but a bit unsteady

_____ Neither unsteady nor weak

R'S COMPREHENSION OF QUESTIONS:

_____ Quick and correct

_____ Slow but correct

_____ Slow and sometimes confused

_____ Quick but often not correct

_____ Barely able to follow

EASE OF ACCESS TO AND FROM QUARTERS:

_____ Dangerous flight of stairs

_____ Easy flight of stairs

_____ Just stoop or porch stairs

_____ No stairs

CONDITION OF FURNISHINGS:

_____ Clean and in good repair

_____ Clean but in poor repair

_____ In good repair, but soiled

_____ Soiled and in poor repair

R'S SOCIOECONOMIC STATUS: (SEE SHEET OF DESCRIPTIONS OF SOCIOECONOMIC RATINGS)

_____ A

_____ B

_____ C

_____ D

_____ E

_____ F

TIME INTERVIEW BEGAN:_____

_____

TIME INTERVIEW ENDED:_____

_____

TOTAL TIME OF INTERVIEW:_____

_____ HRS.

Appendix 3

The Index of
Socioeconomic Status

A MEASURE OF SOCIOECONOMIC STATUS (SES) was required for this study that would be compatible with known characteristics of the older population. Indices that might normally be employed may not be useful in the type of sample dealt with here. Using a standard index, therefore, would produce spurious classifications of individuals and, eventually, spurious categories of status groups.

In the procedure followed, certain known indicators of SES, such as income, education, occupation, father's occupation and so forth, were analyzed according to some behavioral items in the questionnaire that were believed to be class-linked. These items were:

The comparative use of private physicians as opposed to clinics

Having a regular physician as opposed to not having a regular physician

Willingness, as opposed to unwillingness, to go to a neighborhood medical center for advice

Desire or lack of desire to join a social club for older people.

In addition, the interviewer's rating of the person as to SES was also used as a basis for classification. This rating was established on a five-point scale using a set of standard criteria for assessing SES. Three criteria produced the sharpest differences in attitude and practice. These were: (1) occupation, (2) income, and (3) interviewer's rating. These three items then became the basis of the SES index.

The three items produced seven, seven, and six point scales respectively. The following scales and frequencies emerged for each item.

OCCUPATION

Customary occupation	Score	Frequency Number	Per cent
Professional; managerial	1	63	12.6
Semi-professional; sales— e.g., insurance, real estate	2	22	4.4
Skilled worker; foreman; entrepreneur	3	48	9.6
Clerical; sales—e.g., store clerks	4	93	18.6
Semi-skilled; service trades— e.g., deliverman, butler	5	121	24.2
Unskilled worker	6	45	9.0
Service worker—e.g., domestic, janitor, watchman	7	95	19.0
No information	—	13	2.6
		500	100.0

INCOME

Income per week	Score	Frequency Number	Per cent
$150 and over	1	19	3.8
$125 to $149	2	4	.8
$100 to $124	3	9	1.8
$ 75 to $ 99	4	33	6.6
$ 50 to $ 74	5	74	14.8
$ 25 to $ 49	6	116	23.2
Less than $25	7	207	41.4
No answer		31	6.2
"Don't know"		7	1.4
		500	100.0

INTERVIEWER'S RATING OF RESPONDENT'S SES

Description of Rating	Score	Frequency Number	Per cent
All the luxuries available in their community are taken for granted. These are the wealthy, the rich.	I	II	2.2
The comforts and necessities of life are taken for granted. They can afford *more* than one of the luxuries.	2	40	8.0
This group takes the necessities of life for granted, and most of the comforts, if times are good. They must save and plan for any luxury—usually have one.	3	87	17.4
This group has the necessities of life and some of the comforts, if economic conditions are good. Must save for major comforts or a luxury.	4	160	32.0
The minor necessities are taken for granted, and if times are good, some of the comforts are available to them. But they must save up for any major necessity (e.g., overcoat)	5	195	39.0
Abject poverty. Penniless, below subsistence; begging; not sure of next meal.	6	5	1.0
No rating.		2	.4
		500	100.0

Examples of *luxuries:*   new car, radio-phonograph combination, maid, oriental rugs, summer cottage, etc.

Examples of *comforts:*   household appliances such as mix-master, pop-up toaster, vacuum cleaner, automatic washing machine.

Final scores were obtained for each individual by summing his scores for each of the three variables. Scores fell between three and twenty. The full range of scores and their frequencies were as follows:

Score	Frequency	SES Group frequency	Coded by inspection[a]	Total
3	5			
4	10			
5	7	42 High SES	13	55
6	3			
7	5			
8	12			
9	19			
10	21			
11	28	137 Middle SES	11	148
12	32			
13	37			
14	30			
15	34			
16	37			
17	52	268 Low SES	29	297
18	56			
19	58			
20	1			

[a] Fifty-three cases were coded by inspection of the original interview because one or more of the three variables was missing.

Inasmuch as our sampling procedure was designed to obtain a ratio of 6:3:1 corresponding to low, middle, and high SES groups, no regression formula was developed to assist in plotting relative position on the index. Using the criteria described above, we have the following final grouping:

		Frequency	
Score	SES Group	Number	Per cent
3 to 8	High	55	11.0
9 to 13	Middle	148	29.6
14 to 20	Low	297	59.4

The final index approximates the sizes of the three SES groups originally desired. A finer breakdown would have made cross-tabulation employing controlled variables almost impossible with a sample of 500 cases. As employed in this study, the "high" and "middle" categories are combined except in a few places since these yielded, upon extensive analyses, relatively similar findings.

It might be good, in conclusion, to point up certain distinctions between a special group such as the aged and a population of unselected ages. All the points listed bear on the assignment of SES positions.

1. While income and rental for home or apartment may decrease with age, retirement, and widowhood, social position may remain stationary.

2. Education bears less relation to status in younger populations, since more people are receiving more education regardless of class position. Among the present sample, lack of education or foreign schooling may be deceptive, since often a person's social status rose as he prospered in business.

3. Occupation is more complex to score in an aged sample due to retirement and changes occurring in the years immediately preceding retirement. In these latter years, the person may change positions one or more times, often at a lower level of status and income. Occupation should be rated according to his *usual* or *normal* lifetime positions.

4. Establishing a clear-cut group of "middle income" or "middle class" persons in their later years is no simple task. It is of sociological interest that with increasing age there is a gradual evaporation of middle income persons. Retirement, illness, loss of savings, and the reduction of other sources of income tend to throw large numbers of persons, who would formerly have been classed in the middle range of incomes, into the lower income group. Inasmuch as the vast majority of our sample are to be found in the two lowest income groups, it is difficult to separate those of low and those of middle social status and, further, to categorize the borderline cases.

5. Since most (70 per cent) of our sample are foreign-born, income and social status may be quite discrepant. While his income may rise considerably, his social position in the community at large may not reflect this.

It seems probable that as studies of older people increase in number, improved techniques for measuring their socioeconomic status will be developed. A standard measuring instrument is required that will take into account the more usual characteristics of community status as well as those peculiar to an older population.

Appendix 4

Scale Analysis of
Attitude Measures

THE MODEL FOR ATTITUDE MEASUREMENT used in this study is the
Guttman Scale.[1] By using a scale, it is possible to consolidate
responses to a number of questions bearing on a central attitude
rather than placing reliance on a single attitude item. From these
responses a single score can be derived for each individual and
these scores can then serve as the basis for ordering individuals
along an attitude continuum.

In a Guttman scale, the items that comprise it are themselves
ordered in such a way that a scale score is also indicative of the
individual's responses—that is, one knows from a score what items
in the scale were responded to positively and what items were
negatively answered.

One way of illustrating this is to consider the items in terms of
how "easy" or how "hard" they are to answer "correctly." If the
items are put in progressive order of difficulty, the person who is
able to answer a "hard" question should have been able, also,
to answer "correctly" the preceding "easy" items. Suppose, for
example, that we have a five-item scale. The questions are put in
order of increasing difficulty and a score is given for each "correctly" answered question. If we were told that an individual received a total score of 3, we would then predict that he had "correctly" answered the first three items and had "failed" the "harder"
fourth and fifth items.

---

[1] It is not our purpose here to present a detailed theoretical statement. Rather,
the brief description that follows is intended primarily for the general reader who
may not be familiar with Guttman scales.

In dealing with attitudes, of course, we cannot measure the correctness or incorrectness of an answer against some yardstick of truth or fact. The "correct" answers in an attitude scale are merely those responses which for purposes of the scale are given a "plus" score, and "incorrect" answers are merely those which are unscored.

Similarly, it is not possible to prearrange attitude items in an order of difficulty. In attitude scale analysis, the ordering of the component items of a scale is empirically accomplished, the items being arranged in order of greatest to least proportions of scored responses. Thus, in our age conservatism scale the item order is as follows:

	Scored Response: "Agree" Frequency	
	Number	*Per cent*
1. Older people should dress more conservatively than younger people	367	73
2. Older people ought to go around with friends their own age rather than with younger people	273	55
3. You can't expect older people to accept new ways of doing things	208	42
4. It's undignified for older people to be interested in the opposite sex	133	27

If our conservatism measure were a perfect scale, we could accurately predict what items were answered by a scored response merely on the basis of knowledge of the individual's score. We could confidently state that the person who received a score of 3 endorsed the first three items and that a person who scored 2 endorsed the first two items. In actual practice, 100 per cent accuracy in reproducing a response pattern from the score is extremely rare since all individual patterns do not follow the exact scale order of items. It is possible, for instance, for a person to agree with the second item in our age conservatism scale but to disagree with the first item, or to agree with the first and third but to disagree with the second item. In short, we cannot expect that *all* response patterns will follow the item order and that everyone will give perfect scale responses.

The occurrence of imperfect, nonscale responses introduces an error factor, which, of course, reduces the accuracy with which one can predict or reproduce response patterns from knowledge of the scores. In devising scales, the effort is to combine items that will produce minimum error. One set of standards suggests that for a set of items to be acceptable as a scale the incidence of imperfect responses (errors) should not exceed 10 per cent of the total number of responses. Stated in another way, there must be a 90 per cent probability of accurately reproducing from the individual score values the response patterns which they represent. This is generally considered to be a minimum figure and is a criterion for the acceptability of a scale. Other criteria require that:

1. Errors should be randomly distributed—i.e., if an imperfect response pattern occurs more frequently than other imperfect responses, error is not randomly distributed over all the items.

2. Item error should be within certain limits—i.e., the error attributable to each component item of the scale should not exceed 10 to 15 per cent of the total responses to the item. Determination of the acceptable limit is somewhat arbitrary; some suggest that an item error of 15 per cent is acceptable, but others require a more rigorous limit of only 10 per cent error for inclusion of the item in the scale.

Each of the four attitude scales to be discussed here achieves 90 per cent reproducibility or more, thus satisfying this first criterion.[1] They do not, however, uniformly satisfy the remaining criteria. For this reason, it should be noted that, although the term "scale" is used in this report in referring to the measures, this is done with reservations which are noted below.

---

[1] The analysis procedure used is described in: Ford, Robert N., "A Rapid Scoring Procedure for Scaling Attitude Questions," in *Sociological Studies in Scale Analysis*, by Matilda White Riley, John W. Riley, Jr., and Jackson Toby. Rutgers University Press, New Brunswick, N. J., 1954, pp. 273–305.

Morale Scale

The morale scale, used in this study as a measure of adjustment, consists of seven items:

	Response Scored $+1$	Frequency Number	Per cent
1. How often do you feel there's just no point in living?	Hardly ever	389	78
2. Things just keep getting worse and worse for me as I get older.	Disagree	325	65
3. How much do you regret the chances you missed during your life to do a better job of living?	Not at all	252	50
4. All in all, how much unhappiness would you say you find in life today?	Almost none	216	43
5. On the whole, how satisfied would you say you are with your way of life today?	Very satisfied	192	38
6. How much do you plan ahead the things you will be doing next week or the week after— would you say you make many plans, a few plans, or almost none?	Many plans	176	35
7. As you get older, would you say things seem to be better or worse than you thought they would be?	Better	117	23

For the seven items as a whole, the coefficient of reproducibility is 90 per cent.

The morale scale used in this study is an adaptation of one used in the Elmira Study of Aging conducted by the Department of Anthropology and Sociology of Cornell University. The present set of items differs from the original Elmira scale in two respects: (1) As used in Elmira, the response "A few plans" to item 6 was a scored response as well as "Many plans." (2) In the Elmira study an eighth item—the interviewer's rating of the respondent's morale—was included.

It was found in the Kips Bay study that scoring the response, "A few plans," to item 6 increased the error for the scale as a whole as well as item errors. Therefore, in this study, this response was treated as a "negative," nonscored response. This difference in the performance of the scale in the two studies serves to illustrate the point that a scale that meets scaling criteria when used with one population will not necessarily meet the same criteria when used with another population. In this instance, both the Elmira and Kips Bay samples were drawn from a population of aged individuals. In the former, however, the sample was drawn from a predominantly native-born, nonurban population. The Kips Bay sample is a predominantly foreign-born group in an urban setting.

Self-Image

The self-image measure provides a picture of the individual as he sees himself in comparison with others of his own age or his friends. The scale, based upon the person's estimate of whether he feels more or less advantaged than other people, is based on three items:

	Response Scored +1	*Frequency* Number	Per cent
1. Would you say you feel older or younger than most people your age?	Younger	326	65
2. Do you think your health is better or worse than that of people your age?	Better	252	50
3. Would you say it [your standard of living] is better or worse than the standard of living of most of your friends and acquaintances?	Better	70	14

The coefficient of reproducibility is 96.2 per cent.

Age Conservatism Scale

This scale is, in effect, an "attitude toward age" index. It was used to measure the individual's orientation with respect to age, that is, whether one is youth-oriented (low age conservatism) or age-oriented (high age conservatism). The scale is made up of four items:

	Response Scored +1	Frequency Number	Per cent
1. Older people should dress more conservatively than younger people	Agree	367	73
2. Older people ought to go around with friends their own age rather than with younger people	Agree	273	55
3. You can't expect older people to accept new ways of doing things	Agree	208	42
4. It's undignified for older people to be interested in the opposite sex	Agree	133	27

The coefficient of reproducibility is 91.5 per cent. The following should be noted, however.

About 7 per cent of the sample make each of the following imperfect response patterns: (a) The combination of items 3 and 1; (b) The combination of items 4, 2, and 1.

This suggests a more complex relationship than the "unidimensional" scale can handle.

Disposition to Use Health Resources

This scale composed of three items is an index of attitude toward health resources as expressed in readiness to utilize such services. The three items are:

	Response Scored +1	Frequency	
		Number	*Per cent*
1. If you were suddenly taken very sick, where would you turn for help?	Private doctor *or* clinic or hospital	377	75
2. If this neighborhood had a medical center especially for older people, would you go there for advice on your health problems?	Yes	316	63
3. If this neighborhood had a medical center especially for older people, would you go there for treatment, or would you go to a center where they treated people of all ages?	Center for older people, or center for all[a]	303	61

[a] Would go to a center, as opposed to would not go to *any* center.

The coefficient of reproducibility is 91.3 per cent.

To reiterate, although each of the measures discussed here achieves an acceptable coefficient of reproducibility, they do not uniformly satisfy the other criteria for scales. In this study the term "scale" is used to refer to these measures.

BIBLIOGRAPHY

Bibliography

ABRAMS, ALBERT J., "Barriers to the Employment of Older Workers," *Annals* of the American Academy of Political and Social Science, vol. 279, January, 1952, pp. 62–71.

"Discrimination in Employment of Older Workers in Various Countries of the World," *Journal of Gerontology*, vol. 6, July, 1951, Supplement, p. 51. Abstract.

"Job Engineering and Job Re-assignment for the Older Worker in American Industry" in *Growing with the Years*, New York State Joint Legislative Committee on Problems of the Aging. Legislative Document 32, Newburgh, 1954, pp. 99–107.

"National Conference on Aging Sparks Drive for Older Workers," *Employment Security Review*, vol. 17, December, 1950, pp. 3–5.

ADAMS, G. F., "The Social Medicine of Old Age in Northern Ireland," *Ulster Medical Journal*, vol. 21, November, 1952, pp. 130–141.

ADAMS, G. F., AND E. A. CHEESEMAN, *Old People in Northern Ireland:* A Report to the North Ireland Hospitals Authority on the Medical and Social Problems of Old Age. Belfast, 1951. 201 pp.

ADAMS, G. F., AND A. T. WELFORD, "Some Social and Psychological Problems of Ageing," *Nature*, vol. 171, March 7, 1953, pp. 422–423.

ALBRECHT, RUTH, "Relationships of Older People with Their Own Parents," *Marriage and Family Living*, vol. 15, November, 1953, pp. 296–298. Abstract.

"Social Roles in the Prevention of Senility," *Journal of Gerontology*, vol. 6, October, 1951, pp. 380–386.

ALDRIDGE, GORDON J., "Old Age as a Social Problem," *Journal of Public Law*, vol. 2, Fall, 1953, pp. 333–339.

ALLEN, EDWARD B., AND HOLLIS E. CLOW, "The Psychology of Retirement," *Journal of the American Geriatrics Society*, vol. 2, December, 1954, pp. 796–806.

AMERICAN INSTITUTE OF ARCHITECTS, "Buildings for the Handicapped and/or Aged," *American Institute of Architects Bulletin*, vol. 5, November, 1951, pp. 1–14; vol. 6, January, 1952, pp. 1–18; vol. 8, March–April, 1954, pp. 51–56.

AMERICAN NURSES' ASSOCIATION, *The Older Nurse*. New York, 1954. 40 pp.

AMERICAN PUBLIC HEALTH ASSOCIATION, Committee on the Hygiene of Housing, *Housing an Aging Population*. New York, 1953. 92 pp.

AMES, LOUISE B., AND OTHERS, *Rorschach Responses in Old Age*. Paul B. Hoeber, Inc. (Harper and Bros.), New York, 1954. 229 pp.

AMULREE, BASIL W. S. M., *Adding Life to Years*. National Council of Social Service, London, 1951. 101 pp.

ANTMAN, JOSEPH, "Older Parent-Adult Child Counseling," *Jewish Social Service Quarterly*, vol. 25, March, 1949, pp. 331–340.

ARENSBERG, CONRAD M., AND S. T. KIMBALL, *Family and Community in Ireland*. Harvard University Press, Cambridge, 1940. 322 pp.

ARTHUR, JULIETTA K., *How to Help Older People*. J. B. Lippincott Co., Philadelphia, 1954. 500 pp.

BANCROFT, GERTRUDE, "Older Persons in the Labor Force," *Annals* of the American Academy of Political and Social Science, vol. 279, January, 1952, pp. 52–61.

BANKERS TRUST COMPANY OF NEW YORK, editor, *A Study of Industrial Retirement Plans Including Analyses of Complete Programs Recently Adopted or Revised*. New York, 1953. 145 pp.

BARKIN, SOLOMON, "Jobs for Older Workers," *Journal of Gerontology*, vol. 7, July, 1952, pp. 426–430.

"Should There Be a Fixed Retirement Age? Organized Labor Says No," *Annals* of the American Academy of Political and Social Science, vol. 279, January, 1952, pp. 77–80.

BARNETT, DELLA D., "The Barrier of Age Exploded," *Public Aid in Illinois*, vol. 20, June, 1953, pp. 14–17.

BARRON, MILTON L., "Minority Group Characteristics of the Aged in American Society," *Journal of Gerontology*, vol. 8, October, 1953, pp. 477–482.

BARRON, MILTON L., GORDON STREIB, AND EDWARD A. SUCHMAN, "Research on the Social Disorganization of Retirement," *American Sociological Review*, vol. 17, August, 1952, pp. 479–482.

BAY, EMMET B., "Care of the Aged: A Growing Problem," *Medical Clinician of North America*, vol. 35, January, 1951, pp. 289–293.

BELBIN, R. M., "Difficulties of Older People in Industry," *Occupational Psychology*, vol. 27, October, 1953, pp. 177–180. Abstract.

BENNETT, GEORGE K., "A Psychologist's View of Retirement Problems," *Industrial Medicine and Surgery*, vol. 23, May, 1954, pp. 209–212.

BLACKBURN, GEORGE G., "The Problem of the Older Worker," *Canadian Labour Gazette*, vol. 53, February, 1953, pp. 203–215.

BLAU, ZENA S., "Changes in Status and Age Identification," vol. 21, *American Sociological Review*, April, 1956, pp. 198–203.

BLUESTONE, E. M., "Current Problems in Geriatrics: With Special Reference to Medical Care," *Geriatrics*, vol. 9, October, 1954, pp. 465–471.
"Medical Care of the Aged," *Journal of Gerontology*, vol. 4, October, 1949, pp. 305–309.

BOAS, ERNEST P., *Add Life to Your Years*. McBride Co., New York, 1954. 278 pp.

BOND, FLOYD A., AND OTHERS, *Our Needy Aged*. Henry Holt and Co., New York, 1954. 401 pp.

BORTZ, EDWARD L., "Geriatrics as a Specialty" in *Health in the Later Years*, edited by John M. Maclachlan. Institute of Gerontology Series, vol. 3. University of Florida Press, Gainesville, 1953, pp. 11–16.
"New Goals for Maturity," *Journal of Gerontology*, vol. 9, January, 1954, pp. 67–73.

BOSSARD, JAMES H. S., "Marrying Late in Life," *Social Forces*, vol. 29, May, 1951, pp. 405–408.

BOWEN, GEORGENE E., "Philadelphia's Recreational Project for Older People," *Journal of Gerontology*, vol. 3, July, 1948, pp. 215–219.

BOWERS, WILLIAM H., "An Appraisal of Worker Characteristics as Related to Age," *Journal of Applied Psychology*, vol. 36, October, 1952, pp. 296–300.

BOWMAN, KARL M., "Personality Adjustment in Aging Adults," *Geriatrics*, vol. 9, December, 1954, pp. 563–566.

BOYNTON, PAUL W., *Six Ways to Retire*. Harper and Bros., New York, 1952. 145 pp.

BRECKINRIDGE, ELIZABETH L., *Effective Use of Older Workers.* Wilcox and Follett Co., Chicago, 1953. 224 pp.

BRESLOW, LESTER, "Aging and Community Health Programs," *Journal of Gerontology*, vol. 9, April, 1954, pp. 224–227.

BRIGHT, MARGARET L., AND DONALD G. HAY, *Health Resources and Their Use by Rural People:* Ulster County. Bulletin 32, New York State College of Agriculture, Department of Rural Sociology, Ithaca, 1952. 30 pp. Mimeographed.

BRITTON, JOSEPH H., "The Personal Adjustment of Retired School Teachers," *Journal of Gerontology*, vol. 8, July, 1953, pp. 333–338.

BRITTON, JOSEPH H., AND JEAN O. BRITTON, "Work and Retirement for Older University Alumni," *Journal of Gerontology*, vol. 9, October, 1954, pp. 468–474.

BRUNOT, HELEN H., *Old Age in New York City.* Welfare Council of New York City, 1944. 128 pp.

BUCKLEY, JOSEPH C., *Retirement Handbook.* Harper and Bros., New York, 1953. 329 pp.

"BUILDING POSITIVE APPROACHES TO THE CHRONICALLY ILL," *Public Health Reports*, vol. 69, May, 1954, pp. 462–470.

BUNKER, RUTH, "Creative Activity Through Handicrafts," *Annals* of the American Academy of Political and Social Science, vol. 279, January, 1952, pp. 93–97.

BUNZEL, JOSEPH H., AND LOUIS GARE, "Some Factors in Satisfaction with Retirement" in *Report of the Mayor's Advisory Committee for the Aged*, vol. 2, New York, 1953. 15 pp.

BURGESS, ERNEST W., "Family Living in the Later Decades," *Annals* of the American Academy of Political and Social Science, vol. 279, January, 1952, pp. 106–114.
"Social Relations, Activities, and Personal Adjustment," *American Journal of Sociology*, vol. 59, January, 1954, pp. 352–360.

BURGESS, ERNEST W., editor, "Aging and Retirement," *American Journal of Sociology*, vol. 59, January, 1954. Entire issue.

BURNS, ROBERT K., "Economic Aspects of Aging and Retirement," *American Journal of Sociology*, vol. 59, January, 1954, pp. 384–390.

CALIFORNIA ASSEMBLY INTERIM COMMITTEE ON SOCIAL WELFARE, *The Nonpsychotic Seniles and Related Problems:* Report of the Assembly Interim Committee on Social Welfare. Sacramento, 1955. 109 pp.

CALIFORNIA GOVERNOR'S CONFERENCE ON THE PROBLEMS OF THE AGING, *Proceedings*. State Printing Office, Sacramento, 1951. 296 pp.

CANTOR, LEON R., "Cooperation of the Jewish Community Center and Other Agencies to Meet the Needs of Older Adults," *Jewish Social Service Quarterly*, vol. 29, Spring, 1953, pp. 331–336.

CARLSON, ANTON J., AND EDWARD J. STIEGLITZ, "Physiological Changes in Aging," *Annals* of the American Academy of Political and Social Science, vol. 279, January, 1952, pp. 18–31.

CAVAN, RUTH S., "Family Life and Family Substitutes in Old Age," *American Sociological Review*, vol. 14, February, 1949, pp. 71–83.

CAVAN, RUTH S., AND OTHERS, *Personal Adjustment in Old Age*. Science Research Associates, Chicago, 1949. 204 pp.

CHEIN, ISIDOR, STUART W. COOK, AND JOHN HARDING, "The Use of Research in Social Therapy," *Human Relations*, vol. 1, no. 4, 1948, pp. 497–511.

CIOCCO, ANTONIO, AND PHILIP S. LAWRENCE, "Illness Among Older People in Hagerstown, Maryland" in *Illness and Health Services in an Aging Population*. U. S. Public Health Service, Washington, 1952, pp. 26–37.

CLAGUE, EWAN, "Labor Force Trends in the United States," *Journal of Gerontology*, vol. 7, January, 1952, pp. 92–99.

CLEVELAND WELFARE FEDERATION, Occupation Planning Committee, *A Study of Older Woman Clerical Workers in Cleveland*. Cleveland, Ohio, 1952. 5 pp. Mimeographed.

COCHRANE, CRAIG P., "Should There Be a Fixed Retirement Age? Some Managements Prefer Flexibility," *Annals* of the American Academy of Political and Social Science, vol. 279, January, 1952, pp. 74–77.

COHEN, WILBUR J., "Income Maintenance for the Aged," *Annals* of the American Academy of Political and Social Science, vol. 279, January, 1952, pp. 154–163.

COLBY, EVELYN, AND JOHN G. FORREST, *Ways and Means to Successful Retirement*. B. C. Forbes and Sons Publishing Co., New York, 1952. 250 pp.

CORNELL UNIVERSITY, DEPARTMENT OF SOCIOLOGY AND ANTHROPOLOGY, *The Study of Occupational Retirement:* First Progress Report, Ithaca, N. Y., 1953. 34 pp. Second Progress Report, 1955. 12 pp. Mimeographed.

CORSON, JOHN J., AND JOHN W. McCONNELL, *Economic Needs of Older People*. Twentieth Century Fund, New York, 1956. 533 pp.

"COURSE IN MATURITY AT THE UNIVERSITY OF CHICAGO," *Science Digest*, vol. 33, June, 1953, p. 34.

COWDRY, EDMUND V., "The Broader Implications of Aging," *Journal of Gerontology*, vol. 2, October, 1947, pp. 277–282.

COWDRY, EDMUND V., editor, *Problems of Ageing*. 3d ed. edited by Albert I. Lansing. Williams and Wilkins Co., Baltimore, 1952. 1061 pp.

CREEDON, CAROL F., BERNARD KUTNER, AND ALICE M. TOGO, *The Role of Research in Planning Community Services for the Aged*. Cornell University Medical College, New York, 1955. Mimeographed.

CUSHING, J. G. N., "Problems of Retirement," *Mental Hygiene*, vol. 36, July, 1952, pp. 449–455.

DACSO, MICHAEL M., "Physical Restoration in the Older Person" in *Growing in the Older Years*, edited by Wilma T. Donahue and Clark Tibbitts. University of Michigan Press, Ann Arbor, 1951, pp. 99–114.

DEARDORFF, NEVA R., "The Religio-cultural Background of New York City's Population," *Milbank Memorial Fund Quarterly*, vol. 33, April, 1955, pp. 152–160.

DEGRUCHY, CLARE, *Creative Old Age*. National Social Welfare Assembly, New York, 1946. 143 pp.

DERBER, MILTON, editor, *The Aged and Society*. Industrial Relations Research Association, Madison, Wis., 1950. 237 pp.

DERTOUZOUS, D. N., AND JOHN J. PEARCE, JR., "The Older Worker in Industry: A Survey of the Retirement Plans of the Larger New Jersey Manufacturing Establishments," *Journal of Gerontology*, vol. 9, July, 1954, pp. 349–353.

DOFF, SIMON O., "Adequate Medical Care Is Problem of Aged," *Public Health Reports*, vol. 69, September, 1954, p. 858. Abstract.

DONAHUE, WILMA T., "Education's Role in Maintaining the Individual's Status," *Annals* of the American Academy of Political and Social Science, vol. 279, January, 1952, pp. 115–125.

"Psychological Aspects of Aging" in *Problems of America's Aging Population*, edited by T. Lynn Smith. University of Florida Press, Gainesville, 1951, pp. 47–65.

"Trends in Gerontology," *Personnel and Guidance Journal*, vol. 31, May, 1953, pp. 505–508.

DONAHUE, WILMA T., compiler, *Education for Later Maturity*. Whiteside, Inc. (William Morrow and Co.), New York, 1955. 338 pp.

DONAHUE, WILMA T., editor, *Earning Opportunities for Older Workers*. University of Michigan Press, Ann Arbor, 1955. 277 pp.
Housing the Aging. University of Michigan Press, Ann Arbor, 1954. 280 pp.

DONAHUE, WILMA T., WOODROW W. HUNTER, AND DOROTHY COONS, "A Study of the Socialization of Old People," *Geriatrics*, vol. 8, December, 1953, pp. 656–666.

DONAHUE, WILMA T., JAMES RAE, JR., AND ROGER B. BERRY, editors, *Rehabilitation of the Older Worker*. University of Michigan Press, Ann Arbor, 1953. 200 pp.

DONAHUE, WILMA T., AND CLARK TIBBITTS, editors, *Growing in the Older Years*. University of Michigan Press, Ann Arbor, 1951. 204 pp.
Planning the Older Years. University of Michigan Press, Ann Arbor, 1950. 248 pp.

DUNNETTE, M. D., AND W. K. KIRCHNER, "Utilization of Older Employees in Minnesota," *University of Minnesota Business News Notes*, February, 1953, pp. 1–4. Abstract.

DUTCHESS, CHARLES E., "A Retirement Policy—Recommendations and Criteria," *Industrial Medicine and Surgery*, vol. 22, August, 1953, pp. 349–351.

EASTERN STATES HEALTH EDUCATION CONFERENCE, 1949, *Social and Biological Challenge of Our Aging Population:* Proceedings. Columbia University Press, New York, 1950. 183 pp.

FANSHEL, DAVID, BERNARD KUTNER, AND THOMAS S. LANGNER, "Aging: A Cross-Sectional Survey and Action Program," *Journal of Gerontology*, vol. 9, April, 1954, pp. 205–209.

FEDERATION EMPLOYMENT SERVICE, *New Evidence:* Employers Evaluate Older Workers as Productive, Absent Less, and as Adaptable as Younger Workers. New York, 1952. 8 pp. Mimeographed.
Part Time Job Finding for Pensioners: A Report. New York, 1954. 19 pp. Mimeographed.

FEIFEL, HERMAN, "We've Added Years to Life: Let's Add Life to Years," *Menninger Quarterly*, vol. 8, no. 3, 1954, pp. 27–29.

FISHER, GLADYS, "Social Services for the Aged," *New York State Journal of Medicine*, vol. 53, October 15, 1953, pp. 2370–2372.

FOLSOM, JOSEPH K., "Old Age as a Sociological Problem," *American Journal of Orthopsychiatry*, vol. 10, January, 1940, pp. 30–39.

FRANCIS, HELEN, AND OTHERS, "Serving the Older Person: A Multiple Approach by the Family Agency," *Social Casework*, vol. 35, July, 1954, pp. 299–308.

FREEMAN, JOSEPH T., "Patterns in Aging," *Journal of the American Geriatrics Society*, vol. 2, June, 1954, pp. 371–376.

"The Sociologic Aspects of Aging: Gerocomy," *West Virginia Medical Journal*, vol. 50, March, 1954, pp. 73–76.

FRIED, EDRITA G., AND KARL STERN, "The Situation of the Aged Within the Family," *American Journal of Orthopsychiatry*, vol. 18, January, 1948, pp. 31–54.

FRIEDMANN, EUGENE A., AND OTHERS, *The Meaning of Work and Retirement*. University of Chicago Press, Chicago, 1954. 197 pp.

GADEL, MARGUERITE S., "Productivity and Satisfaction of Full- and Part-time Female Employees," *Personnel Psychology*, vol. 6, Autumn, 1953, pp. 327–342.

GALDSTON, IAGO, *The Meaning of Social Medicine*. Harvard University Press, Cambridge, 1954. 178 pp.

GARDNER, L. P., "Attitudes and Activities of the Middle-Aged and Aged," *Geriatrics*, vol. 4, January-February, 1949, pp. 33–50.

GILBERT, JEANNE G., *Understanding Old Age*. Ronald Press Co., New York, 1952. 422 pp.

GINZBERG, RAPHAEL, "Geriatrics and Gerontology in Every-Day Practice," *Individual Psychology Bulletin*, vol. 7, 1949, pp. 21–29.

GOLDFARB, ALVIN I., "Psychiatric Problems of Old Age," *New York State Journal of Medicine*, vol. 55, February 15, 1955, pp. 494–500.

GOLDFARB, ALVIN I., AND JACK SHEPS, "Psychotherapy of the Aged," *Psychosomatic Medicine*, vol. 16, May–June, 1954, pp. 209–219.

GOULDING, W. S., "Housing for Older People," *Canadian Welfare*, vol. 28, December 15, 1952, pp. 38–41.

GRANICK, SAMUEL, "Adjustment of Older People in Two Florida Communities," *Journal of Gerontology*, vol. 7, July, 1952, pp. 419–425.

GRAVATT, ARTHUR E., "Family Relations in Middle and Old Age: A Review," *Journal of Gerontology*, vol. 8, April, 1953, pp. 197–201.

GREENLEIGH, LAWRENCE F., *Psychological Problems of Our Aging Population*. U. S. Public Health Service, National Institute of Mental Health, Bethesda, Md., 1952. 76 pp. Processed.

GRETHER, E. T., "Aging and the National Economy," *Journal of Gerontology*, vol. 9, July, 1954, pp. 354–358.

GROSSMAN, BEN L., "Older People Live in Institutions," *Journal of Ohio Association of Nursing Homes* (Elyria, Ohio), vol. 1, no. 4, 1952, pp. 7–13.

GROUP FOR THE ADVANCEMENT OF PSYCHIATRY, Committee on Hospitals, *The Problem of the Aged Patient in the Public Psychiatric Hospital.* Report no. 14, Topeka, Kan., 1950. 6 pp.

GRUENBERG, ERNEST M., "Community Conditions and Psychoses of the Elderly," *American Journal of Psychiatry*, vol. 110, June, 1954, pp. 888–896.

GUMPERT, MARTIN, "Geriatrics: A Social Problem," *Journal of the Medical Society of New Jersey*, vol. 51, February, 1954, pp. 56–60.

"Old Age and Productive Loss," *Bulletin of the Menninger Clinic*, vol. 17, no. 3, 1953, pp. 103–109.

You Are Younger Than You Think. Duell, Sloan, and Pearce, Inc. (Little, Brown and Co.), New York, 1944. 244 pp.

GUMPERT, MARTIN, AND OTHERS, "Where and with Whom Should Older People Live? Radio Discussion," *University of Chicago Round Table*, September 16, 1951, pp. 1–21.

HALL, HAROLD R., "Activity Program for Retirement by Executives," *Journal of Gerontology*, vol. 9, April, 1954, pp. 214–217.

HARLAN, WILLIAM H., "Community Adaptation to the Presence of Aged Persons: St. Petersburg, Florida," *American Journal of Sociology*, vol. 59, January, 1954, pp. 332–339.

Isolation and Conduct in Later Life: A Study of Four Hundred Sixty-Four Chicagoans of Ages Sixty to Ninety-Five. University of Chicago Libraries, Chicago, 1950. Unpublished doctoral dissertation.

HARRIS, MARSHALL, "Should There Be a Fixed Retirement Age? The Farmer's Viewpoint," *Annals* of the American Academy of Political and Social Science, vol. 279, January, 1952, pp. 80–83.

HARRIS, RAYMOND, "The Challenge of Aging," *Journal of the American Geriatrics Society*, vol. 2, April, 1954, pp. 210–215.

HAUSER, PHILIP M., "Changes in the Labor-Force Participation of the Older Worker," *American Journal of Sociology*, vol. 59, January, 1954, pp. 312–323.

HAVIGHURST, ROBERT J., "Flexibility and the Social Roles of the Retired," *American Journal of Sociology*, vol. 59, January, 1954, pp. 309–311.

Human Development and Education. Longmans, Green and Co., New York, 1953. 338 pp.

"Old Age: An American Problem," *Journal of Gerontology*, vol. 4, October, 1949, pp. 298–304.

"Social and Psychological Needs of the Aging," *Annals* of the American Academy of Political and Social Science, vol. 279, January, 1952, pp. 11–17.

"Validity of the Chicago Attitude Inventory as a Measure of Personal Adjustment in Old Age," *Journal of Abnormal and Social Psychology*, vol. 46, January, 1951, pp. 24–29.

HAVIGHURST, ROBERT J., AND RUTH ALBRECHT, *Older People.* Longmans, Green and Co., New York, 1953. 415 pp.

HIBBARD, DONALD L., AND JOHN P. LEE, "Presbyterian Ministers and Their Widows in Retirement," *Journal of Gerontology*, vol. 9, January, 1954, pp. 46–55.

HILTON, MARY N., AND PEARL C. RAVNER, *Entry and Reentry of the Older Woman into the Labor Market.* U. S. Women's Bureau, Washington, 1953. 20 pp. Multigraphed.

HOLTZMAN, ABRAHAM, "Analysis of Old Age Politics in the United States," *Journal of Gerontology*, vol. 9, January, 1954, pp. 56–65.

The Townsend Movement: A Study in Old Age Pressure Politics. Harvard University, Cambridge, 1952. Unpublished doctoral dissertation.

HOPE, STANLEY C., "Should There Be a Fixed Retirement Age? Some Managements Say Yes," *Annals* of the American Academy of Political and Social Science, vol. 279, January, 1952, pp. 72–74.

HORNEY, KAREN, *The Neurotic Personality of Our Time.* W. W. Norton and Co., New York, 1937. 299 pp.

HOUSING RESEARCH COUNCIL OF SOUTHERN CALIFORNIA, *The Architect Looks at Housing the Aged.* Pasadena, 1954. 16 pp. Processed.

HOWELL, TREVOR H., *Our Advancing Years.* Macmillan Co., New York, 1954. 192 pp.

HOYT, G. C., "The Life of the Retired in a Trailer Park," *American Journal of Sociology*, vol. 59, January, 1954, pp. 361–370.

HUNTER, WOODROW W., "A Proposed Activity Center for Older People," *Geriatrics*, vol. 6, March-April, 1951, pp. 121–128.

HUNTER, WOODROW W., AND HELEN MAURICE, *Older People Tell Their Story*. University of Michigan Press, Ann Arbor, 1953. 99 pp.

ILLINOIS PUBLIC AID COMMISSION, *Studies in Later Maturity and the Aged*. Chicago, 1952. 53 pp. Mimeographed.

INDELMAN, ROCHELLE, "The Application of Two Basic Case Work Concepts in Work with Older Persons," *Jewish Social Service Quarterly*, vol. 28, June, 1952, pp. 388–395.

JACOBSON, EUGENE, AND OTHERS, "Research in Functioning Organizations," *Journal of Social Issues*, vol. 7, no. 3, 1951, pp. 64–71.

JAFFE, ABRAM J., AND R. O. CARLETON, *Occupational Mobility in the United States: 1930–1960*. Kings Crown Press, New York, 1954. 105 pp.

JOHNSON, GEORGE E., "A Program to Prepare College Teachers for Retirement," *Journal of Gerontology*, vol. 9, April, 1954, pp. 218–223.

JOHNSON, WINGATE M., "Adjustments to Age," *Medical Annals of District of Columbia*, vol. 17, December, 1948, pp. 664–667, 701.
"Geriatrics in General Practice," *Maryland Medical Journal*, vol. 1, December, 1952, pp. 582–592.

JOHNSTON, McCLAIN, "Adult Guidance Center, San Francisco," *Public Health Reports*, vol. 68, June, 1953, pp. 590–594.

JONES, HAROLD E., "Longitudinal and Cross-Sectional Methods in the Study of Aging" in *Research on Aging*, edited by Harold E. Jones. Social Science Research Council, New York, 1950, pp. 67–73.

JONES, HAROLD E., editor, *Research on Aging*. Social Science Research Council, New York, 1950. 128 pp. Mimeographed.

KAPLAN, JEROME, "Effect of Group Activity on Psychogenic Manifestations of Older People," *Geriatrics*, vol. 9, November, 1954, pp. 537–539.

KAPLAN, OSCAR J., "Psychological Aspects of Aging," *Annals* of the American Academy of Political and Social Science, vol. 279, January, 1952, pp. 32–42.
"Uses of Sample Survey Methodology" in *Research on Aging*, edited by Harold E. Jones. Social Science Research Council, New York, 1950, pp. 91–93. Mimeographed.

KAPLAN, OSCAR J., editor, *Mental Disorders in Later Life*. Stanford University Press, Stanford, Calif., 1945. 436 pp.

KINKADE, HENRY W., JOHN A. SKIPTON, AND OTHERS, *Ohio Fact Book on Aging*. Ohio State University and Ohio Citizens' Council for Health and Welfare, Columbus, 1954. 32 pp.

KIRCHNER, WAYNE K., AND OTHERS, "Attitudes Toward the Employment of Older People," *Journal of Applied Psychology*, vol. 36, June, 1952, pp. 154–156.

KLEEMEIER, ROBERT W., "Moosehaven: Congregate Living in a Community of the Retired," *American Journal of Sociology*, vol. 59, January, 1954, pp. 347–351.

KLUMPP, T. G., "New Horizons for Old Age," *West Virginia Medical Journal*, vol. 44, February, 1948, pp. 25–30.

KOBAK, ROSE, *Care of the Aged in 1954*. Council of Jewish Federations and Welfare Funds, New York, 1953. 15 pp. Multigraphed.

KOLB, LAWRENCE, *Old Age and Mental Disease:* Supplemental Report of the Philadelphia Mental Health Survey Committee. Philadelphia, 1954. 58 pp. Mimeographed.

KOOS, EARL L., editor, *Kips Bay-Yorkville: 1940*. Department of Public Health and Preventive Medicine, Cornell University Medical College, New York, 1942. 86 pp.

KORENCHEVSKY, V., "The Problem of Ageing: Basic Difficulties of Research," *British Medical Journal*, vol. 1, January 8, 1949, pp. 66–68.

KOSSORIS, MAX D., "Absenteeism and Injury Experience of Older Workers," *Monthly Labor Review*, vol. 67, July, 1948, pp. 16–19.

KRAPF, E. E., "On Ageing," *Proceedings* of the Royal Society of Medicine, vol. 46, November, 1953, pp. 957–963.

KRASNER, I. BIGFORD, "Factors Associated with Status in a Recreational Program for the Aged," *Jewish Social Service Quarterly*, vol. 28, March, 1952, pp. 290–301.

KRAUS, HERTHA, "Community Planning for the Aged: Outline of a Working Hypothesis," *Journal of Gerontology*, vol. 3, April, 1948, pp. 129–140.

"Housing Our Older Citizens," *Annals* of the American Academy of Political and Social Science, vol. 279, January, 1952, pp. 126–138.

"Older Persons Have Special Housing Needs," *Journal of Housing*, vol. 7, January, 1950, pp. 17–20.

KUBIE, SUSAN H., AND GERTRUDE LANDAU, *Group Work with the Aged*. International Universities Press, New York, 1953. 214 pp.

KUH, CLIFFORD, "Employment of the Older Worker—A Challenge to Industry and Public Health," *American Journal of Public Health*, vol. 42, June, 1952, pp. 699–704.

KUHLEN, RAYMOND G., "Problems in the Motivation of Subjects in Research on Aging" in *Research on Aging*, edited by Harold E. Jones. Social Science Research Council, New York, 1950, pp. 82–91. Mimeographed.

KUTASH, SAMUEL B., "Personality Patterns of Old Age and the Rorschach Test," *Geriatrics*, vol. 9, August, 1954, pp. 367–370.

LADIMER, IRVING, "Preparation for Retirement," *Factory*, vol. 3, June, 1953, pp. 88–91.

LANDIS, JUDSON T., "Social-Psychological Factors of Aging," *Social Forces*, vol. 20, May, 1942, pp. 468–470.

LANSING, ALBERT I., editor, *Problems of Ageing*. 3d ed. Williams and Wilkins Co., Baltimore, 1952. 1061 pp. A revision of Edmund V. Cowdry's *Problems of Ageing*.

LAVERTY, RUTH, "Non-resident Aid—Community Versus Institutional Care for Older People," *Journal of Gerontology*, vol. 5, October, 1950, pp. 370–374.

LAWTON, GEORGE, *Aging Successfully*. Columbia University Press, New York, 1946. 266 pp.
"Counselling the Older Person," *Journal of Gerontology*, vol. 3, October, 1948, Supplement, p. 8. Abstract.

LAWTON, GEORGE, editor, *New Goals for Old Age*. Columbia University Press, New York, 1943. 210 pp.

LAWTON, GEORGE, AND MAXWELL S. STEWART, *When You Grow Older*. 2d ed. rev. Public Affairs Pamphlet no. 131, New York, 1954.

LAYCOCK, SAMUEL R., *Many Happy Returns: Needs of Older Folks*. Department of Public Health, Regina, Canada, 1953. Canadian Broadcasting Company Series of Talks.

LEBO, DELL, "Some Factors Said to Make for Happiness in Old Age," *Journal of Clinical Psychology*, vol. 9, October, 1953, pp. 385–387.

LEE, DOROTHY D., AND KENNETH F. HERROLD, editors, "Sociocultural Approaches to Medical Care," *Journal of Social Issues*, vol. 8, no. 4, 1952. Entire issue.

LEGGO, CHRISTOPHER, "Employment of the Aging—Appraising the Barriers," *Industrial Medicine and Surgery*, vol. 23, February, 1954, pp. 73–74.

LEHMAN, HARVEY C., *Age and Achievement*. Princeton University Press, Princeton, N. J., 1953. 358 pp.

"Chronological Age vs. Proficiency in Physical Skills," *American Journal of Psychology*, vol. 64, April, 1951, pp. 161–187.

"Gainful Occupations Engaged in Most Often by Men and Women of Age 65 and Over," *American Psychologist*, vol. 9, August, 1954, p. 414. Abstract.

LEHMAN, MAXWELL, AND MORTON YARMON, *Jobs After Retirement*. Henry Holt and Co., New York, 1954. 241 pp.

LEIGHTON, ALEXANDER H., *The Stirling County Study:* A Research Program in Social Factors Related to Psychiatric Health. Second Annual Report, June 30, 1952. Ithaca, N. Y. 40 pp. Hectographed.

LEMKAU, PAUL V., "The Mental Hygiene of Aging," *Public Health Reports*, vol. 67, March, 1952, pp. 237–241.

LEVINE, HARRY A., "Community Programs for the Elderly," *Annals* of the American Academy of Political and Social Science, vol. 279, January, 1952, pp. 164–170.

LEVINE, SINCLAIR S., "Old Age and Employability," *Connecticut State Medical Journal*, vol. 15, February, 1951, pp. 117–119.

LEWIS, JOHN A., "Mental Health as It Relates to Chronic Illness," *West Virginia Medical Journal*, vol. 50, December, 1954, pp. 355–360.

LEWIS, NOLAN D. C., "Applying Mental Health Principles to Problems of the Aging" in *New Goals for Old Age*, edited by George Lawton. Columbia University Press, New York, 1943, pp. 91–105.

LEWIS, WILLIAM HALL, JR., "Differences in the Rate and Trend of Mortality for Different Age and Sex Groups in Different Eras," *Journal of Gerontology*, vol. 8, July, 1953, pp. 318–323.

LIKERT, RENSIS, *A Program of Research on the Fundamental Problems of Organizing Human Behavior*. Survey Research Center, University of Michigan, Ann Arbor, 1947. 12 pp.

LINDEN, MAURICE E., AND DOUGLAS COURTNEY, "The Human Life Cycle and Its Interruptions—A Psychologic Hypothesis: Studies in Gerontologic Human Relations I," *American Journal of Psychiatry*, vol. 109, June, 1953, pp. 906–915.

LOCKWOOD, WILLIAM V., "Adult Guidance: A Community Responsibility," *Personnel and Guidance Journal*, vol. 31, October, 1952, pp. 31–34.

LORGE, IRVING D., AND KENNETH HELFANT, "The Independence of Chronological Age and Sociopolitical Attitudes," *Journal of Abnormal Psychology*, vol. 48, October, 1953, p. 598.

MACLACHLAN, JOHN M., "Change in Status with Age Called Incongruous," *Public Health Reports*, vol. 69, September, 1954, pp. 857–858. Abstract.

MACLACHLAN, JOHN M., editor, *Health in the Later Years.* Institute of Gerontology Series, vol. 3. University of Florida Press, Gainesville, 1953. 123 pp.

MAHONEY, THOMAS A., "What's Happening to the Older Employee in Industry?" *Labor Law Journal*, vol. 4, May, 1953, pp. 329–333.

MALAMUD, WILLIAM, "The Psychiatric Aspects of Geriatrics," *Journal of Iowa State Medical Society*, vol. 43, November, 1953, pp. 461–466.

MANLEY, CHARLES R., JR., "The Migration of Older People," *American Journal of Sociology*, vol. 59, January, 1954, pp. 324–331.

MARSH, D. C., compiler, "Old People in Wellington City: A Survey" in *Annual Report* of the New Zealand Health Department, 1951–1952, pp. 82–104.

MASON, EVELYN P., "Some Correlates of Self-Judgments of the Aged," *Journal of Gerontology*, vol. 9, July, 1954, pp. 324–337.

MATHIASEN, GENEVA, editor, *Criteria for Retirement:* A Report of a National Conference on Retirement of Older Workers. G. P. Putnam's Sons, New York, 1953. 233 pp.

MAUSER, FERDINAND F., AND JAMES H. BROWN, *Detroit's Senior Citizens:* Their Viewpoints and Attitudes. Wayne University, Detroit, 1955. 53 pp. Multilithed.

MAYOR'S ADVISORY COMMITTEE FOR THE AGED, *New York City's Senior Citizens:* Our Most Neglected Resource; Our Most Important Challenge; Our Greatest Opportunity. New York, 1953. 3 vols. Mimeographed.

McHUGH, ROSE J., "A Constructive Program for the Aged," *Proceedings* of the National Conference of Social Work, 1947. Columbia University Press, New York, 1948, pp. 391–401.

McKAIN, WALTER C., JR., *The Social Participation of Old People in a California Retirement Community.* Harvard University, Cambridge, 1947. Unpublished doctoral dissertation.

McKain, Walter C., Jr., Elmer D. Baldwin, and Louis J. Ducoff, *Old Age and Retirement in Rural Connecticut:* 2. Economic Security of Farm Operators and Farm Laborers. Bulletin 299, Agricultural Experiment Station, Storrs, Conn., 1953. 51 pp.

McMahan, C. A., and Thomas R. Ford, "Surviving the First Five Years of Retirement," *Journal of Gerontology*, vol. 10, April, 1955, pp. 212–215.

Merton, Robert K., and others, editors, "Social Policy and Social Research in Housing," *Journal of Social Issues*, vol. 7, nos. 1 and 2, 1951. Entire issues.

Metropolitan Life Insurance Company, "Widowhood and Its Duration," *Statistical Bulletin Metropolitan Life Insurance Company*, vol. 34, September, 1953, pp. 1–3.

Michelon, L. C., "The New Leisure Class," *American Journal of Sociology*, vol. 59, January, 1954, pp. 371–378.

Michigan State Medical Society, Geriatric Committee, "Preventive Geriatrics," *Journal of the Michigan State Medical Society*, vol. 53, May, 1954, pp. 507–536.

Miller, Frieda S., "Older Workers and Older Women" in *No Time to Grow Old*. New York State Joint Legislative Committee on Problems of the Aging. Legislative Document 12, Newburgh, 1951, pp. 183–191.

Minnesota Commission on Aging, *Minnesota's Aging Citizens*. St. Paul, 1953. 68 pp.

Moberg, David O., "Church Membership and Personal Adjustment in Old Age," *Journal of Gerontology*, vol. 8, April, 1953, pp. 207–211.

Monroe, Robert T., *Diseases in Old Age*. Harvard University Press, Cambridge, 1951. 407 pp.

Moore, Elon H., "Community Organization for Older Persons," *Geriatrics*, vol. 3, September–October, 1948, pp. 306–313.

"Professors in Retirement," *Journal of Gerontology*, vol. 6, July, 1951, pp. 243–252.

Muñoz, Raúl, Belén M. Serra, and Angelina S. de Roca, "Research and Evaluation in a Program of Community Education," *Journal of Social Issues*, vol. 9, no. 2, 1953, pp. 43–52.

Murphy, Gardner, *Personality:* A Biosocial Approach to Origins and Structure. Harper and Bros., New York, 1947. 999 pp.

MYERS, JEROME K., AND LESLIE SCHAFFER, "Social Stratification and Psychiatric Practice: A Study of an Out-Patient Clinic," *American Sociological Review*, vol. 19, June, 1954, pp. 307–310.

NATIONAL ADVISORY COMMITTEE ON THE EMPLOYMENT OF OLDER MEN AND WOMEN, *First Report*. H. M. Stationery Office, London, 1953. 62 pp.

NATIONAL CORPORATION FOR CARE OF OLD PEOPLE, *Annual Report*. London, 1954.

NATIONAL COUNCIL OF SOCIAL SERVICE, National Old People's Welfare Committee, *Age Is Opportunity:* A New Guide to Practical Work for the Welfare of Old People. London, 1949. 147 pp.

Over Seventy: Report of an Investigation into the Social and Economic Circumstances of One Hundred People of Over Seventy Years of Age. National Council of Social Service, London, 1954. 99 pp.

NATIONAL SOCIAL WELFARE ASSEMBLY, National Committee on Aging, *Standards of Care for Older People in Institutions:* A Report of the Project on Standards for Sheltered Care. New York, 1953, 1954. 3 parts.

Sec. 1: Suggested Standards for Homes for the Aged and Nursing Homes, 1953. 112 pp.

Sec. 2: Methods of Establishing and Maintaining Standards in Homes, 1953. 112 pp.

Sec. 3: Bridging the Gap Between Existing Practices and Desirable Goals in Homes for the Aged and Nursing Homes, 1954. 112 pp.

NEWTON, KATHLEEN, *Geriatric Nursing.* 2d ed. C. V. Mosby Co., St. Louis, 1954. 424 pp.

NEW YORK STATE DEPARTMENT OF LABOR, Division of Research and Statistics, *Retirement Under Industry-Wide Pension Programs Established Through Collective Bargaining.* Publication no. B-63, New York, 1952. 30 pp.

NEW YORK STATE DEPARTMENT OF MENTAL HYGIENE, *Annual Report*. Albany, 1952.

NEW YORK STATE JOINT LEGISLATIVE COMMITTEE ON PROBLEMS OF THE AGING, *Age Is No Barrier.* Legislative Document 35, Newburgh, 1952. 171 pp.

Enriching the Years, Legislative Document 32, 1953. 199 pp.

Growing with the Years, Legislative Document 32, 1954. 159 pp.

No Time to Grow Old, Legislative Document 12, 1951. 316 pp.

Young at Any Age, Legislative Document 12, 1950. 192 pp.

NISBET, N. H., "Some Practical Considerations in the Care of the Old," *Lancet*, vol. 1, January 24, 1953, pp. 184–190.

NUFFIELD FOUNDATION, Survey Committee on the Problems of Ageing and the Care of Old People, *Old People:* Report. Oxford University Press, London, 1947. 202 pp. Prepared under the direction of B. Seebohm Rowntree.

OAHU HEALTH COUNCIL AND HONOLULU COUNCIL OF SOCIAL AGENCIES, *A Study of Oahu's Aged.* Honolulu, 1953. 74 pp.

ODELL, CHARLES E., "Employment Problems of Older Workers," *Journal of Rehabilitation*, vol. 18, January–February, 1952, pp. 3–6, 26, 27.

"Employment Services for Older Workers," *Annals* of the American Academy of Political and Social Science, vol. 279, January, 1952, pp. 171–179.

"Policy and Practice in Employing the Aging," *Personnel Guidance Journal*, vol. 31, December, 1952, pp. 152–158.

O'DONNELL, WALTER G., "The Problem of Age Barriers in Personnel Selection," *Personnel*, vol. 27, May, 1951, pp. 461–471.

OGDEN, JEAN, AND JESS OGDEN, "Sharing Community Responsibility," *Annals* of the American Academy of Political and Social Science, vol. 279, January, 1952, pp. 98–105.

OLSON, C. T., "Maintenance of Health in the Elderly Work Force," *Industrial Medicine and Surgery*, vol. 21, December, 1952, pp. 581–582.

PALMER, EDWARD NELSON, "Toward a Sociological Definition of Old Age: A Research Note," *American Journal of Sociology*, vol. 59, July, 1953, pp. 28–29.

PAN, JU-SHU, "A Comparison of Factors in the Personal Adjustment of Old People in the Protestant Church Homes for the Aged and Old People Living Outside of Institutions," *Journal of Social Psychology*, vol. 35, May, 1952, pp. 195–203.

"Problems and Adjustment of Retired Persons," *Sociology and Social Research*, vol. 35, July, 1951, pp. 422–424.

PAULUS, JEAN, "Philosophy of Human Life: Some of the Conditions of a Happy Maturity and Old Age," *Dialectica*, vol. 5, 1951, pp. 393–401.

PAYNE, STANLEY L., "The Cleveland Survey of Retired Men," *Personnel Psychology*, vol. 6, 1953, pp. 81–110.

PEMBERTON, ANNIE MAY, *Helping Older People Who Have Been in Mental Hospitals.* American Public Welfare Association, Chicago, 1954. 16 pp.

PENNINGTON, P. W., "Basic Psychological Needs of the Aged Must Be Met," *Public Health Reports*, vol. 69, September, 1954, pp. 858–859. Abstract.

PENNSYLVANIA JOINT STATE GOVERNMENT COMMISSION, *Sixty-five:* A Report Concerning Pennsylvania's Aged. Report of the Commission to the General Assembly, Harrisburg, 1953. 96 pp.

PERROTT, G. ST. J., AND OTHERS, *Illness and Health Services in an Aging Population.* U. S. Public Health Service Publication no. 170, Government Printing Office, Washington, 1952. 68 pp.

PETERSON, ROBERT L., *The Effectiveness of Older Personnel in Retailing.* Bulletin 607, Business Management Service, University of Illinois, Urbana, 1953. 15 pp.

POLLAK, OTTO, *Social Adjustment in Old Age.* Bulletin 59, Social Science Research Council, New York, 1948. 199 pp.

PRESSEY, S. L., AND ELIZABETH M. SIMCOE, "Case Study Comparisons of Successful and Problem Old People," *Journal of Gerontology*, vol. 5, April, 1950, pp. 168–175.

PRESTON, DAVID, AND ROLAND BAXT, "Techniques in the Placement of Older Workers," *Jewish Social Service Quarterly*, vol. 28, June, 1952, pp. 410–414.

RAMSEY, DOROTHEA, "Community Services for Self-Maintenance in the United Kingdom," *Annals* of the American Academy of Political and Social Science, vol. 279, January, 1952, pp. 139–145.

RAVIN, LOUIS H., "Problems of Counseling and Placement of Older Workers," *Jewish Social Service Quarterly*, vol. 28, June, 1952, pp. 415–422.

RAWLS, WILLIAM B., "Retirement and the Retirement Age," *Journal of the American Geriatrics Society*, vol. 2, 1954, pp. 619–622.

RAY, MARIE BEYNON, *The Best Years of Your Life.* Little Brown and Co., Boston, 1953. 300 pp.

RHODE ISLAND GOVERNOR'S COMMISSION TO STUDY PROBLEMS OF THE AGED, *Old Age in Rhode Island.* Providence, 1953. 143 pp.

RICHARDSON, I. N., "Age and Work: A Study of 489 Men in Heavy Industry," *British Journal of Industrial Medicine*, vol. 10, October, 1953, pp. 269–284.

RIESMAN, DAVID, "Some Clinical and Cultural Aspects of Aging," *American Journal of Sociology*, vol. 59, January, 1954, pp. 379–383.

RINGE, H. R., AND SOPHIA COOPER, *Employment and Economic Status of Older Men and Women*. U. S. Bureau of Labor Statistics Bulletin 1092, Government Printing Office, Washington, 1952. 58 pp. Processed.

ROTH, MARTIN, Discussion of "On Ageing" by E. E. Krapf in *Proceedings of the Royal Society of Medicine*, vol. 46, November, 1953, pp. 963–964.

SANDERSON, W. A., "Problems of Old Age," *Nature*, vol. 163, February 5, 1949, pp. 221–223.

SANDS, S. L., AND D. ROTHSCHILD, "Sociopsychiatric Foundations for a Theory of the Reactions to Aging," *Journal of Nervous and Mental Diseases*, vol. 116, September, 1952, pp. 233–241.

SCHEELE, LEONARD A., "Better Care for Older People," *Public Health Reports*, vol. 69, May 1, 1954, pp. 455–461.

SCHMIDT, JOHN FRANK, "Patterns of Poor Adjustment in Old Age," *American Journal of Sociology*, vol. 57, Part 1, July, 1951, pp. 33–42.

SENSEMAN, LAURENCE A., "Psychiatric Problems Associated with the Aging," *Rhode Island Medical Journal*, vol. 37, January, 1954, pp. 30–34.

SHANAS, ETHEL, AND ROBERT J. HAVIGHURST, "Retirement in Four Professions," *Journal of Gerontology*, vol. 8, April, 1953, pp. 212–221.

SHELDON, J. H., "Old-Age Problems in the Family," *Milbank Memorial Fund Quarterly*, vol. 27, April, 1949, pp. 119–132.

SHELDON, JOSEPH H., *The Social Medicine of Old Age:* Report of an Inquiry in Wolverhampton. Oxford University Press, London, 1948. 250 pp.

SHOCK, NATHAN W., *Classified Bibliography of Gerontology and Geriatrics*. Stanford University Press, Stanford, Calif., 1951. 599 pp.

"Gerontology (Later Maturity)," *Annual Review of Psychology*, vol. 2, 1951, pp. 353–370.

Trends in Gerontology. Stanford University Press, Stanford, Calif., 1951. 153 pp.

SILK, LEONARD S., "The Housing Circumstances of the Aged in the United States, 1950," *Journal of Gerontology*, vol. 7, January, 1952, pp. 87–91.

SIMMONS, LEO W., "Old Age Security in Other Societies," *Geriatrics*, vol. 3, July–August, 1948, pp. 237–244.

The Role of the Aged in Primitive Society. Yale University Press, New Haven, Conn., 1945. 317 pp.

"Social Participation of the Aged in Different Cultures," *Annals* of the American Academy of Political and Social Science, vol. 279, January, 1952, pp. 43–51.

SIMMONS, LEO, AND HAROLD G. WOLFF, *Social Science in Medicine*. Russell Sage Foundation, New York, 1954. 254 pp.

SIMON, ALEXANDER, "Psychological Problems of Aging," *California Medicine*, vol. 75, August, 1951, pp. 73–80.

SLADEN, FRANK J., "The Values of Geriatrics" in *Health in the Later Years*, edited by John M. Maclachlan. Institute of Gerontology Series, vol. 3. University of Florida Press, Gainesville, 1953, pp. 17–30.

SLICHTER, SUMNER H., "The Need for More Employment of Older Workers," *Wisconsin State Federation of Labor*, vol. 36, 1951, pp. 31–32, 36.

SMITH, M. W., "Evidences of Potentialities of Older Workers in a Manufacturing Company," *Personnel Psychology*, vol. 5, 1952, pp. 11–18.

SMITH, T. LYNN, editor, *Problems of America's Aging Population*. Institute of Gerontology Series, vol. 1. University of Florida Press, Gainesville, 1951. 117 pp.

SMITH, WILLIAM M., JR., "Family Plans for Later Years," *Marriage and Family Living*, vol. 16, February, 1954, pp. 36–40.

SROLE, LEO, "Social Integration and Certain Corollaries: An Exploratory Study," *American Sociological Review*, vol. 21, December, 1956. In preparation.

STAFFORD, VIRGINIA, *Older Adults in the Church*. Methodist Publishing House, New York, 1953. 96 pp.

STANTON, JEANETTE E., "How Far Can We Go in Hiring Older Workers?" *Proceedings*, 8th Annual Conference in Restaurant Management, Ohio State University, Columbus, 1951, pp. 8–15.

"Part-time Employment for the Older Workers," *Journal of Applied Psychology*, vol. 35, December, 1951, pp. 418–421.

STEINHARDT, R. W., AND OTHERS, "Appraisal of Physical and Mental Health of the Elderly," *Journal of the American Medical Association*, vol. 151, January 31, 1953, pp. 378–382.

Stern, Karl, "Problems Encountered in an Old Age Counselling Center" in *Conference on Problems of Aging:* Transactions of the 10th and 11th Conferences, edited by Nathan W. Shock. Josiah Macy, Jr. Foundation, New York, 1950, pp. 30–38.

Stern, Karl, Joan M. Smith, and Margit Frank, "Mechanisms of Transference and Counter-Transference in Psychotherapeutic and Social Work with the Aged," *Journal of Gerontology*, vol. 8, July, 1953, pp. 328–332.

Stevenson, George S., "A Guide to a Community Committee on the Mental Health of the Aged," *Mental Hygiene*, vol. 37, April, 1953, pp. 265–277.

Stieglitz, Edward J., *The Second Forty Years*. J. B. Lippincott Co., Philadelphia, 1946. 317 pp.

Stieglitz, Edward J., editor, *Geriatric Medicine*. 3d ed. J. B. Lippincott Co., Philadelphia, 1954. 718 pp.

Stokes, A. B., "Old Age from the Psychiatric Viewpoint," *Canadian Medical Association Journal*, vol. 59, December, 1948, pp. 518–521.

Swartz, Frederick C., "A Wider Concept of Geriatrics," *American Journal of Nursing*, vol. 53, November, 1953, pp. 1327–1328.

Swartz, P. W., "Organized Community Planning for Old Age," *Journal of Gerontology*, vol. 6, July, 1951, Supplement, p. 154.

Switzer, Mary E., and Howard A. Rusk, "Keeping Older People Fit for Participation," *Annals* of the American Academy of Political and Social Science, vol. 279, January, 1952, pp. 146–153.

Taietz, Philip, *Administrative Practices and Personal Adjustment in Homes for the Aged*. Bulletin 899, Cornell University Agricultural Experiment Station, Ithaca, N. Y., 1953. 39 pp.

Temple University, Bureau of Economic and Business Research, *The Problem of Making a Living While Growing Old:* Proceedings of Joint Conference. Philadelphia, 1952. 167 pp.
   The Problem of Making a Living While Growing Old: Proceedings of Second Joint Conference. Philadelphia, 1953. 414 pp.

Thewlis, Malford W., *The Care of the Aged*. 6th ed. rev. C. V. Mosby Co., St. Louis, 1954. 832 pp.

Thewlis, Malford W., and E. T. Gale, "Ambulatory Care of the Aged," *Geriatrics*, vol. 5, November-December, 1950, pp. 331–336.

"Three Challenges of the Future," *Journal of the American Medical Association*, vol. 151, January 17, 1953, pp. 212–213.

TIBBITTS, CLARK, "The National Significance of Aging," *New York State Journal of Medicine*, vol. 53, October 15, 1953, pp. 2363–2367.

"Retirement Problems in American Society," *American Journal of Sociology*, vol. 59, January, 1954, pp. 301–308.

TIBBITTS, CLARK, editor, *Living Through the Older Years*. University of Michigan Press, Ann Arbor, 1949. 193 pp.

"Social Contribution by the Aging," *Annals* of the American Academy of Political and Social Science, vol. 279, January, 1952. Entire issue.

TIBBITTS, CLARK, AND HENRY D. SHELDON, "A Philosophy of Aging," *Annals* of the American Academy of Political and Social Science, vol. 279, January, 1952, pp. 1–10.

TOMPKINS, DOROTHY C., *The Senile Aged Problem in the United States*. Bureau of Public Administration, University of California, Berkeley, 1955. 82 pp.

TRUSTEES OF THE LONDON PAROCHIAL CHARITIES, *Isleden House*. London, 1951, with 1954 insert. 25 pp.

TUCKMAN, JACOB, AND IRVING D. LORGE, "Attitudes Toward Old People," *Journal of Social Psychology*, vol. 37, May, 1953, pp. 249–260.

"Attitudes Toward Older Workers," *Journal of Applied Psychology*, vol. 36, June, 1952, pp. 149–153.

"The Best Years of Life: A Study in Ranking," *Journal of Psychology*, vol. 34, October, 1952, pp. 137–149.

"Classification of the Self as Young, Middle-Aged, or Old," *Geriatrics*, vol. 9, November, 1954, pp. 534–536.

"The Effect of Institutionalization on Attitudes Toward Old People," *Journal of Abnormal and Social Psychology*, vol. 47, April, 1952, Supplement, pp. 337–344.

"Old People's Appraisal of Adjustment Over the Life Span," *Journal of Personality*, vol. 22, 1954, pp. 417–422.

Retirement and the Industrial Worker: Prospect and Reality. Teachers College, Columbia University, New York, 1953. 105 pp.

"Retirement Practices in Business and Industry," *Journal of Gerontology*, vol. 7, January, 1952, pp. 77–86.

"'When Aging Begins' and Sterotypes About Aging," *Journal of Gerontology*, vol. 8, October, 1953, pp. 489–492.

"When Does Old Age Begin and a Worker Become Old?" *Journal of Gerontology*, vol. 8, October, 1953, pp. 483–488.

TUCKMAN, JACOB, IRVING D. LORGE, AND G. A. SPOONER, "The Effect of Family Environment on Attitudes Toward Old People and the Older Worker," *Journal of Social Psychology*, vol. 38, November, 1953, pp. 207–218.

TUCKMAN, JACOB, IRVING D. LORGE, AND FREDERIC D. ZEMAN, "Retesting Older People with the Cornell Medical Index and with the Supplementary Health Questionnaire," *Journal of Gerontology*, vol. 9, July, 1954, pp. 306–308.

TUCKMAN, JACOB, AND OTHERS, "Somatic and Psychological Complaints of Older People in Institutions and at Home," *Geriatrics*, vol. 8, May, 1953, pp. 274–279.

U. S. CONGRESS, Senate, *Retirement Policies and the Railroad Retirement System:* Report of Joint Committee on Railroad Retirement Legislation. 83d Congress, 1st Sess. Senate Report 6, Government Printing Office, Washington, 1953. Part 1, "Issues in Railroad Retirement," 770 pp.; Part 2, "Economic Problems of an Aging Population," 172 pp.

U. S. DEPARTMENT OF HEALTH, EDUCATION, AND WELFARE (formerly Federal Security Agency)

Man and His Years: An Account of the First National Conference on Aging, Health Publications Institute, Inc., Raleigh, N. C., 1951. 311 pp. Sponsored by the Department of Health, Education, and Welfare.

Committee on Aging, *Aging*. Bimonthly (irregular).

Committee on Aging and Geriatrics, *Fact Book on Aging*. Government Printing Office, Washington, 1952. 62 pp.

Division of State Merit Systems, *Problems of Mandatory and Variable Retirement Ages in State Employment*. Washington, 1954. 10 pp. Mimeographed.

Social Security Administration, "Economic Status of Aged Persons and Dependent Survivors, December, 1953," *Social Security Bulletin*, vol. 17, June, 1954, pp. 17–18.

Social Security Administration, *Old-Age Insurance Benefits, 1952*, Analytical Note 73, June, 1953, 6 pp.; *Old-Age Insurance Benefits, 1953*, Analytical Note 76, June, 1954, 6 pp.; *Old-Age Insurance Benefits, 1954*, Analytical Note 78, August, 1955, 7 pp.; *Old-Age Insurance Benefit Awards, January–June, 1955*, Analytical Note 79, January, 1956, 7 pp. Bureau of Old-Age and Survivors Insurance, Division of Program Analysis, Baltimore. Mimeographed.

U. S. DEPARTMENT OF LABOR

Bureau of Employment Security, *Older Workers Seek Jobs*. Washington, 1951. 12 pp. Processed.

Bureau of Labor Statistics, *Budget for an Elderly Couple:* Estimated Cost, October, 1950. Government Printing Office, Washington, 1950. 4 pp.

Bureau of Labor Statistics, *Digest of Selected Health, Insurance, Welfare and Retirement Plans Under Collective Bargaining, Mid-1950.* Special Series No. 6, Government Printing Office, Washington, 1951. 99 pp.

Bureau of Labor Statistics, *Employee Benefit Plans Under Collective Bargaining,* Bulletin 1017, Government Printing Office, Washington, 1950. 7 pp.

Bureau of Labor Statistics, *Fact Book on Manpower.* Bulletin 1171, Government Printing Office, Washington, 1954. 88 pp. Processed.

Intradepartmental Committee on the Older Worker, "Services for Older Workers: The Need for Developing Work Opportunities," *Employment Security Review,* vol. 21, November, 1954. Entire issue.

Women's Bureau. *Bibliography on Employment Problems of Older Women.* Government Printing Office, Washington, 1956. 89 pp.

[U. S.] FEDERAL SECURITY AGENCY. See U. S. Department of Health, Education, and Welfare.

U. S. PRESIDENT'S COMMISSION ON THE HEALTH NEEDS OF THE NATION, *Building America's Health:* America's Health Status, Needs and Resources, vol. 2. Government Printing Office, Washington, 1952. 320 pp.

UNIVERSITY OF CALIFORNIA, Institute of Industrial Relations, "Economic Problems of the Aged," *American Economic Review,* May, 1954, pp. 634–670.

UNIVERSITY OF CHICAGO, Industrial Relations Center, *Aging and Retirement:* Research in Progress. Chicago, 1954. 45 pp. Multilithed.

UNIVERSITY OF MICHIGAN, Bureau of Industrial Relations, *Addresses on Industrial Relations.* Bulletins 20 and 22, Ann Arbor, 1953, 1954.

UNIVERSITY OF WISCONSIN, Industrial Relations Center, *Proceedings* of a Conference on Problems of Older Workers. Madison, 1951. 184 pp. Mimeographed.

VETTIGER, MARGERETE (Gretel), ANIELA JAFFÉ, AND ALBAN VOGT, *Alte Menschen im Altersheim.* B. Schwabe and Co., Basel, Switzerland, 1951. 150 pp.

VISCHER, ADOLF L., *Old Age, Its Compensation and Rewards.* 2d ed. rev. Macmillan Co., New York, 1948. 200 pp. Translation from the German by Bernard Miall.

WAHLSTROM, CATHERINE LEE, *Add Life to Their Years.* National Council of the Churches of Christ in the U.S.A., New York, 1953. 75 pp.

WALKER, KENNETH M., *Living Your Later Years.* Oxford University Press, New York, 1954. 196 pp.

WASHINGTON UNIVERSITY, *Proceedings* of the Second Institute on Aging. St. Louis, 1953. 58 pp.

WATSON, ROBERT I., "The Personality of the Aged: A Review," *Journal of Gerontology*, vol. 9, July, 1954, pp. 309–315.

WEBBER, IRVING L., "The Organized Social Life of the Retired: Two Florida Communities," *American Journal of Sociology*, vol. 59, January, 1954, pp. 340–346.

"The Retired Population of a Florida Community" in *Problems of America's Aging Population*, edited by T. Lynn Smith. Institute of Gerontology Series, vol. 1. University of Florida Press, Gainesville, 1951, pp. 87–101.

WEISS, JOSEPH, "Employment Problems of Older Workers," *Jewish Social Service Quarterly*, vol. 28, June, 1952, pp. 423–427.

WELFARE COUNCIL OF METROPOLITAN CHICAGO, *Services for Older People:* Survey of the Field. Chicago, 1955. 15 pp.

WELFARE COUNCIL OF METROPOLITAN CHICAGO, Community Project for the Aged, *Community Services for Older People:* The Chicago Plan. Wilcox and Follett Co., Chicago, 1952. 240 pp.

WELFORD, ALAN T., "Extending the Employment of Older People," *British Medical Journal*, vol. 2, November 28, 1953, pp. 1193–1197.

WELFORD, ALAN T., AND OTHERS, *Skill and Age.* Oxford University Press, London, 1951. 161 pp.

WENTWORTH, EDNA C., "Economic Situation of Aged Insurance Beneficiaries: An Evaluation," *Social Security Bulletin*, vol. 17, April, 1954, pp. 13–22, 26.

WHEELER, HOWARD, "Creative Activities of Older People," *Annals* of the American Academy of Political and Social Science, vol. 279, January, 1952, pp. 84–92.

WICKENDEN, ELIZABETH, *The Needs of Older People, and Public Welfare Services to Meet Them.* American Public Welfare Association, Chicago, 1953. 146 pp.

WILLARD, JOSEPH W., "Employment Problems of Older Workers," *Proceedings* of the National Conference of Social Work, 1948. Columbia University Press, New York, 1949, pp. 395–402.

"Housing and Living Arrangements for the Aged," *American Journal of Public Health*, vol. 42, November, 1952, pp. 1440–1449.

WILLIAMS, ARTHUR M., *Recreation for the Aging*. Association Press, New York, 1953. 192 pp.

WILLIE, CHARLES V., "Group Relationships of the Elderly in Our Culture," *Social Casework*, vol. 35, May, 1954, pp. 206–212.

WOLFF, HAROLD G., *Stress and Disease*. Charles C. Thomas, Springfield, Ill., 1953. 199 pp.

WOODS, JAMES H., *Helping Older People Enjoy Life*. Harper and Bros., New York, 1953. 139 pp.

YOST, ORIN ROSS, "Geriatrics: A Challenging Field of Problems and New Goals," *Geriatrics*, vol. 8, June, 1953, pp. 342–347.

ZBOROWSKI, MARK, "Cultural Components in Responses to Pain," *Journal of Social Issues*, vol. 8, no. 4, 1952, pp. 16–30.

ZEMAN, FREDERIC D., "Constructive Programs for the Mental Health of the Elderly," *Mental Hygiene*, vol. 35, April, 1951, pp. 221–234.

INDEX

Index

339